ADDISON-WESLEY BOOKS IN
NUCLEAR SCIENCE AND METALLURGY

Bishop—PROJECT SHERWOOD—THE U. S. PROGRAM IN CONTROLLED FUSION

Chastain—U. S. RESEARCH REACTOR OPERATION AND USE

Claus—RADIATION BIOLOGY AND MEDICINE

Clegg and Foley—URANIUM ORE PROCESSING

Cullity—ELEMENTS OF X-RAY DIFFRACTION

Cuthbert—THORIUM PRODUCTION TECHNOLOGY

Goldstein—FUNDAMENTAL ASPECTS OF REACTOR SHIELDING

Goodman—INTRODUCTION TO PILE THEORY
(The Science and Engineering of Nuclear Power, I)

Goodman—APPLICATIONS OF NUCLEAR ENERGY
(The Science and Engineering of Nuclear Power, II)

Guy—ELEMENTS OF PHYSICAL METALLURGY

Holden—PHYSICAL METALLURGY OF URANIUM

Hughes—PILE NEUTRON RESEARCH

Kaplan—NUCLEAR PHYSICS

Kramer—BOILING WATER REACTORS

Lane, MacPherson, and Maslan—FLUID FUEL REACTORS

Norton—ELEMENTS OF CERAMICS

Rough and Bauer—CONSTITUTIONAL DIAGRAMS OF URANIUM AND THORIUM

Sachs—NUCLEAR THEORY

Schuhmann—METALLURGICAL ENGINEERING
VOL. I: ENGINEERING PRINCIPLES

Seaborg—THE TRANSURANIUM ELEMENTS

Starr and Dickinson—SODIUM GRAPHITE REACTORS

USAEC—SHIPPINGPORT PRESSURIZED WATER REACTOR

Zinn and Dietrich—SOLID FUEL REACTORS

U.S. RESEARCH REACTOR OPERATION AND USE

U.S. RESEARCH REACTOR OPERATION AND USE

Edited by

JOEL W. CHASTAIN, JR.

Battelle Memorial Institute

PREPARED UNDER CONTRACT WITH THE
UNITED STATES ATOMIC ENERGY COMMISSION

ADDISON-WESLEY PUBLISHING COMPANY, INC.

READING, MASSACHUSETTS, U.S.A.

PREFACE

This book is intended to be a source of information about research and test reactors in the United States. It is hoped that it will be useful to scientists and engineers—and many of their administrators—who are contemplating owning or using a reactor.

The authors have endeavored to write so that the book will be of orientation value to scientists and engineers, and others, not trained in nuclear science and technology. Although not a textbook, it could serve to introduce reactor engineering courses or as a reference for such courses.

The book undertakes to describe the various types of reactors, their characteristics, operating problems (administrative and legal as well as technical), safety considerations, and costs. It covers reactor theory only enough to provide the reactor user with a few basic concepts and an understanding of some common terms; there are a few simple equations.

For those who want additional information, there are numerous references. The references include a number of publications issued by the Atomic Energy Commission. These are available for inspection at the Commission's depository libraries in the United States and abroad and are sold by the Office of Technical Services, U. S. Department of Commerce, Washington 25, D. C.

While the selection of data, its organization and presentation are the work of the authors in consultation with the editor, the preparation of the book required the efforts of many more people. The authors and I are especially indebted to those who contributed information and illustrations from the reactors with which they are working. We thank them by crediting their organizations in the captions of the figures and by references to their literature. Special credit is due John W. Flora, of Atomics International, for his contribution on the KEWB Experiment.

A number of able technical reviewers called attention to errors in the manuscript and suggested other improvements. Among them we are especially indebted to H. W. Etherington, ACF Industries, Inc.; J. D. Fitzgibbons, Babcock and Wilcox Co.; Serge Golian, Naval Research Laboratory; A. C. Menius, Jr., North Carolina State College; and J. W. Webster, American Standard.

Acknowledgment is made for suggestions and editing by John J. Breslin, of the Battelle editorial group; and by Edward T. Sullivan, James Aswell, and Jefferson D. Bates, of the U. S. Atomic Energy Commission's Industrial Information Branch, Technical Information Service.

Whatever usefulness the book may have is due in large measure to all who have so generously aided us. Any remaining errors and other shortcomings are the responsibility of the editor and authors.

Columbus, Ohio,   Joel W. Chastain, Jr.
June 1958   Editor

AUTHORS

The following members of the staff of Battelle Memorial Institute are contributing authors to this book. Specific credits appear with each chapter.

JAMES N. ANNO, JR.

JOEL W. CHASTAIN, JR.

WILLIAM S. HOGAN

FRANCIS J. JANKOWSKI

HAROLD R. NELSON

ARNOLD M. PLUMMER

ROBERT F. REDMOND

DON H. STALL

CLYDE R. TIPTON, JR.

CONTENTS

CHAPTER 1

THE RESEARCH REACTOR*

1–1. INTRODUCTION

This book was prepared primarily to acquaint persons technically trained, but not in the reactor field, with the operation and use of various types of nuclear research reactors. The intent is not to deal overlong with the physics of reactors, but rather to describe each type in detail and to give information on acquiring and utilizing them. The book will set forth some of the advantages and disadvantages of different reactors, and will discuss problems and costs of acquiring and operating a research-reactor facility.

Such information is becoming increasingly important to research people as more and more research reactors, until recently seen only in government laboratories, are now being built and operated by universities, research institutions, and industry. There are several reasons for growing interest. First, revision of the Atomic Energy Act removes many limitations to reactor construction and operation. Second, the owner may eventually benefit financially from discoveries associated with use of the reactor. Third, there are now abundant supplies of U^{235} available for research reactors. However, the most compelling reason for mounting interest is realization of the tremendous training possibilities and the research potential in physics, engineering, biology, and chemistry associated with reactor use.

As the title indicates, this book will be limited to discussion of research reactors. The term "research reactor," as used here, denotes a reactor built to provide a strong source of neutron and gamma rays for physical research. Other types are production reactors designed to produce fissionable materials such as plutonium and other isotopes, and reactors designed to produce useful power. This method of classifying reactors categorizes them according to their primary purpose.

Another category, frequently grouped with research reactors, includes experimental reactors and critical-assembly facilities. Since these are intended principally to test design concepts rather than to serve as radiation sources, they will not be considered here—except for those employed specifically for research reactor safety studies.

---

* By J. W. Chastain, Jr.

1-2. How Research Reactors Work

All nuclear reactors, regardless of type, are devices in which the process called fission occurs at a rate sufficient to maintain a self-sustaining chain reaction. In the most common form of fission, a thermal neutron (a neutron of relatively low velocity) is absorbed by the nucleus of a U^{235} atom which then splits into two almost equal parts. These two parts, or fission fragments, carry off about 160 million electron volts (Mev)* of kinetic energy in the form of heat. The fission fragments later decay to stable products by emitting beta particles (electrons) with a total kinetic energy of 5 Mev and gamma radiation totaling 6 Mev. At the moment of fission, 6 Mev of gamma rays and usually two or three neutrons are also released. The neutrons, emitted at high energies, are "slowed down" by successive collisions with surrounding nuclei to thermal energies where they may be absorbed by U^{235}, thus propagating the fission reaction.

In a research reactor, the fast neutrons, thermal neutrons, and gamma rays are used for experimental work. Fission fragments and electrons are not generally used because they travel such a short distance in most materials; their energy is dissipated in the neighboring matter and removed as heat by the coolant.

The fission process occurs in the part of the reactor called the *core*, which contains the fuel, generally in the form of thin plates or rods and sometimes as a solution. The core also contains a material used to slow down or moderate the fast neutrons to thermal energies. The moderator must be a material of low mass number and must absorb very few neutrons. The most common moderators are light and heavy water, graphite, and beryllium.

Surrounding the core is the *reflector*, the purpose of which is to reduce neutron leakage by scattering escaping neutrons back into the core; it also slows them down. The reflector permits using a smaller core and less fuel for a given fuel and moderator combination than would otherwise be possible. In addition, the reflector causes a high useful neutron concentration over a greater total volume, an advantage in a research reactor. Since a good reflector material should absorb few neutrons while scattering many, it has properties somewhat similar to those of a good moderator. The most used materials are, again, light and heavy water, graphite, and beryllium.

The reflector, in turn, is surrounded by the *shield*, which protects personnel and instruments from the radiations. The shield must attenuate both the neutrons and gammas. Neutrons, after being reduced to thermal energies, are readily absorbed by most materials and particularly well

---

* 1 Mev is equivalent to 1.60×10^{-13} watt-second. Complete fission of one gram of U^{235} produces an energy of approximately one megawatt-day.

by a few materials such as boron and cadmium. Neutron absorption frequently results in the emission of secondary gamma rays which must be shielded against. Gamma rays are attenuated best by dense materials such as iron, lead, and bismuth. One good shielding material is concrete, particularly some of the dense mixes which contain baryte ore as the aggregate. The hydrogen in the water retained in the concrete and other materials in the concrete slow down the neutrons so they may be absorbed. The density of concrete, while not as great as that of the metals mentioned, is sufficient to reduce the gamma-ray intensity to a safe level if it is used in reasonable thicknesses. Concrete has the further advantage of being comparatively cheap and, consequently, is the most frequently used shielding material.

During operation, the core and the reflector of a reactor are densely populated by neutrons flying in all directions with a wide range of velocities. The intensity of this field of neutrons is expressed as a quantity called the neutron flux, which is the product of the neutron density (neutrons/cm^3) and the average velocity (cm/sec) of the neutrons, and is expressed in n/(cm^2)(sec). Research reactors today have a maximum flux of between 10^6 and 10^{14} n/(cm^2)(sec). Since the power of the reactor is proportional to the product of the thermal-neutron flux and the fuel loading, it is advantageous to keep the critical fuel mass as low as possible in order to obtain the maximum thermal-neutron flux for a given power.

Gamma radiation is generally measured in roentgens/hr (r/hr) although it can be expressed as gammas/(cm^2)(sec). The gamma intensity in the core is proportional to the power divided by the core volume and, therefore, if a high gamma intensity is desired it is beneficial to keep the volume as small as possible. A typical enriched uranium research reactor operating at 1 megawatt has a flux of 5×10^{13} gammas/(cm^2)(sec) or about 2×10^8 r/hr. The fast-neutron flux is also proportional to the ratio of the power to the volume. A reduction in core volume tends to increase the fast-neutron and gamma flux but the volume of the region that can be utilized for experimental purposes is lessened. This decrease in volume can be partially compensated by using a good reflector to produce larger regions of high flux.

The maximum fluxes of fast neutrons, thermal neutrons, and gammas usually occur at the center of the core but are fairly uniform inside the core. Along a radial from the core center, the fast-neutron flux drops off most rapidly, since the fast neutrons are slowed down to form thermal neutrons. The thermal flux also drops off away from the center, but increases somewhat in the reflector because the rate of formation of thermal neutrons just outside the core is about the same as it is just inside but the lifetime of thermal neutrons in the reflector is usually much longer.

In using these fluxes, every effort is made to get close to and sometimes into the core. Of course, by changing the location of the specimen in the reactor, the ratios of the radiations received can be varied. To obtain one radiation relatively free of the others, filters can be used either singly or in combination. For instance, a can of paraffin with cadmium ends can be used to partially eliminate both fast and thermal neutrons, leaving a relatively clean beam of gammas. The cadmium absorbs the thermal neutrons and the paraffin slows down the fast neutrons to thermal energies where they, in turn, can be captured by the cadmium. To obtain slow (thermal) neutrons, a column of graphite, called a thermal column, is used. The graphite absorbs very few thermal neutrons but effectively slows down the fast neutrons. A lead or bismuth slab is used between the core and the thermal column to reduce the number of gamma rays from the core.

1-3. TYPES OF RESEARCH REACTORS

Research reactors can be broadly classified into two groups: those using natural uranium as fuel and those using enriched uranium. The enriched reactors can be further divided into fluid-fuel reactors and solid-fuel reactors. Natural-uranium reactors are big, require large amounts of fuel, and must use graphite or heavy water to moderate the neutrons. The typical core of this type is about a 25-ft cube and requires many tons of graphite and natural uranium. Such a system operating at 25,000 kw can produce a thermal-neutron flux of about 4×10^{12} n/(cm^2)(sec). Characteristics of the natural-uranium reactor result in a high cost per unit of flux, particularly in the case of the graphite-moderated assemblies. There are advantages, however, such as large experimental volumes.

Heavy-water moderated reactors are somewhat smaller, but are expensive because of the quantity of costly heavy water required with natural uranium. Reactors of this type have been used extensively outside the United States.

The first research reactors utilizing enriched uranium were named "water boilers," so called because the gas formed by the disassociation of the water causes bubbling. Such reactors use an aqueous solution of uranyl sulfate or nitrate as fuel. A typical water boiler has a critical mass of less than 1 kg, and the thermal fluxes may be as high as 10^{12} n/(cm^2)(sec) at a power of only 30 kw. Thus the water boiler is characterized by low fuel inventory and a relatively high flux to power ratio. The power is limited, however, to the range of 30 to 50 kw because at higher powers the water dissociates too rapidly and the uranium solution tends to become unstable. The reactor core is small and easily shielded, but its small size also limits the volume available for irradiation experiments.

A second type of enriched-fuel reactor is the pool or tank reactor. The uranium is in the form of solid fuel elements. In the so-called pool reactor the core operates in an open pool of ordinary water, while in the tank reactor the core is enclosed in a tank. In a typical pool reactor, the core is arranged on a grid plate suspended some 20 ft below the water surface from a bridge which can be moved from one end of the pool to the other on rails located on the top of the pool wall. Useful experimental loadings may require from 25 to 30 fuel elements each containing 140 to 200 gm, or a total of 3 to 4 kg of U^{235}. Pool reactors are operating at powers as high as 1000 kw. Power levels up to 5000 kw are now being planned for some reactors and one has operated at this power. At 1000 kw, this type of reactor can provide fluxes of 10^{13} n/(cm^2)(sec) throughout useful volumes of only several cubic feet because the thermal-neutron flux diminishes rapidly in ordinary water.

Pool reactors are attractive for general research work because of their extreme flexibility. The core configuration can be changed quite easily by simply rearranging the fuel elements into solid or hollow rectangles, H- or U-shapes, etc. In addition, the core can be operated in several positions in the pool, which is usually divided into two parts by a removable gate. For large experimental setups such as shielding or experimental loop studies, the core can be moved into one side of the pool, the gate closed, and the other side of the pool drained so that the experiment can be set up. The pool is then refilled, the gate removed, and the core brought to the experiment. Experiments can also be performed simply by suspending the material to be irradiated from the bridge, the water in the open pool serving as a transparent shield.

For fluxes much above 10^{13} n/(cm^2)(sec), a tank-type reactor becomes almost essential. The design of a high-power tank reactor provides the necessary shielding with solid material and consequently avoids the excessive water depth required in a pool reactor. Also, the radioactive nitrogen formed in a light-water moderated system as the water passes through the core can be collected and allowed to decay in a holdup tank. However, the tank-type reactor uses much less water than the pool-type and thus requires more concrete for shielding. The core is stationary, and the containing tank is tightly closed. These reactors allow higher power operation but are more expensive and less flexible than the pool type because the tank and shield must be penetrated not only by piping and control lines, but by numerous beam ports and access holes. However, heavy water can be used as moderator at a fairly reasonable cost in these reactors because of the small water volume. Using heavy water roughly doubles the available thermal-neutron flux for a given power over that attainable in a similar reactor moderated with ordinary water and decreases the critical mass. Otherwise, the tank reactors are similar to the pool-type in critical mass and in flux to power ratio.

There are also reactors designed for studies of power transients and safety, and others intended primarily for training purposes and experiments which can be carried out with relatively low fluxes [10^6 to 10^7 n/(cm^2)(sec)]. An example of the first type is the Boiling Reactor Experiment (Borax), which was used to investigate the stability of water-moderated reactors. One reactor of the second type, the AGN-201, has a core of polyethylene containing dispersed uranium dioxide. The reactor operates from a few milliwatts to 5 watts, and produces sufficient neutrons for many training experiments.

Most research reactors outside the United States for which this country supplies fuel are utilizing uranium 20% enriched in the 235 isotope. However, early in 1958 the U. S. Atomic Energy Commission authorized the transfer of uranium enriched up to 90% for research and materials testing reactors provided individual core loadings do not exceed 8 kg U^{235} and that comprehensive safeguards are in effect or agreed to by the United States and the cooperating nations.

1–4. METHODS OF IRRADIATING SPECIMENS

One of the chief problems in designing research reactors is to make the radiations available. A number of different systems have been developed for exposing specimens of various materials to gamma and neutron fluxes. The most common and frequently used system employs beam tubes, that is, vertical or horizontal tubes or lined openings passing through the concrete shield into the reflector or the core of the reactor. Intense beams of neutrons can be brought out through the tubes for experimentation, or materials may be placed in the tubes for irradiation. The number and sizes of the beam holes vary, but most reactors have from 3 to 16 tubes of 6-in., 8-in., and even larger diameters.

Probably the second most common facility in a reactor designed for research is the thermal column. This is a device for providing large quantities of thermal neutrons for use in a variety of experiments, such as activation analysis and measurement of physics parameters. Another common procedure for exposing materials is to employ small beam holes known as "rabbit tubes." A small encapsulated specimen is shot, by pneumatic or hydraulic means, through a small tube into a region of high flux in a matter of a second or two. Because of the speed of the technique, it is particularly useful in preparing short-lived radioactive materials. Specimens can be removed without shutting down the reactor.

Two other irradiation techniques, applicable mostly to pool or tank reactors, should be mentioned. Experiments can be placed in hollow boxes of the same size and design as the fuel element and inserted in the grid plate near or in the core. This permits using the highest possible flux.

In many pool reactors, a second bridge structure identical to the one supporting the core is used to suspend shelves for instruments or specimens. When the two bridges are in close proximity, a specimen on one of the shelves suspended from the instrument bridge receives very intense radiation.

1–5. Considerations in Choosing a Reactor

There are four basic items which must be considered in planning a reactor facility: (1) safety aspects of the reactor, (2) types of experiments of interest to the owner, (3) supporting facilities required for proper operation of the reactor, and (4) construction and operating costs. Since safety is not a matter of choice, the final design must be a compromise between the requirements of the owner and the costs of building the facility and operating it efficiently.

An examination of the safety aspects should include an analysis of the possible hazards to the public, to the reactor personnel, and to the reactor itself, all of which are important in planning a reactor facility. Safe operation of a particular reactor depends on three things: safety features inherent in the reactor design, features incorporated or built into the facility, and the administrative policy and attitude toward safety.

The inherent safety features in a reactor design involve such things as temperature and void coefficients of reactivity and neutron lifetime. The effect of each of the items on the critical state and operating stability varies among the reactor types. For example, in a properly designed light-water moderated reactor, changes in density and voids formed in the core by the increased temperature tend to shut down the reactor in the case of a power runaway. A heavy-water reactor has this same feature plus a longer neutron-generation time; this is defined as the average time between successive generations of prompt fission neutrons. The power of a reactor in a nonstationary state increases (or decreases) exponentially with time and, as shown in Fig. 9–1, the rate of the increase is lower for a longer neutron-generation time for large reactivity changes.

A graphite reactor also has a relatively long neutron-generation time but, of course, does not have a void coefficient. However, in a power excursion the temperature rise still affects the nuclear cross sections, and causes changes in the density and volume of the reactor core. With proper design, these effects tend to shut down the reactor. The aqueous homogeneous reactors have a further safety feature in that a temperature rise causes the solution to expand, and in a violent excursion fuel is forced out of the core.

Built-in safety can be obtained by providing an exclusion area around the reactor, by using a gastight building, and by utilizing an adequate control system. The reactor designer has some latitude in deciding between an exclusion area and a gastight building; he may use some degree of each in obtaining a safe design. In any event, adequate detecting and controlling instrumentation are always necessary.

Possibly the most important single facet of safety involves the administration and organization of the reactor facility. Safety eventually is determined by operational rules and procedures and by safety evaluations of experiments and operation. In setting these procedures and policies, it is particularly important to consider them in relation to the experimenters who will use the reactor. If properly regulated, a facility can be run with considerable assurance of safe operation and at the same time be very useful for experimentation.

Although there is considerable overlapping in the types of experiments that can be performed with the various reactors, each reactor has, in general, distinct characteristics which make it better for certain kinds of experimentation. The characteristics which determine the area of experimentation are flux levels, volume available for experimentation, and special experimental facilities.

Inexpensive low-power reactors provide sufficient flux and volume for such experiments as danger-coefficient measurements of cross sections, activation analysis, and biological research. For neutron-diffraction- and reflection experiments higher-power homogeneous reactors and most pool reactors are adequate. For engineering and chemical in-pile loop experiments, particularly the larger ones, a higher-powered pool reactor or tank reactor is required. A graphite-moderated reactor is usable for all these experiments, and is particularly adapted to experiments requiring a large volume at a fairly uniform flux. Of course, the graphite system must operate at a much higher power to obtain fluxes at the center approximating those of pool or tank reactors.

The experiments which can be conducted with a heavy-water reactor are quite similar to those mentioned for light-water systems. Heavy-water reactors have the advantage of a larger volume of high thermal flux, but care must be taken to avoid contamination or loss of the heavy water.

For experiments to determine the effects of radiation on fuel specimens, very high fluxes are required if irradiation times are to be reasonably short. To obtain these high fluxes, a closed reactor system is required. To date in the United States, these have been tank reactors using ordinary water as moderator and coolant.

The supporting facilities required for efficient operation of a reactor facility depend on the magnitude of the reactor fluxes and on the extent of the research program. If the reactor has a flux above 10^{12} n/(cm^2)(sec), a hot-cell laboratory for remote handling of irradiated materials is required unless the experimental program is radically limited in scope. The size and number and, consequently, the cost of the hot cells will be determined by the flux level of the reactor and how long the materials are to be irradiated. In general, the cost of hot-cell laboratories is comparable to the cost of the reactors with which they are associated; their cost of operation is, in many cases, higher.

Other supporting facilities include radioisotope laboratories or some means of handling radioisotopes, facilities for measuring the induced activity of foils or wires, and machine shops. In addition, transfer mechanisms and transfer coffins or casks are required for removing radioactive materials produced in the operation of the reactor. Obviously, the cost of these items is again determined by the reactor power and the experimental program.

The costs of reactors, exclusive of supporting facilities, can be broken down into design, engineering, and construction costs. Design and engineering costs include the design of the facility, the evaluation of safety, and the acquisition of the various licenses. Construction costs include the reactor components, instrumentation, building, site preparation, etc. The total costs of a reactor with no supporting facilities range from about $100,000 upward. About $100,000 to $200,000 will purchase a small laboratory reactor capable of delivering fluxes of 10^6 to 10^{11} n/(cm^2)(sec). In general, these reactors have been designed and engineered to meet U. S. Government safety requirements and are sold as a package. Consequently, the design and engineering costs are spread over a number of reactors, and are generally a small part of the total cost. Also, the cost of obtaining a license is relatively small because of the low power and the analysis and precautions previously worked out by the manufacturer. Frequently, the construction costs for such a reactor are only the costs incurred in making minor modifications to an existing building.

The next price range is rather arbitrary but may be considered to be from $350,000 to $1,500,000. The 30- to 50-kw water boilers and the natural-convection pool reactors are available at the lower end of this price range. About $750,000 to $1,500,000 will buy a rather elaborate pool reactor and, possibly, a 1- to 5-Mw ordinary water or even a heavy-water tank reactor.

The actual price for a given reactor will vary considerably, depending on the amount of auxiliary equipment, the number of experimental facilities, and the design of the building. The cost, including cooling towers, etc., of very high-power tank reactors such as the Engineering Test Reactor is about $18,000,000.

The percentage of the total cost that must be allotted to design and engineering increases with the cost of the reactor. A larger percentage is required in more expensive reactors because the higher power and greater complexity require a custom-made installation. Thus the design requires considerably more analysis and, possibly, development work, which increases the cost. In addition, the costs of assuring safe operation and of obtaining a license quite naturally increase with the higher power generally associated with the higher-cost reactors. As has been pointed out, the cost of the reactor facility may run two or even three times the cost of the reactor alone when the necessary supporting facilities are considered.

In choosing a reactor, operating costs are possibly more important than the initial costs of obtaining the reactor. The operating costs of a 1000-kw pool reactor can easily run to $250,000 per year if amortization of the plant is included with actual operating expenses. Operating expenses include such things as salaries of supervisory and operating staff, health-physics services, heat and utilities, insurance, fuel costs, etc. To sustain such a reactor requires a sizable research budget. As a rule of thumb, the cost of the neutrons and gamma rays makes up only 10 to 25% of the cost of a reactor-dependent research program. If 15% is assumed as an over-all average, a reactor with an operating cost of $250,000 requires an annual reactor-dependent research budget of about $1,500,000. Conversely, facilities and staff to handle this volume of research must be available if the reactor is to be operated efficiently.

To summarize, then, there are four important criteria to consider in choosing and planning a reactor system. These deal with reactor safety, experimental requirements, necessary supporting facilities, and costs. These criteria are interrelated, and major changes in one will affect the others, particularly the cost. Even at best, the final choice will be a compromise. It is very important for the prospective reactor owner to evaluate his needs and resources carefully, so as to obtain the best reactor for his use commensurate with his operating budget.

1–6. LEGAL PROBLEMS AND REGULATIONS

In the United States, after the reactor is designed, a license application must be prepared and submitted to the Atomic Energy Commission. This license actually consists of three parts: a permit to begin construction, a license to possess the uranium fuel, and a license to operate a facility. As a part of the application, the party who will be responsible for the reactor must prepare a report describing the facility and analyzing its potential hazards.

Not only must the facility itself be licensed, but also the personnel who operate it. Reactor operators' licenses are issued by the AEC after the trainees have passed a written test and have been checked out on reactor operation.

Liability and property damage insurance have been given considerable attention by those who own and those who plan to own research reactors. While most people are convinced that the probability of an accident resulting in damage claims is very low, still they are interested in having some coverage. The problem of the amount of insurance required and the magnitude of the premiums has not as yet been clearly resolved.

1-7. STARTUP AND OPERATION

A considerable amount of time and effort is involved in what might be termed "precriticality experiments." These are the checkouts and experiments that must be run to assure that the reactor is ready to go critical for the first time. Several months may be required for this work, the actual time depending on the complexity of the reactor and the familiarity of the staff with the various components.

During this precriticality period, all the instrumentation and detecting equipment must be checked out and calibrated and the control system tested to see that all units are operating properly. Some time is required to check all external facilities, cooling towers, heat exchangers, plumbing, and piping. Generally, it is necessary to train personnel in reactor operation, core loading, and health-physics techniques. Before routine operation can begin, a procedure plan for normal operation and special procedures to cover a variety of emergency conditions must be formulated. Schooling of personnel in operation and procedures requires considerable training and drill.

Although a number of the items of calibration, formulation, and training can be carried out simultaneously, this requires a trained, competent staff larger than most new facilities have available. The length of time allotted to this checkout period is frequently underestimated in making up reactor time schedules.

After a working knowledge of the various components has been obtained, and immediately before the first attempt to go critical, a final detailed startup procedure is drawn up. This is a written document which is followed point by point in all later reactor startups. The steps in this procedure should not be modified or changed except as dictated by experience, and then only after due consideration by the supervisory staff.

After the reactor goes critical for the first time, there are a number of experiments that must be performed before routine operation can begin. The duration and, to some extent, the type of experiments will vary, depending on the reactor type and the power level. However, these experiments generally include such things as (1) calibrating control rods, (2) measuring the effect of fuel and other materials on reactor operation, and (3) determining the effect of altering or changing the location of experimental facilities. These experiments are usually carried out at very low power in order to keep the fuel from becoming highly radioactive. In certain reactors, such as pool reactors, it may be necessary to repeat these experiments for a number of core configurations.

Still at reduced power, the neutron- and gamma-ray flux distribution in and around the core and in the experimental facilities is measured. During this period, it is also of interest to determine the temperature and void coefficients, and the drop time of the control rods and their effect on the reactor as a function of time for complete insertion.

At full-power operation, the adequacy of the shielding which has been observed at the lower power levels is again checked carefully. If the reactor has a cooling system, it must be completely checked out at power, as must the radiation monitors and other auxiliary equipment.

Normal routine operation can begin after these several months of testing. The owner of the new reactor will now encounter all the problems that occur only in the routine operation and maintenance. Some of the problems encountered by other operators and their solutions may be beneficial to future reactor owners. These are discussed in a later chapter.

BIBLIOGRAPHY

U. S. ATOMIC ENERGY COMMISSION, *Research Reactors. Selected Reference Material. United States Atomic Energy Program*, USAEC Report TID-5275, 1955.

BECK, CLIFFORD K., *Nuclear Reactors for Research*. Princeton, N. J.: D. Van Nostrand Co., Inc., 1957.

CHARPIE, R. A. et al., *Progress in Nuclear Energy, Series II, Reactors*, Vol. 1. New York: Pergamon Press, 1956.

CHAPTER 2

RESEARCH REACTOR PHYSICS*

The physics of research reactors is essentially the same as the physics of reactors in general. Most research reactors are thermal reactors because, at present, this type of reactor is cheaper to construct, easier to control and operate, and a more versatile research tool. The word "thermal" refers to the energy of the neutrons which produce the majority of the fissions in the reactor. Thermal neutrons are those having a kinetic energy close to the energy of the atoms or molecules of the surrounding material. This energy depends on the temperature of the material and is called *thermal energy*.

2-1. PRELIMINARY CONSIDERATIONS

The fission event consists of splitting a U^{235} nucleus into two or more fragments of lower mass and atomic number. The first step in the process is the absorption of a neutron. The nuclear reaction is written as

$$_0n^1 + {}_{92}U^{235} \rightarrow {}_{92}U^{236},$$

where the subscripts indicate the atomic number or number of protons (charge), and the superscripts indicate the atomic mass (the sum of the protons and neutrons). The U^{236} nucleus which results from the above reaction is in an excited state. It returns to stable U^{236} by emitting a gamma ray in 16% of the cases; in the remaining 84% the result is fission. The nucleus of the U^{236} can split in a number of ways, one of which is shown by the following:

$$_{92}U^{236} \rightarrow {}_{56}Ba^{139} + {}_{36}Kr^{94} + 3{}_0n^1 + \text{energy.}$$

Here, the neutron has caused the uranium to fission into two major fragments, barium and krypton. In addition, three neutrons are emitted which can be used to induce more fissions and, consequently, a self-sustaining chain reaction is possible. This self-sustaining characteristic is one of the factors which sets fission apart from other nuclear reactions. A second characteristic is the large amount of energy emitted in this process as compared with the energy in other nuclear reactions. This

---

* By R. F. Redmond and J. W. Chastain, Jr.

energy per fission, about 190 Mev, is quite small, since it takes 3.3×10^{10} fissions/sec to generate 1 watt of power. On the other hand, it is possible to obtain large energy releases per unit time in a reactor from fission because of the high fission rates possible.

In the example 3 neutrons were liberated, but the number can vary from 1 to 6. On the average, about 2.5 neutrons are emitted for each fission, considering all modes of decay for U^{236}. About 2.1 neutrons are produced for each neutron absorbed in U^{235}, since 16% of the neutrons absorbed produce gamma rays.

Consideration of the physics of a thermal reactor will perhaps make clearer some of the reasons for certain design features. The neutrons resulting from the fission of U^{235} are quite energetic, with speeds of approximately 10^9 cm/sec. However, the U^{235} nucleus absorbs neutrons much more readily when the neutrons are moving with slower speeds. In fact, the slower the neutron, the more readily it is captured by the U^{235} nucleus. If this energetic neutron were located in a large volume of material whose atoms could not absorb the neutron but which could scatter the neutron by elastic collisions, the neutron would travel a jagged path, each elastic collision with a nucleus tending to change the direction of the neutron's path. If the atoms of the material had no thermal motion, the neutron would gradually slow to zero velocity because of the transfer of momentum (the product of the mass of a particle and its velocity) from the neutron to the atomic nuclei through elastic collisions. However, the atoms of the material do have thermal motion, so that a neutron whose kinetic energy is less than that of the nucleus can collide with a nucleus in thermal motion and gain kinetic energy. Thus, if there is a large number of neutrons in the material, the neutrons will ultimately be in thermal equilibrium with the material and, instead of zero velocity, the average equilibrium neutron velocity will be several thousand meters per second. The neutrons in such a thermal equilibrium have a Maxwell-Boltzmann distribution of velocities characterized by the temperature of the material but otherwise independent of the material properties. The neutrons in thermal equilibrium have a velocity distribution comparable to that of gas molecules in a closed container.

The nuclei of any material will absorb neutrons to a certain extent, so that ultimately all neutrons initially present will be absorbed. However, if, as in most thermal reactors, the reactor materials (other than U^{235}) do not appreciably absorb neutrons, the neutrons that are degraded to low energy will still have many characteristics of Maxwell-Boltzmann distribution.* In fact, this is the distinguishing feature of a thermal reactor;

---

* The graph of the Maxwell-Boltzmann distribution is a curve that rises sharply to a peak and then diminishes for a time, almost as quickly. It then levels off gradually.

most of the neutrons are absorbed after they have been slowed down to a velocity distribution similar to a Maxwell-Boltzmann distribution.

It should not be inferred that the neutrons must be slowed down to thermal energies in order to maintain a chain reaction. However, research reactors are generally thermal reactors, of which the slowing-down process is an essential feature.

2–2. Moderator, Reflector, and Reactor Size

The size of a thermal reactor depends to a large extent upon the moderating material used to slow down the neutrons. A good moderator (1) effectively slows down the high-speed neutrons and (2) does not readily absorb neutrons. The materials which slow down the high-speed neutrons most efficiently are the light nuclei, i.e., those with small mass numbers. The neutron can transfer more energy to the moderator in an elastic collision with these than with heavier nuclei. The moderators normally used are water, heavy water, graphite, beryllium, and beryllium compounds.

A thermal reactor can be visualized as an arrangement of moderating material and U^{235}. The reactor may be a vessel of water with a uranium salt in solution or it may be a large mass of graphite with uranium contained in metallic rods placed throughout the graphite. The reactor must be the right size and contain the proper amounts of the various atoms to sustain the chain reaction.

Because of the finite size of a reactor, some neutrons from the fissioning uranium escape before they can be slowed down and absorbed inside the reactor. For example, in a graphite-moderated reactor, a neutron from a fission event will travel, on the average, 3 or 4 ft from the point where it was born before it is absorbed; in a water-moderated reactor, the distance may be as small as 6 in. To minimize the escape of neutrons, a material which scatters escaping neutrons back into the reactor is put around the reactor. This material around the reactor is termed the "reflector" material, and normally a good moderator is also a good reflector.

2–3. Criticality and Critical Mass

Suppose a reactor contains the proper materials and is the right size so that a self-sustaining chain reactor occurs. That is, for every neutron which is absorbed in the reactor or escapes from the reactor in a given time interval, one neutron is created by a fission event in the same interval. This reactor is then said to be "just critical" or to have attained *criticality*. An important aspect of the critical state of a reactor should be emphasized.

In a given time interval there may be a certain number of neutrons emitted, but the reactor will still be in a critical state so long as the number of neutrons which are absorbed and which escape, in total, equals the number emitted. A critical reactor can, in principle, have any value for the rate of fissioning or for the power level at which it operates.

The rate of reaction for fission events in a reactor is generally given in terms of a power level. Since, on the average, each fission releases a certain amount of energy, it is clear that the rate of energy release or power of the reactor is proportional to the fission rate. However, criticality and power level are not directly related, and a critical reactor can operate at almost any power.

On the other hand, if n neutrons are created in a given time interval and if in the same interval more than n neutrons are absorbed and escape from the reactor, the reactor will be subcritical. Conversely, a supercritical reactor is one in which more neutrons are produced than are absorbed and escape from the reactor in the same period. The power level in a subcritical reactor decreases with time, while in a supercritical reactor it increases with time.

The quantity of U^{235} required to make a reactor just critical is called the *critical mass* of the reactor. Critical mass depends on the nuclear properties of the materials in and around the reactor and upon the shape and size of the reactor. As an example of the variation in critical mass for typical research reactors, the Armour Reactor (a salt of "enriched" uranium in a water solution contained in about a 1-ft-diameter sphere) has a critical mass of about 1.2 kg of U^{235}, while a graphite reactor containing natural uranium metallic rods in a cube 22 ft on a side has a critical mass of about 0.67 ton of U^{235} contained in about 93 tons of natural uranium.

One of the fundamental problems in reactor physics is to determine (1) the circumstances in which a system will become critical, and (2) the spatial distribution of the neutrons in the critical system. This problem involves equations which represent a detailed balance of the neutrons in the system. Generally these are complicated partial differential equations and are not easily solved. However, numerical techniques have been developed for solving approximations to the correct equations.

For example, a "two-group" theory has been developed which gives approximate results for thermal reactors. In this theory the neutrons are lumped into two energy states instead of being continuously distributed over the full energy spectrum from fission energy to thermal energy. One energy state corresponds to the thermal energy part of the spectrum and the other represents an average energy state of the neutrons above thermal energies. The neutrons in the high-energy group originate from fission events induced by the absorption by U^{235} of neutrons in the thermal group. These fast neutrons are then considered to diffuse and finally to degrade in energy to the thermal group. Some of the fast neutrons leak from the system and are lost. Those degraded in energy to the thermal group diffuse until they are absorbed or leak from the system. When a neutron balance throughout the system has been reached, the reactor system is just critical. The spatial distribution of neutron flux in the reactor for the two energy groups can then be calculated.

The energy spectrum can also be divided into several energy groups. Numerical techniques have been developed for solving core design problems by these multigroup schemes and many of these techniques have been adapted for high-speed electronic computers.

2–3.1 Fuel enrichment. Research reactors in the United States have been fueled with either natural uranium or uranium highly enriched (about 90 a/o*) in the U^{235} isotope. Some countries have or are obtaining research reactors fueled with 20% uranium. It appears that any reactor which uses fully enriched uranium can be modified in design to operate on 20% fuel.

The additional U^{238} in the 20% enriched fuel acts as a neutron absorber which tends to increase the critical mass of the reactor. This effect is small in reactors which already have significant amounts of absorption in the moderator and structural materials. In these reactors, if the U^{235} loading per fuel element is the same for both enrichments, the critical mass and the core size are approximately the same. For example, the Bulk Shielding Reactor, a light-water moderated pool reactor, has a critical mass of 3.5 kg. The Swiss reactor at Wuerenlingen (formerly the Geneva Conference Reactor of 1955) has a critical mass of about 3.6 kg using 20% enriched fuel in a similar core size and arrangement. (See Table 3–4.)

In a reactor where absorption of neutrons in nonfuel materials is small, the effect on the critical mass of the additional U^{238} may be more significant. The critical size of a heavy-water reactor using uranium enriched to 20% is about 1.8 times that of a similar reactor using highly enriched fuel. The critical mass is increased correspondingly.

2–4. NEUTRON FLUX AND SPECTRUM

An important physics concept in reactor technology is that of neutron flux. It will be seen later how this quantity enters into the calculation of the rates of nuclear reactions involving neutrons. Neutron flux has the units of neutrons per unit area per unit time. Physically, neutron flux is a measure of the total length of travel of all the neutrons in a unit

---

* a/o = atomic percent.

volume in a unit time interval. Hence, the neutron flux can be thought of as the intensity of the total neutron motion. The neutron flux is defined as the product of the neutron density and the neutron velocity.

From this definition, the neutron velocity would, of course, have to be representative of the neutrons described by the neutron density term. Ideally, if the neutrons all had the same velocity or kinetic energy there would be no ambiguity. However, in actuality the neutrons will be spread more or less continuously over a large energy range. To be more precise, one should speak of a neutron density and a neutron flux per unit energy interval. Thus, $n(E) \, dE$ is the density of neutrons in the energy interval from E to $E + dE$, and $v(E)n(E) \, dE$ is the flux of neutrons in the energy interval from E to $E + dE$, where $v(E)$ is the velocity of the neutron with kinetic energy E. In these relationships, it is supposed that dE is a small quantity, in fact, a differential quantity, so that there is no ambiguity in the velocity to be used. Since the neutrons are assumed to be continuously distributed in energy, $n(E)$ is the number of neutrons of energy E per unit energy interval per unit volume. Thus, the density of neutrons with energy E in the interval from E_1 to E_2 is $\int_{E_1}^{E_2} n(E) \, dE$, and as the energy interval becomes smaller and smaller the integral approaches zero. Thus, in this description of the neutrons, $n(E)$ may be considered as the spectral distribution function for the neutrons and gives a complete picture of how the neutrons are distributed over the energy range. In the same way, $v(E)n(E)$, usually denoted by $\phi(E)$, gives a complete picture of how the neutron flux per unit energy varies over the energy range.

Actually, the thermal neutrons are in a rather small energy interval compared with the total energy range of the neutrons of a reactor and are, therefore, characterized by the ideal situation noted in the previous paragraph, i.e., the neutrons all have essentially the same velocity. Because of the way the thermal neutron flux is determined experimentally, it is usually given in terms of the total neutron density over the thermal-energy range times a characteristic velocity. It is common usage to use a velocity of 2200 m/sec as the characteristic velocity regardless of the true spectrum of the thermal neutrons. This convention, which may appear somewhat arbitrary, does have a certain utility in calculating reaction rates. The physical significance of the 2200 m/sec velocity is that it corresponds to the neutron energy for which there is a maximum in the thermal flux spectrum $\phi(E) = n(E)v(E)$, when a Maxwell-Boltzmann distribution at a temperature of 25°C is used.

In a reactor there are neutrons from almost zero energy to the maximum energy, i.e., fission neutrons of about 10 Mev. Figure 2–1 shows the neutron spectrum at the center of a typical light-water moderated reactor. It will be noted that a different variable, the lethargy, u, has been used

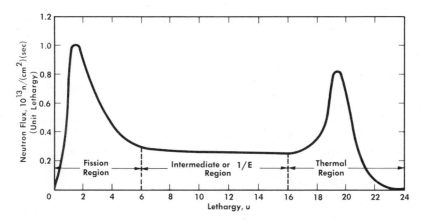

Fig. 2–1. Flux spectrum in typical water-moderated reactor.

rather than the energy, E. These variables are related as shown by the expression

$$u = \log_e \frac{E_0}{E}, \qquad (2\text{--}1)$$

where u = lethargy of neutron, $E_0 = 10^7$ ev (electron volts), and E = energy of neutron in ev units. The flux per unit lethargy, $\phi(u)$, is related to the flux per unit energy, $\phi(E)$, by

$$\phi(u) = -\phi(E) \frac{dE}{du} = E\phi(E). \qquad (2\text{--}2)$$

The lethargy variable is a convenient one, since the energy of most reactor neutrons ranges from several hundredths of an ev to 10^7 ev, whereas the corresponding lethargy values range from about 20 to 0.

Three regions of the neutron-flux spectrum are worth noting and are apparent in Fig. 2–1. The first region is the fission-energy region. In this region the neutron flux has a peak because neutrons of about this energy are created by the fission events and are the most energetic ones in the reactor. The shape of the flux curve in this region follows somewhat the energy distribution of the neutrons released by the fission process. The second region of interest is the intermediate or $1/E$ region. The term $1/E$ refers to the fact that in this region $\phi(u)$ is approximately constant, and hence $\phi(E)$ is proportional to $1/E$. In this region of the spectrum the fission neutrons are being slowed to thermal neutrons by colliding with the moderator atoms. The third region is the thermal-energy region. In this part of the energy spectrum the neutrons are in thermal equilibrium with the moderator atoms. As mentioned previously, the shape of the flux spectrum in this region is essentially a Maxwell-Boltzmann distribution. Most of the neutrons are absorbed after they have entered the thermal-energy region because most moderator materials slow the neutrons down before they can be absorbed. The neutrons over the entire neutron spectrum are of interest for various research applications. Thermal-flux values for research reactors range up to 10^{13} or 10^{14} n/(cm^2)(sec).

As an aid in visualizing the population of neutrons in a reactor, it may be noted that neutron densities of up to perhaps 10^9 n/cm^3 may exist in a research reactor. This number may be contrasted to the density of atomic nuclei in the reactor, which may be of the order of 10^{22} or 10^{23} nuclei/cm^3. Thus, compared with the population of atomic nuclei, the neutron population is exceedingly small.

Attention thus far has been given to how the reactor neutron flux varies with neutron energy. However, mention should also be made of the variation of neutron flux throughout the reactor. In general, the flux level will tend to decrease away from the center of the reactor, although the thermal-neutron flux may not always follow this pattern. Details of the spatial variation of the neutron flux will be described in the chapters which describe the specific reactor types.

2–5. Cross Section and Reaction Rates

Nuclear reactions are frequently characterized by a "cross section" which expresses the likelihood that the given reaction will occur. The cross-section concept is quite fundamental in discussing reaction rates involving reactor neutrons. The rate of neutron absorptions or the reaction rate for absorption by a material when placed in a flux ϕ is given by $\Sigma_a\phi$, with units of neutron absorptions per unit volume per unit time. The quantity Σ_a is termed the *macroscopic cross section* for neutron absorption for the material, and has the units of inverse length. Since the flux can be considered the total path traversed by the neutrons per unit volume per unit time, the macroscopic cross section Σ_a can be interpreted as the probability per unit path length that a neutron will be absorbed. As defined, Σ_a is a macroscopic quantity and depends upon the density of the material, the nuclear properties, and the velocity of the neutrons. If Σ_a is the macroscopic absorption cross section for all absorption processes, then $\Sigma_a\phi$ is the total number of neutrons absorbed by a process per unit volume in unit time. However, Σ_a can be broken down into various components, such as the fission cross section, radiation capture cross section where a gamma ray is emitted, etc. The product of the flux and the macroscopic cross section for a particular process gives the reaction rate for that process.

Cross sections on a per atom basis are termed *microscopic* cross sections. For a material containing only one kind of atomic nucleus the relationship between macroscopic and microscopic cross sections for a given reaction is given by

$$\Sigma = N\sigma, \tag{2–3}$$

where Σ = macroscopic cross section, in inverse length, N = atoms or nuclei per unit volume of material, σ = microscopic cross section, in area per atom. The microscopic cross section for a given reaction depends on the nuclear properties and on the energy of the neutrons. The quantity σ can be thought of as an effective area per nucleus for the particular reaction, although this is not strictly true. If a material has a mixture of different atoms then the macroscopic cross section for the mixture is given by the sum of the macroscopic cross sections for each kind of atom.

A neutron can be scattered in traversing material, as well as absorbed. Thus $N\sigma_s$ denotes the probability per unit path length that a neutron will be scattered in a material containing N atoms per unit volume with a scattering cross section per atom of σ_s.

Experimental techniques for measuring cross sections are explained in Chapter 10.

Frequently, a neutron absorption reaction produces a radioactive material. This activation can be measured to determine neutron flux if the cross section is known, or vice versa, or the resulting radioisotope may be used in research. Since each neutron absorbed results in the production of a radioactive nucleus, the rate of formation of the active species is $\Sigma_a \phi$ nuclei per second per unit volume. However, the decay of the radioactive material occurs to some extent while it is being produced. If λN is the number of disintegrations per second, the net rate of increase of the active species at any instant is

$$\frac{dN}{dt} = \Sigma_a \phi - \lambda N, \tag{2–4}$$

where N is the number of active nuclei per unit volume present after t sec of exposure of the material to the neutron flux ϕ. The solution to this equation is

$$N = \frac{\Sigma_a \phi}{\lambda} (1 - e^{-\lambda t}), \tag{2–5}$$

if $N = 0$ when $t = 0$.

The activity A of the foil measured by a counter with 100% efficiency is equal to λN, which is the rate of emission of charged particles (or photons) per unit volume, so that

$$A = \Sigma_a \phi (1 - e^{-\lambda t}). \tag{2–6}$$

If exposure to neutrons is continued for some time, so that t is large and $e^{-\lambda t}$ is small compared with unity, Eq. (2–6) becomes

$$A_\infty = \Sigma_a \phi, \tag{2–7}$$

which is called the saturation activity. It is the maximum or limiting activity the material can acquire in the specified neutron flux.

After removing the activated material from the neutron flux at time t_0, it continues to decay, and at any subsequent time t the activity is

$$A_t = \Sigma_a \phi (1 - e^{-\lambda t_0}) e^{-\lambda(t-t_0)}$$

$$= \Sigma_a \phi [e^{-\lambda(t-t_0)} - e^{-\lambda(t)}]. \tag{2-8}$$

By determining the activity of the foil in a counter, after a period t_0 of exposure to neutrons, a delay $t - t_0$ before counting, and making allowance for decay during the process of counting, it is possible to evaluate the saturation activity $\Sigma_a \phi$ from Eq. (2-8). Hence if Σ_a is known, ϕ can be determined.

Typical materials used for flux measurements are gold, indium, and manganese.

A term frequently encountered in reactor work is "cadmium ratio." If a wire or foil of a detecting material such as indium is exposed to the flux in a reactor, it is activated by both thermal-energy and intermediate-energy neutrons. However, if indium is covered with cadmium, the cadmium will absorb almost all the neutrons below 0.4 ev. Thus the resulting activation of the indium is induced by neutrons with energy greater than 0.4 ev. The cadmium ratio, R_{Cd}, is defined as

$$R_{Cd} = \frac{A_t + A_i}{A_i}, \tag{2-9}$$

where A_t and A_i are the activations due to neutrons of thermal and intermediate energies, respectively. Since these activations can be related to the fluxes, the cadmium ratio can be used to obtain the ratio of the thermal and intermediate flux to the intermediate flux. If, in addition, a calibrated source or counter is available, the activation by the intermediate neutrons can be related to the absolute intermediate flux. The absolute thermal flux can be derived from the difference between the two activations.

The value of the cadmium ratio depends on the detecting material used, since the activation induced in the material depends on the variation of cross section with energy as well as on the neutron spectrum in the reactor.

2-6. Kinetics, Delayed Neutrons, Reactivity

As mentioned previously under the discussion of criticality, power in a subcritical reactor without an external source of neutrons decreases with time, while in a supercritical reactor the power level increases with time.

Thus the condition of the reactor with respect to the critical condition affects the reactor kinetics.

The existence of delayed fission neutrons has an important influence on reactor kinetics. Although over 99% of the fission neutrons are emitted virtually instantaneously, there is a small fraction (about 0.7% for U^{235}) which have a variety of half-lives associated with their emission following the fission event. These neutrons, called delayed neutrons, act as a damping influence on the time rate of change of the neutron flux. Were it not for the delayed neutrons, a reactor would be extremely difficult to control.

The term "reactor period" is used to describe the transient character of the neutron flux. This quantity is defined by

$$T = \left[\frac{1}{\phi} \frac{d\phi}{dt} \right]^{-1}, \tag{2–10}$$

where T = reactor period in sec, ϕ = reactor flux in n/(cm^2)(sec), and t = time in sec. If Eq. (2–10) is integrated with respect to time and T is constant, we find that the neutron flux in a supercritical reactor has an exponential rise characterized by the period T. The more supercritical the reactor the faster the flux will rise and the shorter the period will be.

Whereas the period describes the transient behavior of the reactor flux, the reactivity gives the state of the reactor with regard to criticality. In the previous discussion, a critical state was said to exist if for every neutron which is absorbed or escapes in an arbitrary time interval, there is just one neutron created by fission in the same time interval. This definition can be modified to include reactor states which are not just critical but are characterized by an "effective multiplication constant," k_{eff}. Suppose that for every fission in a reactor ν fission neutrons are released and that ν can have any value desired; then if a value ν_0 makes the reactor just critical, the k_{eff} for the reactor can be defined by

$$k_{\text{eff}} = \frac{\nu}{\nu_0}, \tag{2–11}$$

where k_{eff} = effective multiplication constant, ν = actual average number of fission neutrons per fission, and ν_0 = required average number of fission neutrons per fission for criticality.

Hence when $k_{\text{eff}} = 1$, the reactor is truly critical, but if k_{eff} is greater than unity the reactor is supercritical, and when k_{eff} is less than unity it is subcritical. Thus reactivity can be defined as

$$\rho = \frac{k_{\text{eff}} - 1}{k_{\text{eff}}} = \frac{\Delta k_{\text{eff}}}{k_{\text{eff}}}, \tag{2–12}$$

where ρ = reactivity.

The reactivity is then seen to be zero for a just critical reactor, greater than zero for a supercritical reactor, and less than zero for a subcritical reactor. The relationship between reactivity and period is discussed in Chapter 9, on reactor safety.

For a given composition of materials in the reactor the value for k_{eff} will depend on the reactor size and the reflector properties. However, if one imagines that the reactor is increased in size indefinitely so that the leakage per unit volume of neutrons from the system is reduced to zero, the k_{eff} will approach a value independent of the reactor size and the reflector properties. This limiting value for k_{eff} is termed the "infinite multiplication constant" of the material and is often designated by k_{∞}. Usually the k_{∞} value for a reactor material composition represents the maximum attainable value of k_{eff}. Therefore, k_{∞} must be greater than unity in order for a reactor of finite size of the given material composition to be critical. The amount that k_{∞} exceeds unity will determine the size of the critical reactor. In general, the more k_{∞} exceeds unity the smaller the reactor can be made. As examples, the k_{∞} for a natural uranium-graphite reactor may be about 1.05 and thus it has to be a very large reactor, about a 25-ft cube; for an enriched uranium-water reactor k_{∞} may be about 1.6, and thus the reactor can be quite small, perhaps a 1.5-ft cube.

2–6.1 Reactor control and reactivity effects. If the power level of a reactor is to be controlled, then some means must be incorporated into the reactor for varying the reactivity. For example, if it is desired to increase the reactor power from some initial level to some final level, the reactivity must be made positive until the final power level is attained and then reduced to zero. The usual way for effecting these reactivity changes is by means of a rod which absorbs neutrons and which can be moved in and out of the reactor. When this control rod is inserted into the reactor, it takes neutrons from the system and causes a decrease in reactivity. Conversely, when the rod is withdrawn, more neutrons are available for fissioning and the reactivity increases.

The need for a control rod to make power-level adjustments is just one example of the necessity of having some control over reactor criticality. A reactor which is made just critical at a desired power level will not maintain its critical condition because the number of U^{235} atoms is continually decreasing and fission products, some of which are good absorbers, are continually being formed. Thus, if initially the reactor is just critical with a control rod fully inserted, the control rod must be withdrawn gradually to maintain criticality. Eventually, of course, the control rod will be fully withdrawn and the reactor must be refueled. Neutron absorption by the experimental devices located in or around the reactor is

TABLE 2–1

ESTIMATED REACTIVITY REQUIREMENTS FOR 6 DAYS' CONTINUOUS
OPERATION OF A POOL REACTOR AT A POWER OF 1 MEGAWATT

Item	Reactivity, $\dfrac{k_{\text{eff}} - 1}{k_{\text{eff}}}$
Control	0.003
Temperature	Negligible
Fission-product poisons	0.020
Beam tubes	0.005
Core experiments	0.015
Total	0.043

another factor which may alter the criticality. Although this effect is generally small, a research reactor facility must include means for accommodating the criticality effects of possible experiments.

These reactivity requirements mean that more U^{235} must be available in the reactor core than would be necessary to make the reactor just critical at the start of operation. That is, fuel must be added to allow for burnup, experiments, temperature effects, and fission-product poisons. Table 2–1 gives estimated values for some reactivity effects encountered in a typical 1-megawatt pool reactor.

To provide safe control of the typical reactor of Table 2–1, the control rods must have a reactivity "worth" greater than the total requirements of $0.043 \ \Delta k_{\text{eff}}/k_{\text{eff}}$. For reactor shutdown safety it is customary for research reactors to have total control rod worths about twice the reactivity requirements.

In addition to the reactivity effects of normal operation the effects of abnormal operation also affect reactor safety. For example, abnormal operation in a water-cooled reactor may cause the water to boil, and so affect reactivity. Such effects as these are generally given in terms of a reactivity coefficient which is the ratio of an incremental reactivity change to the corresponding change in the affected reactor parameter. These coefficients are discussed more fully in Chapter 9.

2–7. RADIATIONS

Of particular interest in a discussion of the physics of research reactors are the kinds of radiation made available by a reactor. The radiations and particles released within a critical reactor include gamma rays, electrons, and neutrons. However, usually only gamma rays and neutrons are of interest; hence attention will be focused on these. Gamma rays and neutrons are penetrating and interact with matter to a significant extent. The electrons released in the reactor are stopped close to their origin, and hence are not easily utilized. The neutrinos (particles with no charge and no mass at zero velocity) released in a reactor are of little practical interest, since they interact with matter to such a very small extent. However, the neutrino is of fundamental interest in nuclear physics and the reactor is a rich source of these particles. Indeed, the existence of neutrinos was established by experiments which employed a reactor as the source of these elusive particles.

A source of the great majority of the neutrons in the reactor is the fission process. A gamma ray impinging on a beryllium atom can eject a neutron. This reaction is expressed as $Be(\gamma, n)$. Initially these fission neutrons have an energy distribution like that shown in Fig. 2–2. The energy spectrum of the neutrons at the particular place where they are to be used depends partially on the location with respect to the core. For example, if a high intensity of fast (high-energy) neutrons is desired, it is necessary to locate the sample in a region near the fuel, where the high-energy neutrons are produced in fission. If the sample is located some distance from the reactor fuel, many of the fission neutrons will be degraded appreciably in energy due to collisions with the intervening material before reaching the specimen.

Neutrons of all energies, from fission energies to close to zero energy, exist in the reactor and its surroundings. The spectral distribution of these neutrons varies considerably with position in the reactor and, consequently, the best location in the reactor for a particular test depends on

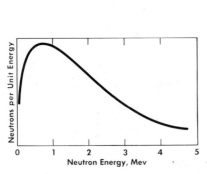

Fig. 2–2. Fission neutron energy spectrum.

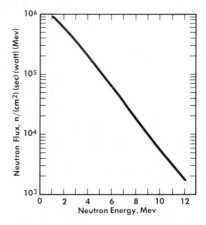

Fig. 2–3. Fast neutron leakage spectrum of the BSR.

the test requirements. The spectrum of high-energy neutrons leaking from one reactor is shown in Fig. 2–3.

The gamma rays appearing in the reactor originate in a variety of nuclear reactions. A number of gamma rays occur at fission, and decay of the fission fragments supplies additional gamma rays at varying times after the fission event. The neutrons are inelastically scattered and absorbed by the core materials, producing more gamma rays. When the reaction of a neutron with material results in the emission of one or more gamma rays, it is termed a neutron-gamma reaction, abbreviated (n, γ). (Reactions involving other nuclear radiations are expressed in a similar manner.) The nuclei resulting from neutron capture are frequently radioactive and also emit gamma rays.

Distribution of gamma-ray sources in the reactor is much more complex than the distribution of the neutron sources. As an indication of the gamma-ray spectrum to be found in a reactor, Fig. 2–4 shows the spectrum measured at the face of the BSR.

The gamma rays from the reactor may heat materials near the reactor core, and consideration must be given to this heating problem in designing some experiments. For example, in the Battelle Research Reactor (BRR) for some materials this effect amounts to as much as 0.3 watts/g of material at 1-Mw reactor power.

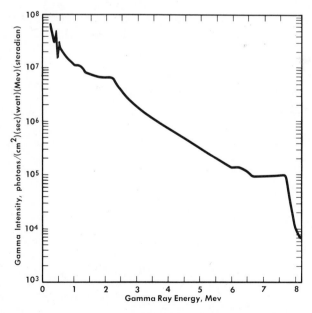

FIG. 2–4. Gamma-ray spectrum at surface of BSR core.

2–7.1 Shielding. Although radiations from reactors are useful for research, they present a serious hazard to human beings. Both gamma rays and neutrons can cause serious biological damage, and the reactor facility must include adequate features to safeguard the health of those who work with it. At the face of the BSR core the gamma-ray intensity and the neutron flux are both about 10^{10} times the maximum permissible value accepted for safe human tolerance.

The usual way of reducing these radiation levels is to surround the reactor with materials which will absorb the radiations to the required extent. These materials form what is termed the *reactor shield*. In research reactor installations the shield is normally water and/or concrete which may incorporate a dense material as the concrete aggregate. Table 2–2 shows some shield thicknesses for several representative reactors. Design of a research reactor shield is complicated by the fact that the shield must be penetrated by tubes and other facilities in order to make the radiations available. These penetrations require careful design to ensure that the radiations do not stream through the shield penetrations and lead to dangerous radiation levels outside the shield.

The analysis of the attenuation of radiations as they penetrate materials is not, in general, straightforward. In the case of gamma rays much is known about the attenuations through materials containing a single element; however, for materials containing a number of different elements little information on attentuation is available. Besides the gamma rays which originate in the reactor, the gamma rays which result from neutron captures in the shield itself must be considered. Thus the shield analyst

TABLE 2–2

SHIELDS FOR FOUR TYPES OF REACTORS

Reactor	Power	Shield component	Shield thickness
BNL (Graphite)	28 megawatt	High-density concrete	5 ft
Armour (Homogeneous)	50 kilowatt	High-density concrete	5 ft
BRR (Pool)	1 megawatt	Light water (vertical shield)	22 ft
AGN (Solid homogeneous)	0.1 watt	Lead and light water	4 in. lead and 22 in. water

must determine where the neutrons are absorbed before he can completely specify the sources of gamma rays in the system.

The determination of neutron attenuation and neutron capture in shield materials is also a complex problem to analyze. Approximate analytical techniques used in conjunction with experimental data are usually employed to estimate neutron attenuations. In most cases for research reactors using concrete shields or water shields, the shield requirements will be determined primarily by the attenuation required for the reactor gamma rays.

Several useful references for making shield evaluations are included in the supplementary reading list at the end of this chapter. However, it should be noted that the design and construction of a safe and economical shield requires the attention of an experienced shield designer.

REFERENCES

1. S. GLASSTONE and M. C. EDLUND, *The Elements of Nuclear Reactor Theory*. Princeton, N. J.: D. Van Nostrand Co., Inc., 1952.

2. C. F. BONILLA (Ed.), *Nuclear Engineering*. New York: McGraw-Hill Book Company, Inc., 1957.

3. D. J. HUGHES, *Pile Neutron Research*. Cambridge, Mass.: Addison-Wesley Press, Inc., 1953.

4. T. ROCKWELL, *Reactor Shielding Design Manual*. New York: McGraw-Hill Book Company, Inc., 1956.

5. *The Reactor Handbook, Vol. 1, Physics*, USAEC Report AECD-3645, 1955.

6. B. T. PRICE et al., *Radiation Shielding*. New York: Pergamon Press, 1957.

CHAPTER 3

LIGHT-WATER MODERATED HETEROGENEOUS REACTORS*

3-1. GENERAL DESCRIPTION

The most commonly used research reactor in the United States is the light-water moderated heterogeneous type. In this reactor, the fuel (generally in the form of metal-alloy plates) is located in a pool or tank of light-water moderator. Since the fuel and moderator are physically separated, the reactor is termed heterogeneous, as opposed to a homogeneous system which has a uniform mixture or solution of the two. The use of light water as moderator sets this type of reactor apart from systems moderated with heavy water (D_2O) even though fuel elements for the two may be identical.

Frequently, the light-water moderated heterogeneous reactors are designated as "MTR-type" reactors, since the cores of all research reactors of this type now operating are patterned after that of the Materials Testing Reactor at the National Reactor Testing Station. However, the designation is misleading when applied to the reactor proper—the MTR core is in a closed tank, while many other reactors with MTR-type fuel elements are suspended in large open pools of water and are often called "pool reactors."

The design of the light-water heterogeneous reactor began in December, 1945, at the Oak Ridge National Laboratory (ORNL), with work leading to the Materials Testing Reactor, a high-flux installation for testing materials in intense radiation fields. As design progressed, it was decided that a mockup of the reactor should be built to test several engineering features. When completed, it was designated the Low Intensity Test Reactor (LITR) and was used in its original design as a mechanical and hydraulic mockup of the MTR. It was later converted, first to a training reactor, then to a research reactor, with its power being increased in each of three modifications.

Using data made available in the design of the MTR and the LITR, a low-cost research reactor facility was constructed to obtain bulk-shielding information. This reactor, called the Bulk Shielding Reactor (BSR), first went into operation in December, 1950, with an MTR-type core suspended in a large pool of water from a movable bridge. The water served as the coolant, shield, and moderator, and permitted the flexibility

---

* By J. N. Anno, Jr., and A. M. Plummer.

and accessibility needed for bulk-shielding studies. Just as the MTR was the first high-flux tank reactor, so the BSR may be considered the prototype for pool reactors. Although still much used for bulk-shielding research, the flexibility of the pool design allows its use for many other types of research, and consequently a wide variety of programs has been developed. The sketch in Fig. 3–1, of the BSR as first designed, demonstrates the general features of this type of reactor. Control rods operate in special fuel elements and are suspended from the bridge on extension rods. The control panel was first at one end of the bridge, but now there is a separate control room. Several modifications and improvements have been made since 1950, but the simplicity of design shown in the sketch has been retained.

The Atomic Energy Act of 1954 encourages the use of reactors as research tools for industry, universities, and government laboratories. In 1955, the first nongovernment light-water heterogeneous reactor was built to operate at 100 kw at Pennsylvania State University. Patterned closely after the BSR, this reactor had the important innovation of beam ports at one end of the pool to supply neutron beams to a general laboratory area (Fig. 3–2). The general trend in pool reactor development has been to divide the pool into two interconnected portions. With the reactor

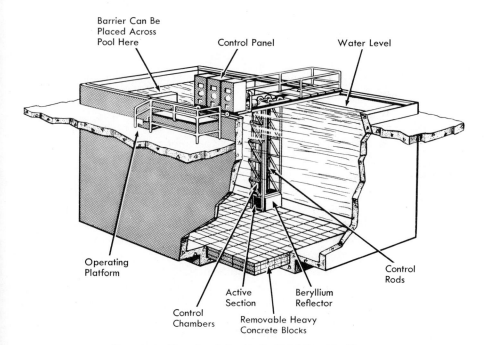

FIG. 3–1. Sketch of the Bulk Shielding Facility.

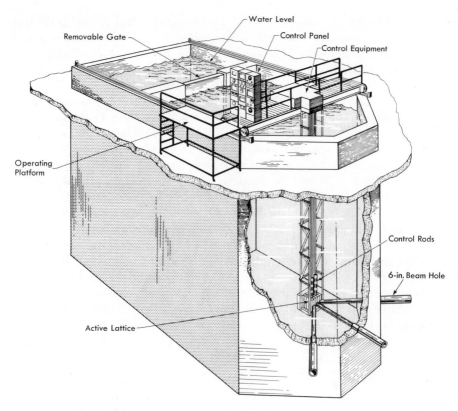

FIG. 3–2. Sketch of the Pennsylvania State University Pool Reactor. (Courtesy of Pennsylvania State University.)

core supported from a movable bridge, one portion, an "open pool," is used for bulk shielding or large loop experiments and for storage; the other contains a stall area where beam tubes and other experimental facilities provide access to radiations from the core (Fig. 3–3).

The tank reactor, like the pool reactor, has grown in popularity. The startup of the MTR (Fig. 3–4) in 1952 and its power-level increases demonstrated the utility of this type of high-flux materials testing reactor. Although operated primarily for testing materials, the reactor also supports a varied research program.

Development of various tank reactors modeled on the MTR has proceeded in two directions. One (exemplified by the 175,000-kw Engineering Test Reactor) provides high fluxes for large engineering test experiments, usually in the form of operating test loops (see Chapter 10). The second (exemplified by the 5000-kw Omega West Reactor) has been a modification for research using lower fluxes.

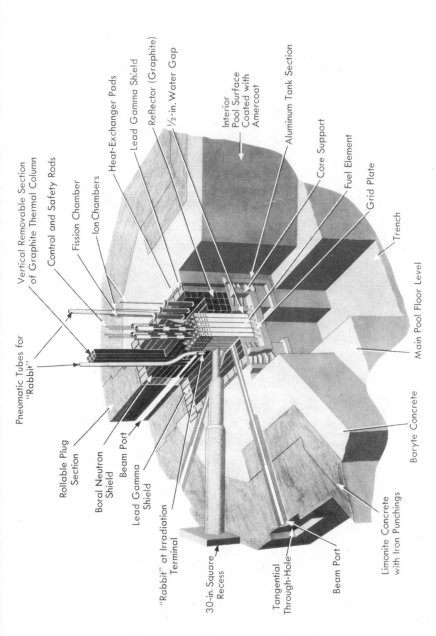

Pneumatic Tubes for "Rabbit"

Vertical Removable Section of Graphite Thermal Column

Control and Safety Rods

Fission Chamber

Ion Chambers

Heat-Exchanger Pads

Lead Gamma Shield

Reflector (Graphite)

½-in. Water Gap

Interior Pool Surface Coated with Amercoat

Aluminum Tank Section

Core Support

Fuel Element

Grid Plate

Trench

Main Pool Floor Level

Baryte Concrete

Limonite Concrete with Iron Punchings

Beam Port

Tangential Through-Hole

30-in. Square Recess

"Rabbit" at Irradiation Terminal

Lead Gamma Shield

Beam Port

Boral Neutron Shield

Rollable Plug Section

FIG. 3–3. Cutaway sketch of stall area of Naval Research Reactor. (Courtesy of Naval Research Laboratory.)

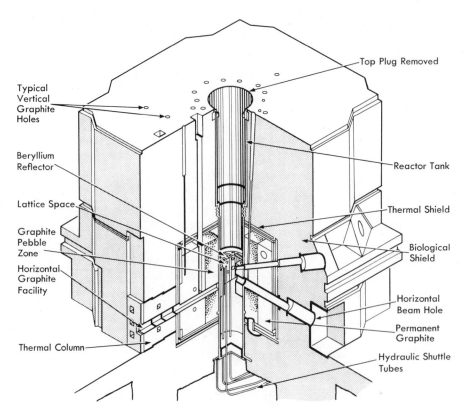

Fig. 3–4. Sketch of the Materials Testing Reactor. (Courtesy of Phillips Petroleum Co.)

High-flux testing reactors now in operation (MTR, ORR, and ETR) are extremely important. At present they provide the only sources of high-intensity neutron and gamma radiation for determining the effects of these radiations on various reactor fuels, coolants, and components. Such testing is of particular value in developing power reactors. Materials or components placed in a loop passing through the core of a testing reactor can be exposed to severe radiation, as strong or stronger than that expected in the power reactor of which they are to become a part. If development of power reactors continues to increase as has been estimated, engineering test reactors will become increasingly important.

The remainder of this chapter will be devoted to the design features, physics, and operational characteristics of light-water moderated heterogeneous reactors. Table 3–1 lists more than 20 reactors of this type being operated or constructed in the United States.

TABLE 3–1

LIGHT-WATER MODERATED RESEARCH REACTORS IN THE UNITED STATES

Installation	Location	Power, kw of heat	Status	Reference
Pool-type reactors				
Ground Test Reactor	USAF,[1] Fort Worth, Texas	100	Operating	—
Naval Research Reactor	Naval Research Laboratory, Washington, D. C.	100	Operating	*NRL Research Reactor*, Nuclear Engineering, Chem. Eng. Prog. Symposium, Part I, vol. 50, No. 11, 1954
Pennsylvania State University Reactor	Pennsylvania State University, University Park, Pennsylvania	100	Operating	*LPE with Penn. State Univ. Reactor*, NYO-7895, Sept., 1956
Bulk Shielding Reactor	ORNL,[2] Oak Ridge, Tennessee	100[3]	Operating	*New Bulk-Shielding Facility at Oak Ridge*, ORNL-991, May 8, 1951
Tower Shielding Reactor No. 1	ORNL, Oak Ridge, Tennessee	100–500	Operating	CF-55-1-165
Aircraft Shield Test Reactor	Fort Worth, Texas	1,000	Operating	—
Battelle Research Reactor	Battelle Memorial Institute, Columbus, Ohio	1,000	Operating	*Hazards Summary Report for BRR*, BMI-ACRS-601 (Rev.), April 1, 1955

(continued)

TABLE 3-1 (*Continued*)

Installation	Location	Power, kw of heat	Status	Reference
Ford Nuclear Reactor	University of Michigan, Ann Arbor, Michigan	1,000	Operating	*Nuclear Research Reactor at Univ. of Mich.*, MMPP-75-1, Nov. 27, 1953
Livermore Pool Reactor	University of California,[4] Livermore, California	1,000	Operating	*The LPTR*, UCRL-4919, July, 1957
Curtiss-Wright Reactor	Curtiss-Wright Corporation, Quehanna, Pennsylvania	1,000	Under construction	*Prelim. Hazards Evaluation Report on CWRR*, CWR-431, Aug. 24, 1956
Ordnance Materials Research Reactor	Watertown Arsenal, Watertown, Massachusetts	1,000	Under construction	Nuclear Engineering, Chem. Eng. Prog. Symposium, No. 12, Part II, 1954
University of Virginia Reactor	University of Virginia, Charlottesville, Virginia	1,000	Under construction	—
Tower Shielding Reactor No. 2	ORNL, Oak Ridge, Tennessee	5,000	Under construction	—
Industrial Research Laboratory Reactor	Industrial Research Laboratories, Inc., Plainsboro, New Jersey	5,000	Under construction	*U. S. Research Reactors*, BMI for USAEC, TID-7013, Aug. 1, 1957
Union Carbide Nuclear Research Reactor	UCNC,[6] Orange County, New York	5,000	Under construction	—
Nuclear Engineering Test Reactor	WADC,[5] Dayton, Ohio	10,000	Under construction	—

Tank-type reactors

Reactor	Location	Power	Status	Reference
Radiation Effects Reactor	USAF, Marietta, Georgia	10,000	Under construction	—
Brookhaven Medical Research Reactor	BNL,[7] Upton, Long Island, New York	1,000	Under construction	*Medical Reactor at Brookhaven*, Journal of the Franklin Institute, 261, 238–9 February, 1956
Low Intensity Test Reactor	ORNL, Oak Ridge, Tennessee	3,000	Operating	Geneva Conference Paper 486, 1955
Omega West Reactor	LASL,[8] Los Alamos, New Mexico	5,000	Operating	*Status of the Los Alamos Omega West Reactor*, ANS paper, June, 1956
NACA,[9] Reactor	NACA, Sandusky, Ohio	10,000	Under construction	—
Westinghouse Testing Reactor	Westinghouse Electric Corporation, Waltz Mill, Pennsylvania	20,000	Under construction	*Nucleonics*, November, 1956
Oak Ridge Research Reactor	ORNL, Oak Ridge, Tennessee	20,000	Operating	*ORR, A General Description*, ORNL-2240
Materials Testing Reactor	NRTS,[10] Idaho	40,000	Operating	*Nucleonics*, November, 1954
Engineering Test Reactor	NRTS, Idaho	175,000	Operating	*Nucleonics*, March, 1957

1. USAF, United States Air Force.
2. ORNL, Oak Ridge National Laboratory of the USAEC.
3. Operated up to 1000 kw for short times.
4. Livermore Laboratory operated for the USAEC.
5. WADC, Wright Air Development Center.
6. UCNC, Union Carbide Nuclear Company.
7. BNL, Brookhaven National Laboratory of the USAEC.
8. LASL, Los Alamos Scientific Laboratory of the USAEC.
9. NACA, National Advisory Committee for Aeronautics.
10. NRTS, National Reactor Testing Station of the USAEC.

3–2. Design Features

In the following qualitative description of the light-water moderated heterogeneous research reactor the advantages, disadvantages, and design features will be pointed out. Effective utilization of the reactor will be emphasized in the discussion of design features.

3–2.1 Core. The core of the Materials Testing Reactor may be considered as fairly typical of those of all light-water reactors. It is composed of a number of fuel subassemblies or elements positioned by a grid plate attached to the tank of the reactor. This arrangement makes many fuel configurations possible and adds to the flexibility. Fluxes in experi-

(a)   (b)   (c)   (d)

Fig. 3–5. MTR-type elements used at the Naval Research Reactor. A single fuel plate is shown (a), with a fuel assembly (b), control rod element (c), and control rod (d). (Courtesy of Naval Research Laboratory.)

mental facilities can be controlled to some extent by arrangement of fuel
elements and reflector assemblies that have the same dimensions as the
fuel subassemblies.

A typical MTR-type fuel element, shown in Fig. 3–5, is composed of
18 curved fuel-containing plates, with a cylindrical plug at the bottom
that fits into a hole in the grid plate to support and position the element
in the core.   Both ends of the element are open to allow coolant flow
between the plates.   Figure 3–6, a cross section of an MTR element,
shows the fuel alloy sandwiched between the aluminum cladding.

Fuel elements for the Westinghouse Testing Reactor (Fig. 3–7) represent
a major change from the MTR type.   Each element is made up of three
concentric fuel-bearing cylinders held together by a central mandrel tube,

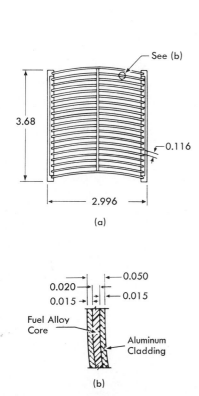

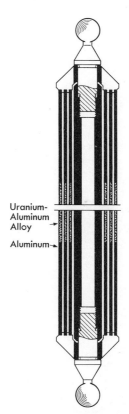

FIG. 3–6. Cross section of the central part of an MTR element fuel
plate. The fuel-bearing part of the element measures 3 by 3 in. by 2 ft in
length.

FIG. 3–7. The WTR fuel assemblies
are made up of three concentric fuel-
bearing cylinders supported by a central tube. (Courtesy of Westinghouse
Electric Corporation.)

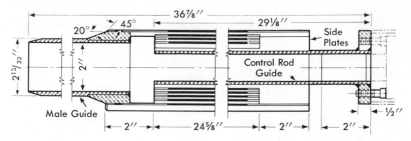

Section A-A of Special Fuel Element Assembly

(a)

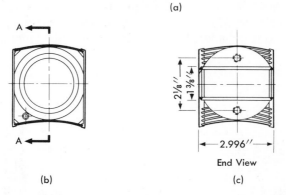

(b)   (c)

FIG. 3–8. Special fuel element for control rod used at the BSR. This element is typical of those used in pool reactors.

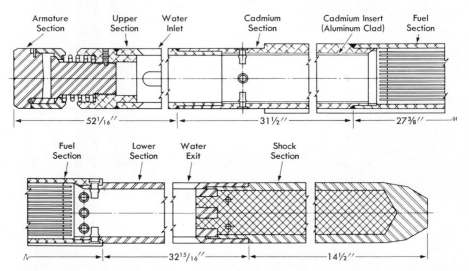

FIG. 3–9. MTR shim-safety rod. The upper section of the rod contains cadmium, while the lower section has fuel-bearing plates similar to those of the fuel assemblies.

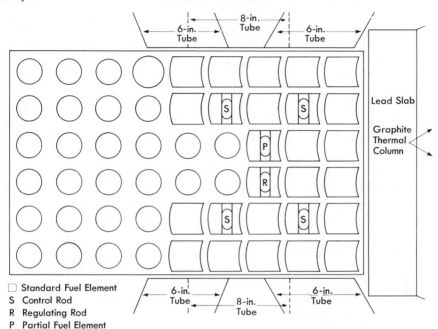

Fig. 3–10. A typical loading configuration of the Battelle Research Reactor. This loading provides maximum neutron fluxes to the beam tubes and thermal column.

a spoked aluminum bracket, and a threaded stainless-steel fitting at each end. The spherical ends provide for handling the symmetrical assemblies with special tools.

A special fuel element used to accommodate control rods in the core is shown in Fig. 3–8. The outside dimensions are the same as those of regular fuel assemblies, but some of the fuel-bearing plates have been removed from the center, leaving a channel for the control rod. The top of the element is fitted with a stainless-steel or aluminum shock-absorber seat which also supports the control-rod guide tube. A control-rod element used at the Materials Testing Reactor (see Article 3–2.7) is shown in Fig. 3–9. As the cadmium section is withdrawn from the core, a lower section containing fuel is pulled into the active lattice. Similar control rods having a beryllium lower section are used in the beryllium reflector which surrounds the core.

As mentioned previously, the use of small fuel subassemblies in the pool and tank reactors makes core configuration quite flexible. For example, Fig. 3–10 shows a typical core loading of the Battelle Research Reactor. The U-shaped arrangement provides maximum fluxes to the six beam tubes and thermal column. Many critical configurations can be formed for special purposes with very little trouble; in fact, the only pattern which is not available is one placing all control rods in a single row across the small dimension of the grid plate. Some special loadings at the Naval Research Reactor are shown in Fig. 3–28.

Another advantage of using separate fuel elements is the ease with which core loadings can be changed. Special handling tools, manipulated from the top of the pool or tank, are used to grasp the elements and remove them from the core. The removed units are then transferred either through a discharge tube (in tank reactors) or directly to underwater storage racks (in pool reactors). Loading is also accomplished easily. In this respect, pool reactors are more convenient than tank reactors because the core is accessible at all times from the top of the pool. With tank types, of course, the tank cover must be removed for fuel-loading changes.

3–2.2 Core container. Using a pool as the core container provides a high degree of accessibility and permits, in most cases, a flexibility of core location. However, engineering and radiation generally restrict a pool-type unit to power levels lower than those necessary for high-flux engineering test reactors.

With pool reactors, the core can usually be operated from several positions in the pool which, in most reactors, is divided into two parts by a removable gate. Generally, one part of the pool is a stall in which beam tubes, thermal columns, and other experimental facilities converge toward the core. The other part is an unobstructed open area that can accommodate apparatus for shielding and engineering experiments or can be used to store radioactive materials for cooling; this part can be drained and, with the core in the stall position (shielded by the water in that section of the pool), the equipment for large experimental setups can be installed on the pool floor. The pool can then be refilled, the gate removed, and the core run up against the apparatus.

The walls of the pool are usually constructed of concrete, reinforced with steel. Regular concrete is used for portions of the pool walls where sufficient radiation shielding is provided either by the pool water itself or by earth outside the wall. For example, the Pennsylvania State Reactor pool (see Fig. 3–2) is set into the side of a hill and earth gives added shielding on three sides of the pool, so these sides are constructed of regular concrete. For portions of the pool wall which are near the core or where the outer wall surface sees working areas of the reactor building, a high-density concrete containing barytes or other heavy aggregate is used to provide the required radiation shielding at minimum thickness. Typical density of barytes concrete is about 3.5 g/cm^3, compared with about 2.3 g/cm^3 for regular concrete. Wall thickness is varied to satisfy the particular strength and shielding requirements, but usual thicknesses

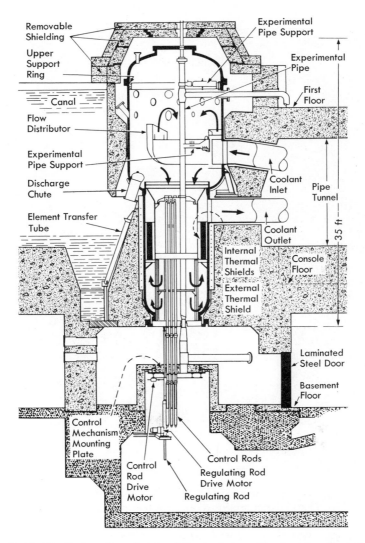

Fig. 3–11. Vertical section sketch of the tank-type Engineering Test Reactor.

are 1 to 3 ft for regular concrete walls used primarily for containment (as opposed to shielding) and 3.5 to 6 ft for barytes concrete walls for shielding at the base of the stall position of the pool.

To provide the required structural strength, the concrete is generally reinforced with $\frac{1}{2}$-in.-diameter steel rods arranged in a 6-in. lattice. Large pools rest on reinforced concrete several feet thick.

The inner wall of the pool is generally lined with tile or special tank

Fig. 3–12. This picture was taken looking down into the Omega West Reactor (OWR) tank. Thermal-column head, control rod system, and the lid of the reactor tank have been removed. The thermal column (A), the grid plate with several dummy elements in position (B), and several of the experimental ports (C) can be seen. The dark square at the bottom is a pit for the storage of hot fuel elements. (Courtesy of Los Alamos Scientific Laboratory.)

lining paint.* Tile protects the concrete from spalling, aids visibility, and is more easily decontaminated than a concrete surface. Several installations have combinations of tile and paint. White is the color generally used because it gives maximum visibility.

The size of the pool is dictated by shielding requirements and antici-

---

* An exception is the Oak Ridge Research Reactor (ORR) which has the pool walls lined in $\frac{1}{4}$-in. welded aluminum plate.

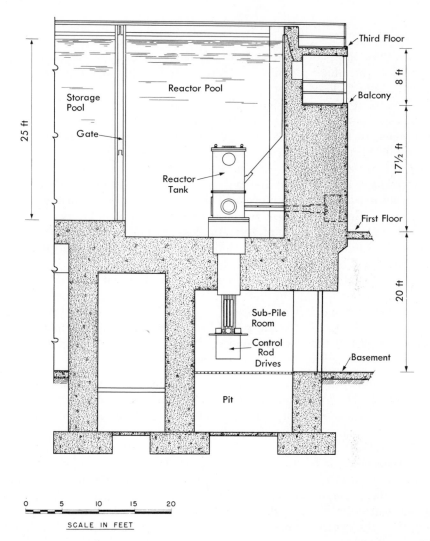

FIG. 3–13. Vertical section of ORR reactor structure. (Courtesy of Oak Ridge National Laboratory.)

pated research needs. Pool volumes vary from 53,000 gal (Ford Nuclear Reactor at the University of Michigan) to 150,000 gal (Naval Research Reactor).

To produce fluxes much higher than 10^{13} n/(cm²)(sec), a tank reactor is almost essential if ordinary water is used as the moderator. This type of reactor provides the necessary shielding in the form of solid material without the excessive water depth that would be required for a high-power pool reactor. In addition, the radioactive nitrogen formed in the cooling water as it passes through the core can be handled more effectively in the closed system. The tank-type reactor is surrounded by much less water than the pool type, and consequently requires more concrete for radiation shielding. Usually the core is immovable and the containing tank is tightly closed.

The aim of the tank design is to achieve both a high fast-neutron and a high thermal-neutron flux. To achieve a high flux at a given power, it is necessary to have a small core volume (i.e., a high power density). A high flux also depends on maximizing the heat transfer from each gram of U^{235} to permit a high specific power. In tank reactors, the specific heat-transfer area is about 100 cm^2/g. This is 10 to 15 times that in un-enriched reactors (see Chapter 6). The largest tank reactor in the United States, the Engineering Test Reactor, is shown in Fig. 3–11.

The tank, usually made of 1-in. stainless steel or aluminum, is approximately 5 ft in diameter, to allow sufficient space for the core and reflector. The Omega West Reactor (OWR) tank is shown in Fig. 3–12.

The ORR, a combination pool and tank type designed for 20-Mw operation, has its core near the bottom of an aluminum tank approximately 15 ft in height and 5 ft in diameter. The tank itself is located in a large pool (Fig. 3–13). Use of the pool provides several desirable features: it serves as part of the shielding and as storage area, and it adds flexibility for transfer of highly radioactive fuel elements.

3–2.3 Moderator. The purpose of the moderator was discussed in Chapter 2. Heterogeneous reactors, both pool and tank type, use ordinary water as moderator, coolant, shield, and often as reflector. As a moderator, ordinary water is an efficient energy absorber, but it is also a strong absorber of neutrons in comparison with other moderators.

The mass of the hydrogen atom is about the same as that of a neutron and, consequently, in a collision between the two, the neutron can lose all its energy and, on the average, does lose half its energy. Thus, ordinary water scatters and slows down neutrons effectively but, because of absorption, the neutron economy is not as good as in a graphite, beryllium, or heavy-water reactor. However, ordinary water is inexpensive and available, and with its dual use as coolant and shield, it is a practical material.

3–2.4 Reflector. By reflecting neutrons which have leaked back into the core, the reflector reduces the critical mass of the core and increases the specific power (power for a given weight of fuel). As with the moderator, a light material with high scattering probability and low absorption probability for neutrons makes a good reflector. Pool reactors frequently use the ordinary water in the pool as the only reflector. This is generally satisfactory, since for pool reactors there is not so much emphasis on maximizing the fast and thermal flux as there is in tank reactors. However, in several pool facilities either a permanent reflector other than the water is designed into the system or portable reflectors are provided. Figure 3–3 shows the permanent graphite reflector on three sides of the NRL reactor core when it is in the stall or "niche" position. Portable reflectors have been constructed in the form of large slabs to be positioned along the faces of the core, or special reflector cans with the same dimensions as the fuel elements can be placed in the grid plate. An example of the use of the latter type of reflector is shown in Fig. 11–5.

To achieve maximum thermal- and fast-neutron flux, the core of a tank reactor is generally surrounded by a beryllium or graphite reflector, usually consisting of pieces fitted around the core. Frequently, the tank is itself surrounded by a secondary reflector of graphite or water. Cooling required in the reflector of high-power reactors is accomplished by diverting part of the core coolant through the reflector. However, the graphite reflector of the Brookhaven Medical Research Reactor is forced-air cooled.

3–2.5 Shield. Water and concrete are the primary shielding materials for the light-water reactors, although additional shielding by lead, steel, cadmium, or Boral is frequently employed. The type and quantity of the material used in the shield must be arranged so that (1) fast neutrons from the core are slowed down, (2) slow (thermal) neutrons are captured, and (3) gamma radiation is reduced to a safe level. Since the size of the shield is not critical for research reactors (except as it affects beam length) the shields of most facilities are overdesigned. In general, shielding is usually provided to reduce the radiation at the external face of the shield to $\frac{1}{5}$ to $\frac{1}{10}$ or less of the allowable tolerance level.

Fast neutrons are slowed down effectively by the moderator and reflector materials in light-water moderated heterogeneous reactors. Consequently, fast-neutron shielding is generally not a problem; the principal difficulties with shielding against fast neutrons occur around ducts (such as beam tubes or piping), where streaming paths exist. The absorption of slow neutrons is likewise not a serious shielding problem for most reactors of this type, provided the secondary gammas formed in neutron absorption are attenuated. Although reflector materials have a low probability for neutron absorption, sufficient quantities can attenuate the thermal-neutron radiation below harmful levels. This point is illustrated in the graph of Fig. 3–14, which shows the thermal-neutron flux in the BSR pool water as a function of distance from the core face. At a distance of only 100 cm from the face of the core, the thermal-neutron flux is diminished by a factor of roughly 3×10^6. Additional neutron attenuation is provided by other biological shielding (usually concrete) surrounding the reflector.

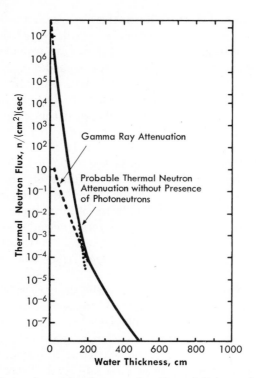

Fig. 3–14. Thermal-neutron flux as a function of distance from the BSR.

The gamma radiation determines the shielding requirements in a research reactor. In general, the denser the material, the more effectively it absorbs gammas. For this reason, regular and heavy concretes are common gamma shields; lead is even more effective, but its use is restricted by its structural properties and relatively high cost. Water, of course, plays an important role in the gamma shielding of light-water reactors even though it is a less effective absorber than concrete or lead. The shielding provided by water is shown in Fig. 3–15, where the gamma dose rate is given as a function of distance from the BSR core. This curve was obtained with a new set of fuel elements in the core, so that there was little effect of fission-product gamma-ray activity. As seen from these data, 500 cm of water attenuates the dose rate by a factor of 10^9. For 1000-kw reactors of this type, about 20 ft of water is commonly used above the core to keep gamma radiation below tolerance values at the pool surface. At 1000 kw, forced circulation used to cool the core will essentially eliminate the hazard from N^{16} due to its decay while circulating through the cooling system.

In the stall areas of pool reactors and in tank reactors it is not practical to use such large thicknesses of water horizontally around the core. Hence,

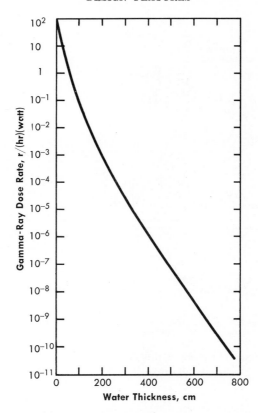

Fɪɢ. 3–15. Gamma-ray dose rate as a function of distance, from the BSR.

the water shield thickness is greatly reduced by using concrete or concrete and lead for at least a portion of the shielding in this area. Thus the shielding for these reactors consists of a composite of neutron-slowing-down material, thermal-neutron-absorbing material, and gamma-absorbing material.

Figure 3–16 shows the composite shield for the stall area of the Naval Research Reactor. The shielding in the horizontal direction is of graphite, lead, and heavy concrete. Vertical shielding is provided by about 17 ft of water above the core. The horizontal shielding is complicated further by the experimental facilities extending through the shield. The ports to the core are stepped to minimize radiation streaming. Although this is a 100-kw reactor, the same general arrangement is used for most light-water reactors.

For example, the MTR core is surrounded by a beryllium reflector, which in turn is surrounded by a minimum of 40 cm of graphite outside the core tank. A 9-ft thickness of barytes concrete serves as the final biological shield. Because of the high heat generated by radiation absorp-

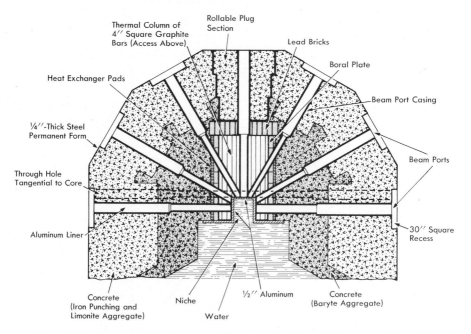

FIG. 3–16. General shielding arrangement in the stall area of the Naval Research Reactor. (Courtesy of Naval Research Laboratory.)

tion, a "thermal shield" of 4-in. air-cooled steel plate separates the graphite reflector and the concrete. The thermal shield reduces the neutron and gamma flux incident on the concrete enough to keep the temperature drop across the concrete shield to less than 50°F, which is the temperature differential that can be tolerated without danger of the concrete structures' failing from thermal stresses. The heat generated in the thermal shield is about 95 kw at a reactor power of 30 Mw, requiring air cooling.

3–2.6 Instrumentation. A control system has two functions: protection against an accident which could endanger personnel and the reactor, and regulation, necessary for startup and shutdown and also for controlling the neutron flux over the entire operating range. The safety function is further divided into two functions: warning the operator to take action, and automatically reducing the power level.

Most reactor control systems consist of six basic parts: (1) the startup or pulse channel, (2) the linear-servo channel, (3) the log N and period channel, (4) the safety channel, (5) manual controls, and (6) monitors for supporting facilities. Each of these and its basic components are discussed below. A block diagram of a representative system is shown in Fig. 3–17.

(1) In the *startup* or *pulse channel* the detector is generally a fission counter whose pulse output is amplified by a linear preamplifier and amplifier and fed through a logarithmic count-rate meter to a recorder. The output of the rate meter is differentiated electronically, and appears as a period signal in the low-level period amplifier. This channel contains interlocks to prevent startup if no neutron source is present in the core and to scram* the reactor if the rate of increase of neutron density exceeds some preset limit. The maximum rate usually used for starting up reactors of this kind is an increase in neutron density by a factor of e ($=2.718$) in a period of 20 to 30 sec. The scram point is ordinarily set for a 3 to 5-sec period.

(2) In the *linear-servo channel*, the current output of a compensated ion chamber is fed to a micromicroammeter which in turn drives a linear power recorder. A signal from the recorder slide wire is fed to a servo controller, where it is compared with the output from a power-set potentiometer. Any unbalance in the controller bridge due to a difference in the two signals drives the regulating rod in the proper direction (when the operator has selected automatic operation) to bring the reactor power level back in balance. Interlocks in this channel warn the operator when a large servo deviation occurs and when the regulating rod nears its limits of travel. Some systems automatically begin inserting control rods when these conditions occur.

(3) The detector for the *log N* and *period channel* is also a compensated ion chamber. The chamber signal is fed to a logarithmic amplifier (log N) which drives the log power recorder. The amplifier output is also differentiated by a period amplifier which yields a period signal, as in the startup channel. In addition to a period scram interlock, there is a high power level scram (usually at 150% full power) and warning signals for short period (10 sec) and 110% full power. Another interlock sometimes located in this channel shuts down the reactor at powers above 100 kw if the forced cooling system fails.

(4) The *safety channel* supplies current to the safety- and control-rod magnets. The outputs from two or more parallel-plate (uncompensated) ion chambers are amplified in this channel and initiate the level scram when the power level exceeds 150% full power.

(5) The *manual controls* represent at least a portion of the operator's functions in the control system. The most important of these are the rod drives (with associated position indicators) and controls for cooling-system pumps and valves.

(6) The *monitors for supporting facilities* provide measurements of the various temperatures, pressures, and flow rates of the cooling system, and the radiation levels around the reactor.

---

* The term "scram" is used to indicate an irreversible shutdown, i.e., one or more of the control rods is released and falls or is driven into the core.

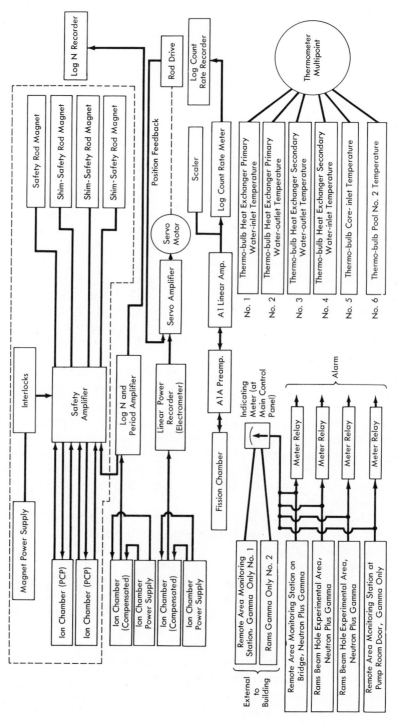

FIG. 3–17. Block diagram of control system instrumentation.

In addition to the basic reactor instrumentation needs, outlined above, the control systems of most reactors also contain some optional equipment. Few reactors, even of the same type, have exactly the same controls and interlocks.

An interlock system (sometimes called the facility scram) should be included for use with experiments. It provides protection for experiments which will damage themselves or the reactor if a malfunction occurs. At the Materials Testing Reactor, for example, five rates of automatic shutdown are available to experiments. The rate permitted for a particular experiment is the minimum required to prevent damage if trouble develops. These rates are (1) scram: all shim safety rods are dropped into the lattice; (2) junior scram: two of the shim safety rods in the beryllium reflector are dropped; (3) reverse: motor-driven insertion of all shim safety rods; (4) fast setback: logarithmic reduction to 1% of full power in 90 sec; and (5) slow setback: logarithmic reduction to 1% of full power in 420 sec.

The Ford Nuclear Reactor also utilizes interlocks for automatic rundown. These operate in the same manner as the "reverse" of the MTR. Certain abnormal but not particularly dangerous conditions cause the control rods to be driven rather than dropped into the core. Since this action has no effect on the normal operation of the scram circuits, needless shutdowns are often avoided with no loss in safety.

3–2.7 Control rods. In all light-water pool and tank research reactors currently operating or under construction, reactivity of the core is changed with mechanically operated control rods, usually cans of oblong cross section containing boron or cadmium as the principal neutron-absorbing material. The special fuel assemblies previously described contain the control rods. In an alternate (less common) control scheme, flat blades of a highly absorbing material (hafnium, cadmium, boron, etc.), slide between the fuel assemblies rather than inside special assemblies.

The most widely employed method of supporting control rods is by suspension from electromagnets. The excitation of these lifting magnets is controlled by the reactor safety system. For rapid shutdown, the current to the electromagnets is interrupted and the rods fall by gravity into the core. Hydraulic or pneumatic systems are sometimes used to obtain more rapid and positive insertion, although these systems are usually complicated and are used in very few light-water research reactors.

A typical control rod (Fig. 3–18) contains boron carbide (B_4C) as the principal neutron-absorbing medium. The boron carbide is in an aluminum jacket with two tubes of lead running the length of the rod to add ballast and rigidity. This type of rod weighs about 9 lb (6.5 lb in water). Rods of this type are used both for safety and for coarse adjustment of the critical state of the core. As an initial step in startup, some of the safety

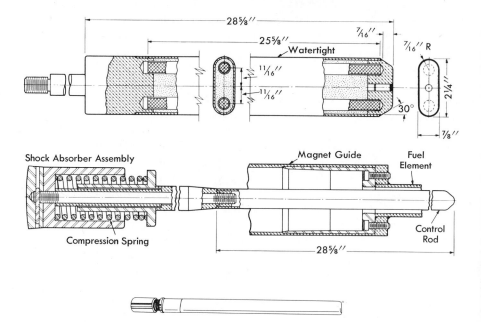

FIG. 3–18. Sketch of typical control rod for pool reactors.

rods are withdrawn from the core; the reactivity worth of these rods is then available for rapid core shutdown. After these safety rods have been withdrawn completely from the core, the rest of the heavy (large reactivity) rods are then partially withdrawn to bring the reactor to a critical or near critical condition. During operation, large adjustments of the core reactivity (for example, to compensate for poison buildup) are made with the latter rods. In this sense, they are sometimes referred to as "shim" rods. Some light-water reactors use one set of control rods for both safety and shimming purposes and usually designate these rods as "shim-safeties." These rods have a reactivity worth of from 2 to 4% $\Delta k_{\text{eff}}/k_{\text{eff}}$.

For fine control of the core, a more simply constructed regulating rod is employed. This rod (often just a stainless-steel tube) is a weaker neutron absorber, and has a total reactivity worth of about 0.5% $\Delta k_{\text{eff}}/k_{\text{eff}}$, much less than that of the safety and shim rods. It is generally connected to the servo drive systems for automatic operation. Table 3–2 summarizes the various operational purposes of the control rods.

Control rods are moved by means of individual mechanical drive units. A complete control assembly usually consists of a motor geared to a rack-and-pinion drive, an extension tube, an electromagnet, an armature, a

TABLE 3–2

PURPOSES OF VARIOUS TYPES OF CONTROL RODS IN REACTOR
OPERATION

Control-rod type	Purpose	Typical operation
Safety	Safety	Removed from core prior to startup
Shim	Coarse adjustment (shimming)	Startup and large adjustments during operation
Shim-safety	Both safety and coarse adjustment	Same as above
Regulating	Fine control	Automatic operation at fixed power level

shock absorber, and the control rod (Fig. 3–19). Such an assembly is used primarily for the safety and shim rods; the regulating rod usually is not magnetically coupled, since its contribution to shutdown in a scram is small. The drive motors are synchronous and operate at constant speed. The motor drive is geared so that the rods move very slowly. Typical drive speeds are about 0.5 ft/min. The total rod travel is approximately 2 ft for most light-water moderated reactors, so that 4 to 5 min are required to withdraw a rod completely from the core. Many reactors have provision for "gang-driving" several rods simultaneously.

The rod drives are usually mounted at the top of the tank or pool and are connected through the water to the magnets by long extension tubes. The magnets must support the weight of the armature, shock absorber, and control rod. A plunger-operated switch attached to the magnet transmits a signal to the control console when the magnet and armature are coupled. The shock absorbers (both hydraulic and spring types) prevent damage to the control rod and the fuel element when the rod is dropped by a scram.

Although the control rods of most light-water reactors are suspended from structures above the core, several of the more recent reactors (ETR and ORR) have the control rods entering the core from below (Figs. 3–11 and 3–13). The principal advantage of this scheme is that access to the core from above is not obstructed by control rods and drives.

Another type of control rod not mentioned above is the shim-safety rod containing a fuel section, like those in use at the MTR (Fig. 3–9). This

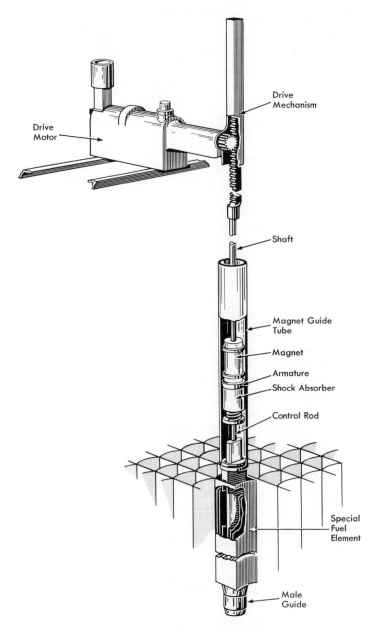

FIG. 3–19. Components of a complete control assembly.

FIG. 3–20. The core support tower and bridge of a typical pool reactor.

rod has an upper section of cadmium absorber and a lower portion similar to a standard MTR fuel element. As the rod is withdrawn, the fueled section is drawn into the core. When the rod is inserted the fuel is removed from the core and the cadmium inserted. The principal advantages of this type of rod are the increased rod worth (fuel plus absorber) and the uniformity of the core resulting from replacing poison with fuel as the rod is withdrawn.

3–2.8 Structural components. The bridge and core support are common features of all pool-type reactors (see Fig. 3–1). The core is suspended in

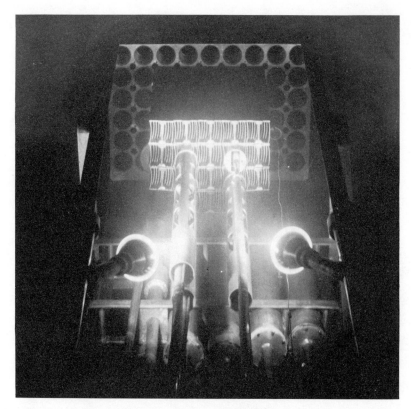

FIG. 3–21. The core of the Pennsylvania State University Reactor. (Courtesy of Pennsylvania State University.)

the pool on a tower (frame) fixed to a bridge that rolls on rails at the edge of the pool. Figure 3–20 is a photograph of a typical bridge and tower structure under construction. The grid plate is fastened to the lower end of the tower, and control-rod drive units are located at the top, where their positions can be changed easily for different core loadings. In the BSR installation the ion-chamber power monitors are outside the tower structure; in others (Fig. 3–26), the chambers are suspended inside the tower above the core.

Figure 3–21, a photograph of a core, shows clearly the grid plate and fuel elements. The cylindrical tubes extending above the elements are guide tubes for the control rods and magnets. The ion chambers and fission chamber are at the back of the tower and above the core.

Vertical section drawings of two tank-type reactors are shown in Figs. 3–4 and 3–11. The grid plate is fixed within a tank surrounded by a concrete

Fig. 3–22. A view into the tank of the ETR during construction. The grid plate can be seen in its position in the tank. (Courtesy of Phillips Petroleum Co.)

shield. Access to the core during shutdown is gained by removing the shielding at the top of the tank. As Fig. 3–11 shows, the control-rod drives of the ETR are at the bottom of the tank, while those of the MTR are at the top and are removed with the shielding plug. Ion chambers and other flux monitors are in holes piercing the concrete shield. Figure 3–22 illustrates other features of the ETR during construction of the reactor. Figure 3–23 is a plan view showing the core loading and locations of the various core components. Unlike the other light-water reactors, the ETR is designed for a fixed loading configuration. Because it is intended primarily for large engineering loops, no experimental facilities penetrate the shield.

The Livermore Pool Reactor, with a pool about $6\frac{1}{2}$ ft in diameter, is similar in appearance to a tank reactor, but is classified as a pool or well reactor because it is not enclosed at the top, and control rod drives enter from the top.

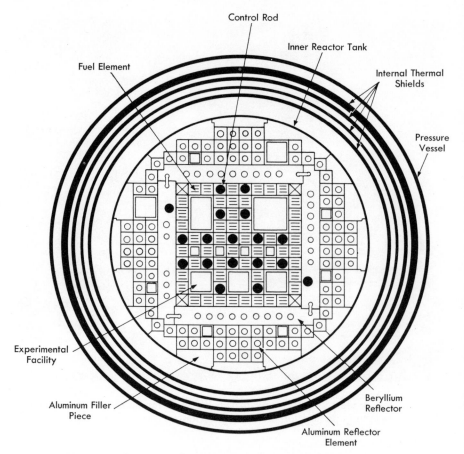

FIG. 3–23. Sketch of the grid plate of the ETR, showing the arrangement of core and experimental components.

3–2.9 Cooling and purification systems. Pool reactors designed for operation at power levels up to 100 kw do not have provisions for forced cooling. They are cooled by natural convection; the lower side of the grid plate is open to allow unrestricted coolant flow up through the fuel elements. The limiting factor with this type of cooling, in addition to the obvious limitation of heat transfer, is the presence of radioactive N^{16} at the top of the pool. The N^{16} formed in the core is carried to the surface by convection and, in spite of its short half-life (7.3 sec), can constitute a source of moderately hazardous external radiation at power levels above 100 kw. So far as cooling is concerned, there is evidence that pool reactors can operate safely at 1000 kw with natural-convection cooling (see Sec-

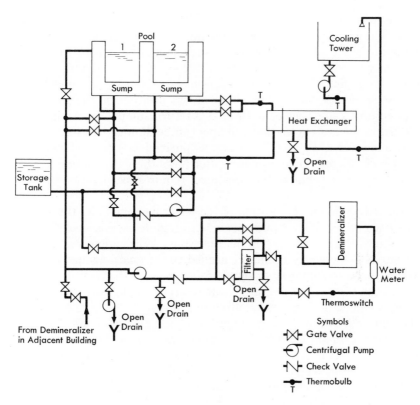

FIG. 3–24. Schematic diagram of BRR cooling system.

tion 3–4). At BSR underwater jets are used to diffuse the N^{16} just above the core; this permits running the reactor at several hundred kilowatts.

Pool reactors operating at power levels of 1000 kw and higher use a cooling system in which the pool water is pumped through the core into a heat exchanger and returned to the pool. Forcing the water down through the core tends to reduce the N^{16} activity above the core. In some cases, when the circulation time through the cooling loop is not long enough for the activity to decay significantly, a holdup tank is incorporated in the loop. The flow rate, the length of the primary loop, and the degree to which the water is diffused when it returns to the pool determine the necessity for a holdup tank.

Figure 3–24 is a schematic diagram of the cooling system of the BRR, which has a primary flow rate of about 900 gpm and a secondary flow rate of 700 gpm. The secondary system and heat exchanger are designed to remove 1000 kw of heat from the primary loop. The heat exchanger is a

U-tube type tube-and-shell exchanger with the primary flow through the tubes. The primary piping, primary pump, and heat-exchanger tubes are of aluminum, while the heat-exchanger shell is stainless steel. All valves in the primary system are of stainless steel; secondary piping is cast iron and steel. The piping and valves of the primary system are arranged so that the reactor can be operated at either of two positions in the pool and the water returned to either or both of two return sumps. A storage tank is included in the system, so that the pool can be drained without discarding the demineralized water. The water is purified in a bypass loop with a capacity of 20 gpm. The primary water flows through a filter and mixed-bed ion-exchange column. The deionizer requires regeneration every 4 to 5 weeks.

A hinged section in the bottom of the water plenum under the grid plate drops open when coolant flow stops, allowing convection cooling to start if the forced-convection system malfunctions. This action also scrams the reactor. No emergency cooling is needed to safeguard against damage to the core if the cooling system should fail, provided that shutdown occurs. Natural convection and the large heat reservoir of the pool are more than ample to handle heat generated after shutdown.

The flow pattern of the very large ETR tank reactor (Fig. 3–25) is similar to that shown in Fig. 3–24, but with several significant differences. The first, of course, is that this system is designed to transfer 175 Mw of heat from the reactor. Four primary pumps and four banks of three heat exchangers each are used in the primary system, which has a flow rate of

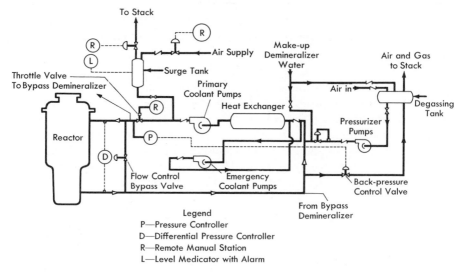

FIG. 3–25. Schematic diagram of the primary cooling system of the ETR.

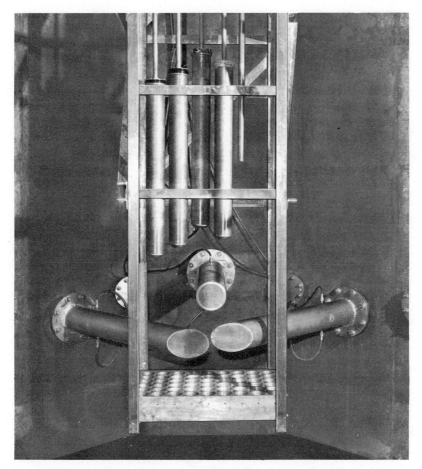

FIG. 3–26. The beam tubes of the Pennsylvania State University Reactor. The grid plate and ion chambers for measuring neutron flux are also shown. (Courtesy of Pennsylvania State University.)

44,000 gpm. Because of the high heat generation in the core and the relatively small volume of water in the tank, emergency cooling must be provided to prevent damage to the core if the regular system fails.

The heat flux in the ETR is very high, and degassing facilities are included to remove any dissolved gases from the primary system that might adversely affect the heat-transfer properties of the coolant. For the same reason, demineralizers maintain the concentration of dissolved solids in the water to less than $\frac{1}{2}$ ppm.

3–2.10 Experimental facilities. Experimental facilities in light-water reactors include those common to most research reactors: thermal columns,

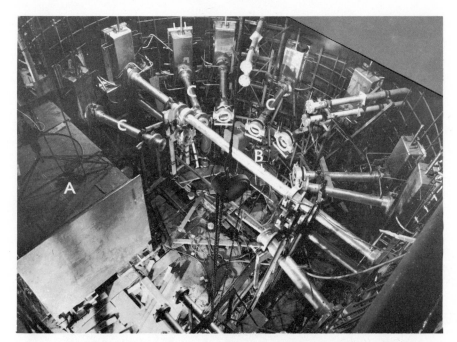

FIG. 3–27. Early construction photograph showing the thermal column (A), through facility (B), and beam ports (C) of the Ford Nuclear Reactor. (Courtesy of the University of Michigan.)

beam tubes, through tubes, pneumatic and hydraulic tubes (rabbits), and irradiation cells in the core and reflector. They are designed to make the most efficient use of high fluxes from the reactor core.

Typical beam tube installations are shown in Figs. 3–26 and 3–27. The number, size, and location of the tubes depend upon the use for which the reactor is intended.

Thermal columns that provide a means for obtaining a flux of predominantly thermal neutrons are useful in operating subcritical assemblies, and with a converter plate of U^{235} can be used for fission-spectrum studies. The high and easily accessible thermal-neutron fluxes also make thermal columns useful for absorption cross-section measurements with a pile oscillator. The thermal column is usually a column of high-purity graphite (heavy water can also be used) which penetrates the shield. The core end of the column is separated from the core face by several inches of lead to shield against gamma radiation. The thermal column at the Ford Nuclear Reactor is shown in Fig. 3–27.

Test spaces in the reactor core and reflector provide a convenient means of obtaining high fluxes for irradiating small specimens. ETR has several large test cells in the active lattice and numerous others in the reflector surrounding the core (Figs. 3–22 and 3–23).

3–3. PHYSICS CHARACTERISTICS

This section describes the physics of the light-water moderated heterogeneous reactor system. Experimental results of critical mass, flux distribution, reactivity, and control requirement determinations are presented for representative reactors. Reactor theory is minimized in this presentation; for elaboration of theory the reader is referred to the references at the end of Chapter 2.

3–3.1 Critical mass. The critical mass of the light-water reactors is strongly dependent on the core geometry, reflector, and proportion of moderator to fuel. Smaller effects are introduced by core structures (such as control-rod channels) and differences in fuel enrichment. The critical mass of these reactors varies from 1.5 to 5.0 kg of U^{235}, depending on the combination of these factors.

The effects of geometry on the critical mass are illustrated in Fig. 11–5. As seen in this figure, radical changes in the core geometry of the BRR caused the critical mass to vary from about 2.8 kg for very compact core (near minimum critical mass for this reactor) to 4.8 kg. The effects of inhomogeneities, such as control-rod channels, on the critical mass are shown in the same figure for two loadings of the NRR. This effect is much smaller than the geometry effect.

The effect of the reflector on the critical mass of MTR-type cores is shown in Table 3–3, which gives the results of criticality experiments at ORNL.

Table 3–3 shows that, as compared with water, an efficient reflector such as beryllium halves the critical mass. The last column of the table shows the critical mass predicted by simple two-group theory (see Chapter 2).

TABLE 3–3

CRITICAL MASSES OF U^{235} FOR MTR-TYPE CORES*

Reflector	Aluminum-to-water ratio	Observed critical mass, kg		Calculated (two-group) critical mass, kg
		Gross	Corrected for empty control-rod ports, etc.	
D_2O	0.88	2.48	2.40	2.64
D_2O	0.76	2.23	2.15	2.43
Be	0.76	1.54	1.42	1.54
H_2O	0.76	3.29	3.22	3.34
H_2O	0.66	2.82	2.72	3.04

* From *Progress in Nuclear Energy*, Series II, "Reactors," 1956, p. 51.

These calculated values are in good agreement with the experimental determinations, considering the approximations made in the two-group theory.

The effect of varying the ratio of moderator to fuel can be demonstrated by comparing the two water-reflected cases in Table 3–3. In general, MTR-type cores are undermoderated, so that a decreasing aluminum-to-water ratio reduces the critical mass (see Chapter 2). The choice of aluminum-to-water ratio is determined by the heat-transfer surface needed and a desire to maintain an undermoderated condition for safety. MTR-type cores now in use have aluminum-to-water ratios varying from 0.35 to about 0.8.

Although most cores are closely packed clusters of fuel elements, some interesting results have been obtained at the Naval Research Laboratory using a core separated into two parts by a central row of graphite reflector elements about 3 in. thick. The core, with an aluminum-to-water ratio of about 0.73, has a normal water-reflected critical mass of approximately 3.2 to 3.4 kg. Dividing the core by the row of graphite reflector elements increased the critical mass to 3.7 kg. Two core loadings are shown in Fig. 3–28 to illustrate the change. The advantage of using a split-core arrangement is primarily one of providing a more thermalized neutron flux to the experimental facilities at the center of the core.

Although highly enriched U^{235} is often used in U. S. MTR-type cores, 20% enrichment was used for the Aquarium Reactor exhibited at the 1955

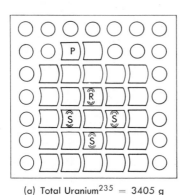 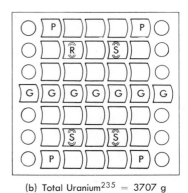

(a) Total Uranium^{235} = 3405 g   (b) Total Uranium^{235} = 3707 g

☐ Standard Fuel Element
G Graphite
P Partial Fuel Element
R Regulating Rod
S Control Rod

FIG. 3–28. Core loadings for Naval Research Reactor: (a) Loading 1M, water reflected core, (b) Loading 10H, slit core with central row of graphite reflectors.

TABLE 3–4

COMPARISON OF CRITICAL MASS OF A HIGHLY ENRICHED
CORE WITH A CORE 20% ENRICHED

	BSR	Aquarium
U^{235} enrichment, %	90	20
Lattice	5×6	5×5
Number of elements	28	25
Approximate U^{235} content of standard element, g	140	170
Critical mass, kg of U^{235}	3.5	3.6
Loading	3.92	4.25

International Conference in Geneva. The lower enrichment has also been used for one cycle of operation at the MTR. So long as the amount of U^{235} in the fuel elements is the same, little effect on the critical mass by use of 20% enrichment has been observed. Characteristics of the BSR are compared with the Aquarium Reactor in Table 3–4.

3–3.2 Flux distributions. Flux distributions in the reactor are important from both the operating and the experimental points of view. From an operating standpoint, distribution of thermal neutrons in the core can be used to determine fuel burnup and power level. Fluxes external to the core are important to experimenters since, in most research reactors, experimental facilities are located about the core face. In experimental regions, fast-neutron and gamma fluxes are often of as much or more interest than thermal-neutron fluxes. Radiation effects on chemical systems are caused by fast neutrons and gamma rays, and fast neutrons are also of special interest in the study of radiation effects on semiconductors. Gamma-ray fluxes must be known to determine their contribution to energy absorption and to calculate gamma heating in materials placed near the core.

Thermal-neutron fluxes are usually determined from the activation of gold, cobalt, or indium foils or wires. Wires (long enough to extend the entire active length of a fuel element) are used in measuring flux distributions within the active lattice. After exposure, they are either cut into convenient lengths for counting or are counted intact by a wire scanner [1]. Some flux distributions obtained at the MTR in one fuel element with three different conditions of fuel burnup are shown in Fig. 3–29. These distribution curves are from cobalt wires counted with the wire scanner.

Figure 3–30 shows the flux distribution in an element of the BRR as indicated by the activity of a manganese-iron wire placed in the element.

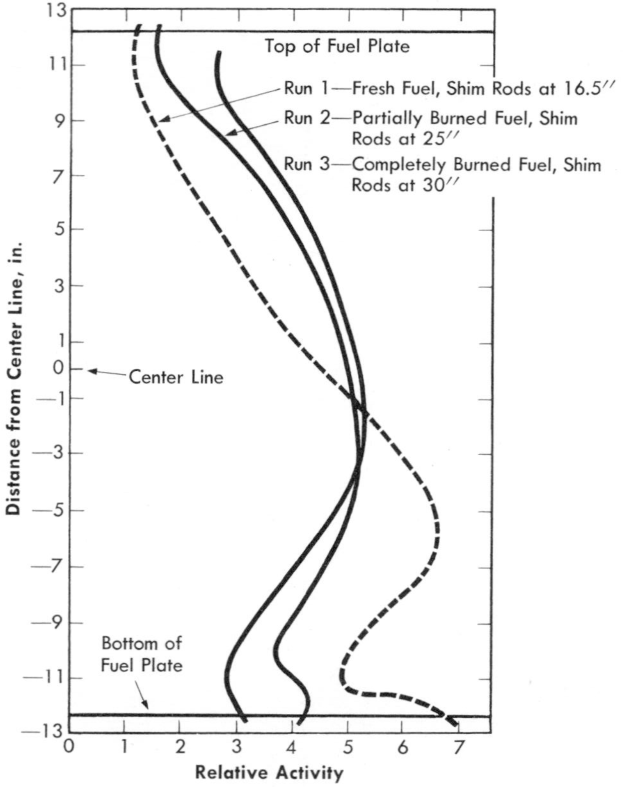

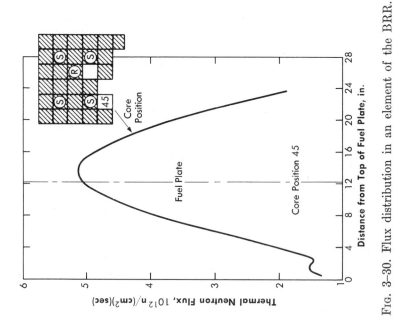

Fig. 3–30. Flux distribution in an element of the BRR. The position of the element in the core is shown at the upper right.

Fig. 3–29. Flux distributions in a fuel element of the MTR under different burnup conditions. The distribution for the fully poisoned reactor (Run 3) is nearly a cosine except at the ends of the plates.

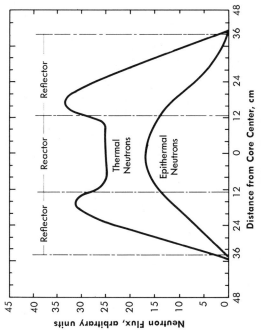

FIG. 3–32. Thermal flux distribution through the core and reflector of the MTR. Note the peaking of the flux in the beryllium reflector.

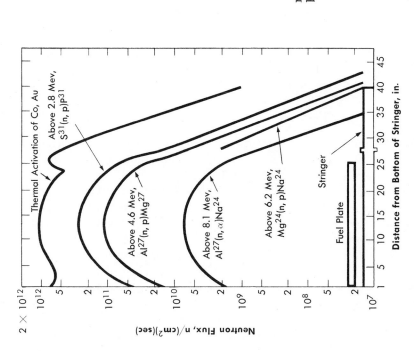

FIG. 3–31. Thermal and fast neutron fluxes through an element in the BSR for 100-kw operation. The threshold reactions used to obtain fast flux distributions are noted.

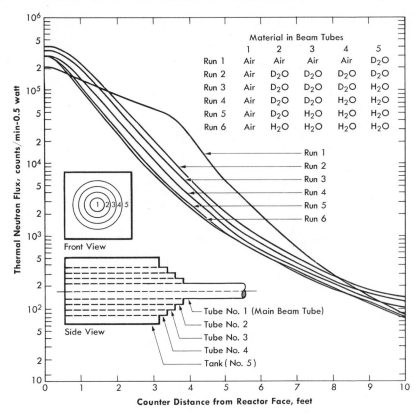

Fig. 3–33. Flux distributions in a mock beam tube experiment at the BSR. The beam tube is surrounded with various combinations of air, light water, and heavy water.

The wire was cut into 1-in. segments for counting. The relative activities of the wire segments are normalized to the absolute flux determined from gold foils irradiated at one position on the wire.

Figure 3–31 is a plot of both thermal- and fast-neutron fluxes through an element in the BSR. The fast-neutron fluxes are from measurements by threshold detectors, which utilize the characteristics of certain reactions caused only by neutrons above a certain energy. An interesting feature of these curves is the peaking of the thermal-neutron flux in the moderator above the fuel plate. This effect is shown more dramatically in Fig. 3–32, which is a plot of the neutron distribution through a narrow beryllium-reflected slab loading of the MTR.

The thermal flux distribution in a mockup beam tube at the BSR is shown in Fig. 3–33. These curves show some results of an experiment to determine the effect on beam-tube fluxes of surrounding the tube with a

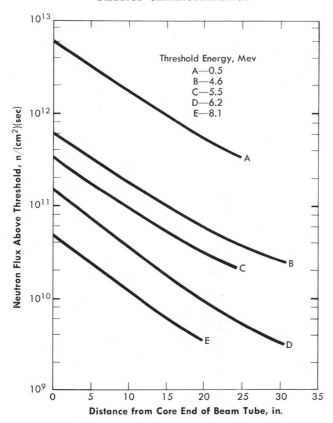

FIG. 3–34. Fast-neutron flux distribution in a beam tube at the BRR. Threshold detectors were used to measure these fluxes.

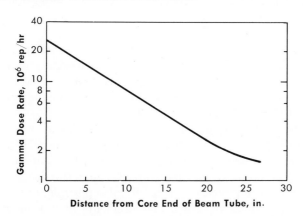

FIG. 3–35. Gamma dose rate in a beam tube at the BRR. Measurements were made with a 10-cm³ graphite-walled ionization chamber.

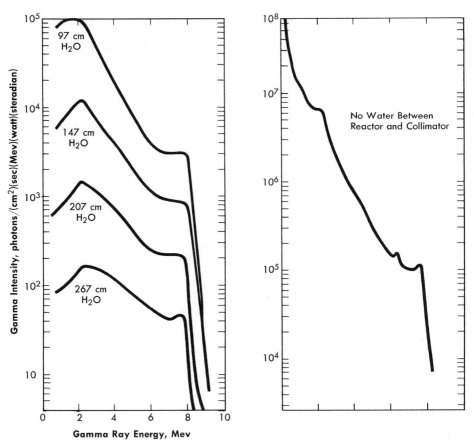

FIG. 3–36. Gamma flux measurements in the BSR, using the multicrystal gamma spectrometer.

heavy-water reflector [2]. Fast-neutron fluxes in a beam tube of the BRR are shown in Fig. 3–34. Threshold detectors were used to obtain these data.

Gamma-ray measurements in reactors are usually made as dose-rate rather than as flux measurements. Gamma ion chambers are rather easily calibrated to read dose rate and can be used directly in the high gamma-ray fields encountered in reactors. Results of measurements of the gamma dose rate in one of the beam tubes of the BRR are shown in Fig. 3–35. These measurements, made with a 10-cm^3 ion chamber immediately after startup of a clean core, do not show the decay gamma contribution. Gamma-flux measurements are also possible, but require much more elaborate equipment. Such measurements have been made at the BSR using a multicrystal gamma spectrometer [3]. Some of the results of gamma-attenuation measurements in the water shield are given in

Fig. 3–36. The peak in each of the four lower curves is attributed to capture gammas from the water and aluminum structures of the reactor.

3–3.3 Excess-reactivity requirements. All light-water reactors require extra fuel or excess reactivity above the critical condition to compensate for changes in the multiplication state of the core due to fission-product poisons, temperature, and absorbing experiments. Also, some allowance must be made for control purposes, i.e., to increase the power level of the reactor, the reactor must be made supercritical until the desired power is attained. A small amount of reactivity must be available for this purpose.

Several fission products formed during reactor operation are strong neutron absorbers (poisons). As these products increase with reactor operating time (and power), excess reactivity is required to override their poisoning effect on the neutron economy of the core. Principal offenders are Xe^{135} and Sm^{149}. Since Xe^{135} is radioactive, the poison effect reaches an equilibrium value where the rate of production of xenon is equal to the rate of decay of xenon plus the burnup of xenon through neutron capture. The effects of xenon on high-power reactors is significant, and considerable reactivity allowance must be made. On the other hand, Sm^{149} is stable, and hence continues to build up during the operation of the reactor. The only loss of samarium comes through its burnup by neutron capture.

The limiting value of reactivity required to compensate for xenon poison at equilibrium is about 5%, compared with a limiting value of about 0.4% for samarium. Thus, the reactivity requirements for fission-product

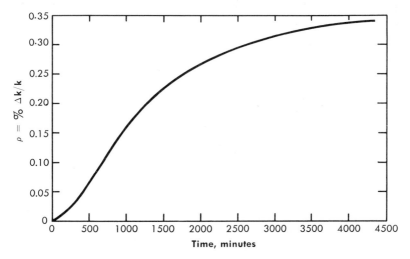

FIG. 3–37. Fission-product poison effects for 100-kw operation of the BSR.

poisons vary with reactor power from essentially zero for very low-power reactors (less than 1000 kw) to a maximum value of about 5% for the very high-power reactors such as the MTR and ETR. The buildup of poison with operating time for 100-kw operation of the BSR is shown in Fig. 3–37. Approximately 0.35% reactivity is required to compensate for the poison buildup at equilibrium.

The behavior of poison buildup with time and reactivity effects after shutdown (due to continued buildup of Xe^{135} from I^{135} decay after shutdown) are described in Chapter 11 for the MTR.

In general, temperature changes in the core affect reactivity. For most changes encountered in normal operation, the reactivity required to compensate for temperature effects is small. The temperature coefficient (see Chapters 9 and 11) for most light-water reactors is in the order of -0.005 to $-0.01\%/°F$ in the normal operating range. Thus changes in temperature must be in the order of tens of degrees before the excess reactivity requirements become significant. However, for reactors operating on very limited excess reactivity, this effect must be considered.

Changes in the reflector region of the core caused by the presence of experimental facilities can bring about significant reactivity changes. The effect can be positive if a more efficient reflector is added by the experimental facility (such as moving the reactor next to a graphite thermal column) or negative if reflector is removed (such as replacing with an air-filled beam tube). The magnitude of these effects can be deduced from the information presented in Table 11–1. As a rule, beam-tube effects are in the order of tenths of a percent of reactivity.

Some excess reactivity must be allotted for effects of experiments placed in or near the core. The experiments either absorb neutrons or displace moderator or reflector, and hence have a negative reactivity effect. Experiments can have a positive effect if they contain fuel, or better moderator or reflector materials than those normally in the core. Usually experiments in low- and intermediate-power research reactors require much less than 1% reactivity. Large engineering test reactors may require as much as 5% reactivity for special experiments.

The need for a small amount of excess reactivity for control has been mentioned. Since the reactor can be placed on a 20-sec positive period from a critical condition by introducing 0.2% reactivity, this may be taken as the approximate reactivity required to increase the power level. For best automatic control of the critical state at a set power level, the regulating rod must respond rapidly to any deviations. Thus the regulating rod should be in an effective range and not completely withdrawn from the core. The 0.2% allotted for power change is nearly sufficient to meet this second requirement.

For a reactor with a design power level in the range 0 to 100 kw, the above requirements dictate total excess reactivities in the range of 0.5 to about 2%. The excess reactivity required by a 1000-kw pool reactor is about 2 to 5%, and by high-power engineering test reactors about 10 to 20%.

To operate reactors with considerable built-in excess reactivity requires that the reactivity worth of the rods be greater than the reactivity requirements. As a rule of thumb, the minimum total rod worth is usually taken as about twice the total reactivity required for safety. For low-power reactors, this condition is easily met, and usually the total control-rod worths are much greater than twice the requirements. However, for very high-power reactors with small cores, obtaining sufficient rod worth becomes a problem. For this reason, the cadmium and fuel combination control rod previously described was devised for the MTR. The worth of this type of rod is about three times that of the conventional boron or cadmium control rod.

3–4. OPERATIONAL CHARACTERISTICS

The characteristics of light-water moderated research reactors are rather low fuel requirements and high thermal- and fast-neutron fluxes. The simplicity of the loading procedures and (in the pool type) the easy accessibility to the reactor core make these reactors attractive.

3–4.1 Fuel requirements. Representative fuel requirements for various light-water reactors have been discussed (Section 3–3). Actual operating requirements are somewhat higher than the figures given because excess reactivity (fuel) is needed to compensate for the effects of experiments, fission-product poison buildup, temperature, and fuel burnup, which vary considerably with operating power level and experimental requirements. For example, a reactor operating at 1000 kw will burn up an average of about 15% of the fissionable material in its initial loading in about 2 yr. In a pool reactor, this is a practical estimate because it is feasible to rotate fuel subassemblies to achieve nearly uniform burnup in the horizontal plane.

On the other hand, in reactors operating at higher power, burnup occurs at a correspondingly higher rate, and it may not be practical to rotate elements often enough to achieve uniform burnup. Some rotation is desirable from an economic standpoint, however. For example, the MTR originally operated on a "burnup cycle" (i.e., the reactor was operated until burnup had depleted the fuel to the point where the reactor shut itself down) of 30 to 40 days, and a complete new fuel loading was installed at that time. The reactor is now operated on a 3-week cycle which utilizes a loading containing both new and partially burned elements. The savings in fuel costs with this procedure have been significant.

3–4.2 Power range. Light-water reactors may be divided into three groups, according to their operating power levels: (1) those reactors operating at powers up to 100 kw, (2) those operating at from 100 kw to 1000 kw, and (3) those operating at above 1000 kw. At present all pool reactors fall in the first two groups, i.e., under 1000 kw. Several of these reactors, however, have been designed for operation at higher power, with plans to increase their power level when sufficient operating experience has been gained. All in the third group are tank-type reactors.

Reactors operating at power levels up to 100 kw utilize natural-convection cooling. However, measurements made at the BSR on fuel-plate surface temperatures indicate that a reactor can be operated at 2000 kw with natural-convection cooling without causing local boiling [4]. Continuous operation at this level is not implied, of course, since the bulk pool temperature will rise until boiling eventually occurs and N^{16} is far above tolerance.

Reactors in the second group have forced-convection cooling systems which allow 1000-kw operation with ambient pool temperatures in the range of 90°F. Most of these facilities have plans for adding heat exchangers and cooling towers for operation at as high as 5000 kw.

One limiting factor in operating pool reactors at higher power is the problem of radiation and thermal shielding. Thermal shielding can be added by incorporating steel plates around the core to protect the pool walls from thermal stresses. Additional radiation shielding is difficult to provide at power levels above 5000 kw, since it becomes impractical to increase the height of water above the core. Fuel handling and other manipulations are difficult through 20 ft of water; there is a practical limit to the working depth. The second limiting factor is the N^{16} problem mentioned before.

Tank reactors solve the shielding problems of high-power light-water reactors. The shielding on the top of the tank supplies the additional shielding in a dense solid form, making it possible to operate at a high power with water not too deep for convenient handling of fuel elements.

3–4.3 Operating stability. Light-water reactors are quite stable in operation; those of lower power can supply nearly constant fluxes to experiments for several weeks. In high-power testing reactors, changes in flux distribution and magnitude occur because of fuel burnup and consequent movement of the control rods. In attempt to minimize these changes, the ETR employs a burnable poison (boron) intimately mixed with the fuel. Ideally, the poison burns out as the fuel is depleted, keeping the reactivity and flux more or less constant throughout the operating cycle.

Startup and shutdown are easily accomplished in the light-water reactors, and the rate of power change in each case can be controlled over a wide range. A typical pool reactor can reach a power level of 1 Mw from source level in as short a time as 20 min or, if conditions warrant, can attain the same power level in a matter of hours. The servo control system can maintain the power constant to within $\pm 1\%$ of the set value. Because the heat capacity of the system is fairly large, sudden temperature changes do not occur. However, temperature changes from day to day influence the rod positions somewhat, which causes variations in the flux distribution. Generally, these changes are small and not objectionable. The periodic fuel-element changes cause fluctuations in the flux values which may occasionally affect an experiment.

3–5. SUMMARY

Light-water moderated heterogeneous reactors are characterized by flexibility, versatility, and accessibility. In 10 years of existence they have demonstrated their utility as research tools, as evidenced by the rapid growth of the use of this type of reactor in the United States. A wide power range is available with present light-water reactors (100 to 175,000 kw). Correspondingly, the maximum neutron fluxes available in this power range vary from about 10^{12} to 10^{15} n/(cm^2)(sec). The choice of a pool- or tank-type reactor depends on the research needs. The power level of a pool reactor is restricted to several thousand kilowatts; a tank reactor may be operated at several hundred thousand kilowatts. On the low end of the power scale, the pool reactor offers a unique flexibility in core arrangement and experimental access at relatively low cost. On the high end, the light-water tank reactor offers the highest fast-neutron flux of any research reactor.

Light-water reactors have critical masses in the order of several kilograms. For low-power reactors the fuel lifetime is several years, being limited in some cases by the durability of the fuel assemblies rather than by burnup. For high-power engineering test reactors, the fuel cycle is several weeks, and is limited by a combination of fuel burnup and fission-product poison buildup. The light-water reactor, if properly designed, is very safe because of the negative temperature coefficients and the (usually negative) void coefficients.

From an operational standpoint, light-water moderated heterogeneous reactors are very stable. Those of high power must cope with poison buildup and rapid fuel depletion, but these factors tend to decrease the power at any given time, and hence increase inherent safety. The operational history of these reactors has been excellent.

References

1. R. J. Preston, *The MTR Automatic Wire Scanner*, USAEC Report IDO-16243, Phillips Petroleum Co., Sept. 29, 1955.

2. K. M. Henry et al., Effect of Reflector on the Neutron Flux in an ORR Beam Hole Mockup, in *Applied Nuclear Physics Division Annual Report for Period Ending September 10, 1956*, USAEC Report ORNL-2081, Oak Ridge National Laboratory, Nov. 20, 1956.

3. F. C. Maienschein, *Multiple-Crystal Gamma-Ray Spectrometer*, USAEC Report ORNL-1142, Oak Ridge National Laboratory, Apr. 14, 1952.

4. K. M. Henry and J. N. Anno, Temperature Distribution in the BSR Under Natural Convection Cooling, in *Applied Nuclear Physics Division Annual Report for Period Ending September 10, 1956*, USAEC Report ORNL-2081, Oak Ridge National Laboratory, Nov. 20, 1956.

CHAPTER 4

HEAVY-WATER REACTORS*

4–1. General Description

In physical appearance and operation, heavy-water reactors do not differ greatly from light-water moderated reactors. However, certain significant divergences arise from the cost of heavy water and its low absorption cross section. Although, unlike light-water reactors, heavy-water reactors can employ natural uranium as fuel, both heavy-water research reactors in the United States (listed in Table 4–1) are designed as highly enriched systems. This type will be emphasized in the present chapter. Characteristics which these reactors share with light-water reactors will be treated less fully than features peculiar to the heavy-water designs.

Ordinary water contains 1 part in 6500 of heavy water. Chemically like so-called "light water" (H_2O), heavy water has deuterium (D), with twice the mass of ordinary hydrogen, in place of hydrogen (H) in its molecule. Consequently, the molecular weight of heavy water is 10% greater than that of light water. The price of heavy water is relatively high ($28 per lb) because of the cost of separating it from light water. Therefore, precautions must be taken to prevent loss or dilution. A sealed system is required to contain the heavy water as it circulates through the reactor tank, the core, and a light water-cooled heat exchanger.

Table 4–1

Heavy-Water Research Reactors
Operating in the United States

Name and location	Power, kw	Reference
CP-5 (Chicago Pile No. 5) Argonne National Laboratory (USAEC), Lemont, Illinois	4000	*Peaceful Uses of Atomic Energy*, vol. 2, pp. 458–470
Massachusetts Institute of Technology Reactor, Cambridge, Massachusetts	1000–5000	*Nucleonics*, **15**, No. 1, Jan. 1957, pp. 38–40

* By F. J. Jankowski and R. F. Redmond.

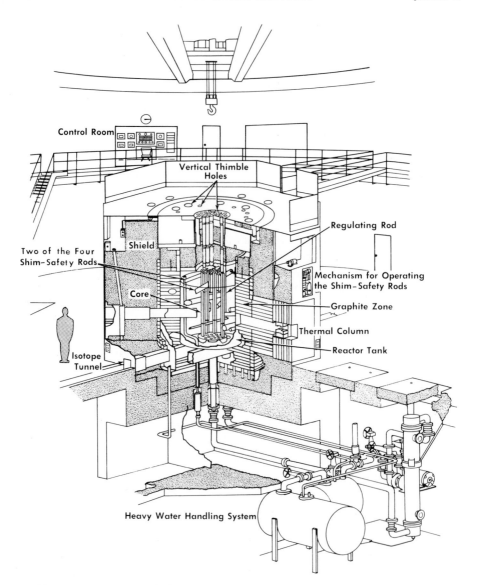

FIGURE 4–1. Pictorial drawing of the Argonne Research Reactor (CP-5) showing the principal features. This reactor is located in the center of the room, permitting experimental facilities on all sides and on top of the reactor; irradiation tunnels pass beneath it. Normal water is used to cool the heat exchanger in the lower right corner. (Courtesy of Argonne National Laboratory.)

Heavy water has a very low cross section for absorbing thermal neutrons. The cross section of a deuterium atom is approximately 0.00046 barn, as compared with 0.33 barn for a hydrogen atom. The resultant saving of neutrons makes possible a lower critical mass and a lower power for a given thermal-neutron flux than in a light-water moderated system. In a heavy-water reactor, the fuel elements can be spaced relatively far apart because of the low neutron absorption cross section of the moderator. The average fast-neutron flux is low compared with the thermal-neutron flux. However, by locating an experiment close to or within a fuel element, it is possible to get a relatively high fast flux. Fuel elements for the highly enriched heavy-water reactors are of uranium-aluminum alloy, clad with aluminum. Both curved-plate MTR-type fuel assemblies and concentric-cylinder arrangements are in use.

Critical masses of D_2O reactors using highly enriched fuel range from 1.5 to 4 kg. The core is approximately 2 ft high and 2 ft in diameter, a slightly larger core volume but with less uranium than light-water reactors of comparable power.

Control rods may be vertically driven, as in light-water reactors. Semaphore blades pivoted at the top edge of the reactor core are also attractive for this type of reactor because there is ample room between the fuel elements for movement of the blades. This control element requires less vertical space but its reactivity response is less linear. This type leaves the top of the reactor free for experimental facilities and fuel handling.

Arrangements for experimental facilities are quite similar to those of light-water reactors, although the closed system and the need for preventing contamination of the heavy water make the core less accessible. Therefore, the facilities must be carefully designed into the system when it is built.

The shielding of heavy-water research reactors closely resembles that for light-water tank reactors.

Figure 4–1 shows the general features of heavy-water research reactors.

The CP-3 reactor (now dismantled) at the Argonne National Laboratory, was first fueled with natural uranium, then converted to highly enriched elements. The Canadian NRX and NRU reactors use natural uranium fuel, which requires both large critical mass and large size. This has advantages and disadvantages over the highly enriched system. Canadian reactors use heavy water as moderator, but are cooled with light water.

Slightly enriched uranium fuel offers interesting possibilities for heavy-water research reactors. If the U^{235} enrichment is merely doubled, the critical mass can be far less than with natural uranium fuel. Using a fuel enrichment of 20% by weight U^{235} will result in a reactor with physics characteristics similar to those of highly enriched reactors. Such reactors are now under construction by U. S. firms in Italy and in Japan. The Italian reactor is patterned after the MIT reactor and the Japanese reactor more closely resembles CP-5.

4–2. DESIGN FEATURES

4–2.1 Core. The core of the heavy-water research reactor is somewhat larger than that of a comparable light-water reactor. The height is about the same but the diameter is greater, with the result that the core volume is three to four times that of a light-water reactor of the same power. The CP-5 and the MIT reactors have from 12 to 19 fuel elements, each approximately 3 in. across and 24 in. long, spaced so that the distance between elements approximates their width. The reactors operate at temperatures between 95 and 140°F, well below the boiling point of water, which permits the use of aluminum in components.

Both existing reactors have complete flexibility in the choice of type of fuel. One fuel element design, now in the MIT reactor, has plates of highly enriched uranium-aluminum alloy clad with aluminum. In some elements, some of the plates are omitted to allow sample access and to provide high thermal flux at certain of the ports. The fuel plates are brazed to opposite walls of a long square box of the MTR fuel-assembly type. In a second design, now used in the CP-5, the sandwich-type elements are formed into concentric cylinders (Fig. 4–2). Either arrangement makes it possible to insert experiments into the center of the elements in a high fast-flux region. In the box-type assembly the number of fuel plates depends chiefly on the heat-transfer surface required. To operate at 4 Mw the CP-5 requires a minimum of 16 fuel elements with 12 plates in each. In both the CP-5 and the MIT reactors, a plenum top plate with holes positions the fuel elements and provides a lower plenum chamber which directs the flow of the heavy water through the elements.

Both reactors have a heavy-water reflector region at the bottom of the core. The lower end of the fuel element is machined to make a tight fit to the plenum top plate so that the coolant flow is directed through the element for maximum cooling efficiency. The element support tube has coolant discharge openings above the fuel level, allowing the heavy water to spill into the space between and around the elements. The tube can contain thermocouples for measuring the coolant outlet temperature and also contains provisions for emergency cooling of the element should the main heavy-water tank rupture. The topmost section of the element support tube is incorporated into a shielding plug that serves as part of the top shield of the reactor and aligns the element in the tube.

Since the flow through the element is upward, a velocity head is added to the pressure head of the water. This feature is used to measure the flow

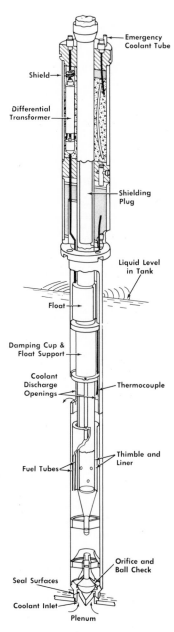

FIG. 4–2. Isometric sectional view of a fuel element for the CP-5, showing features generally incorporated into elements for heavy-water reactors. The cylindrical fuel tubes permit insertion of experiments along the centerline of the element; flat-plate elements may also be used in heavy-water reactors. (Courtesy of Argonne National Laboratory.)

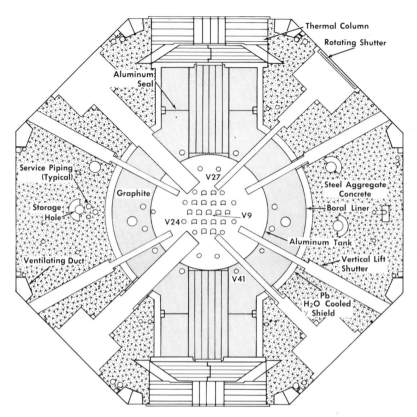

FIG. 4–3. Section through the CP-5 reactor, showing fuel-element locations, reflectors, shielding, and many experimental facilities. (Courtesy of Argonne National Laboratory.)

in the following manner. The support tube enclosing the element contains a float connecting it to the core of a differential transformer in the shield section above. The position of this float changes the output of the differential transformer, thus indicating the velocity head and consequently the coolant flow in the element.

A large core tank provides a substantial D_2O reflector thickness which lowers the critical mass. However, such a tank naturally requires a large volume of costly heavy water and also built-in thimbles for access to the high flux at the core surface. Not only do these built-in thimbles increase the cost, but they are the tank components most likely to fail. On the other hand, although a small tank produces a less efficient reflector, requiring a greater critical mass, it does use less heavy water. In addition, the beam ports and irradiation facilities need not be brought through the tank to reach a region of high flux.

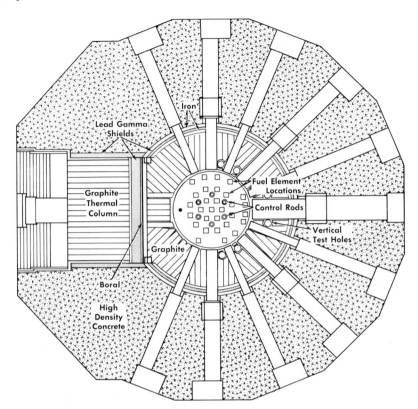

FIG. 4–4. Cross section of the MIT Research Reactor showing fuel-element and control-rod locations, reflector, shield, and many experimental facilities. Note that the beam holes do not penetrate the reactor tank and that there are fuel-element locations in front of most of the beam holes to permit increasing the neutron flux in these regions. (Courtesy of Massachusetts Institute of Technology.)

Through-holes, thimbles, and beam ports can be built into the tank. Inlet and outlet pipes for heavy water and helium blanket are also required. Gas lines draw off and recombine the oxygen and deuterium formed by dissociation. A method is also provided for removing spent fuel elements and for operating control rods.

Figures 4–3 and 4–4, cross sections of two heavy-water research reactors, show the relation of the core tank to the reflector, shield, and experimental facilities. Figure 4–5 is a cross-sectional view of the core tank in Fig. 4–3.

4–2.2 Moderator. Because of the low neutron absorption of the heavy water, most of the neutrons absorbed in the reactor are absorbed in the fuel or in experiments and thus are utilized efficiently. On the other hand,

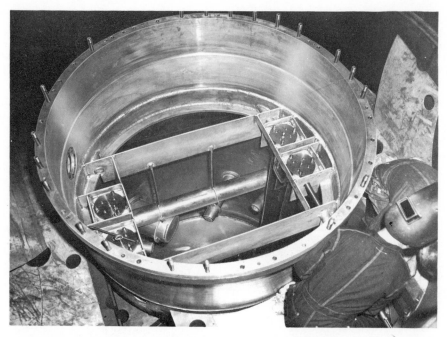

Fig. 4–5. Reactor core tank for the CP-5 reactor. Note thimbles for the beam holes and through tubes entering the core; also the brackets at the top of the tank for holding semaphore-type control rods. (Courtesy of Argonne National Laboratory.)

since heavy water does not slow fast neutrons as effectively as does light water, a reactor must have greater volumes of heavy water as moderator. Hence, although larger as a rule, the heavy-water reactor makes better use of the neutron yield from identical fuel materials than does the light-water reactor. These features explain why relatively large spaces are available within the core for experiments and why these reactors achieve a high thermal flux per unit power and per unit mass of fuel. Thus the characteristics of a heavy-water research reactor favor low operating costs per unit of flux.

The use of heavy water as a moderator increases the safety of a research reactor because the high thermal flux per unit power results in a lower buildup of fission-product activity within the core than with other reactors of the same flux. The low neutron absorption in the moderator results in long neutron lifetime, which makes for easier control. In addition, if the power becomes too high, water in the fuel element channels will boil. The displacement of moderator by the void formation tends to shut down the reactor.

Fig. 4–6. Graphite reflector for a heavy-water reactor prior to the insertion of the reactor tank. (Courtesy of Argonne National Laboratory.)

The combination of these features—the relatively large volume in a region of high neutron flux, the low operating cost, and the increased safety of the system—makes the use of heavy water as a moderator especially suitable for installations where the primary interest is research in nuclear and neutron physics.

4–2.3 Reflector. Heavy water is an efficient reflector material. However, it is too expensive to be utilized for more than a partial reflector that extends from the edge of the fuel elements to the core tank wall. The thickness of the heavy-water reflector varies from a few inches to more than a foot, as seen in Figs. 4–3 and 4–4.

In both designs a graphite reflector outside the core (inner) tank further reduces neutron losses. The graphite, accurately cut from blocks and fitted into place in a steel (outer) tank, is from 1 to 2 ft thick, depending on the thickness of the heavy-water reflector within the core tank. The graphite reflector region is shown in Figs. 4–3 and 4–4; Fig. 4–6 shows a graphite reflector in place. Graphite is also placed beneath the tank to serve as a reflector. Because it is difficult to place solid reflector and shielding above the core, the height of the heavy water above the core is increased to obtain more complete neutron reflection.

The heavy water, serving as both reflector and moderator, is circulated for cooling through the heat exchanger. The graphite reflector requires little cooling; relatively low temperatures are maintained because heat escapes to the outer and inner tank walls. A helium atmosphere within the tank aids this heat transfer. Heat produced in the shield and graphite reflector amounts to only 2 to 3% of total reactor heat.

4–2.4 Shield. The shield surrounding the cylindrical reflector tank could be round, but it is more easily constructed with eight or more flat sides, which provide convenient surfaces for attaching and aligning experimental equipment. The relation of the shield to the rest of the reactor facility is apparent in Fig. 4–7.

The shield is made in several layers. Since the ratio of slow to fast neutrons entering the shield is very high, it is effective to use a layer of slow-neutron absorbing material, such as Boral, on the side nearest the

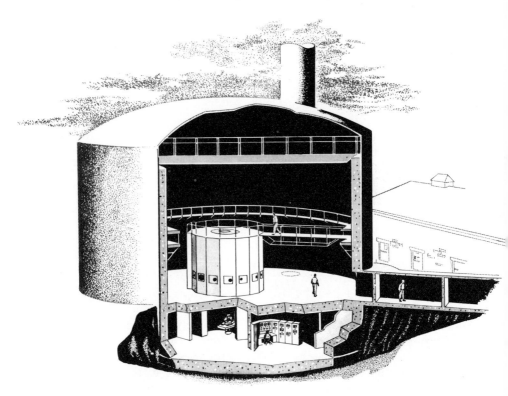

Fig. 4–7. Cutaway view of the MIT Research Reactor building showing the location of the reactor in the room, permitting experiments on all sides, and the experimental room beneath the reactor, which is primarily for medical research.

core, as in both the CP-5 and MIT designs. To be most effective this material should not emit hard gamma radiation by neutron capture. Boral, a mixture of boron carbide in aluminum clad with aluminum, has this property, and only a thin layer is needed to give a large attenuation of the thermal-neutron flux; i.e., $\frac{1}{4}$ in. gives an attenuation of approximately 10^4.

Outside the graphite reflector is a layer of dense material that absorbs gamma rays to keep them from overheating the concrete which constitutes the outer layer and major part of the shield. This gamma-absorbing layer (thermal shield) consists of several inches of lead or lead and steel. The concrete, containing higher density aggregate, serves as a biological shield and reduces the remaining fast neutrons and gamma flux to a safe level. It varies in thickness, depending on the power rating of the reactor. The over-all dimension of the reactor from one side of the radial shield to the other is about 20 ft.

On top, the shield has an opening as large as the graphite reflector. This opening is filled with two sections, or slabs, of shielding material which can be removed with a crane, to permit changing fuel elements or even the reactor tank or reflector material. The two slabs are said to constitute the top shield. The one next to the reactor is composed of an annular ring resting on top of the graphite reflector and a central plug fitting the ring and covering the reactor tank. The plug is pierced by openings sized to fit the fuel element plugs.

The upper top shield slab is also made in two parts, an annular ring resting on the radial concrete shield (or on the steel structure which contains the radial concrete shield) and a central plug for access to the core tank. This central plug is supported by the upper annular shielding ring. The top shielding pieces are made by filling steel shells with high-density concrete. Figure 4–8 shows a shielding plug for a heavy-water reactor. This plug can be seen at top center in Fig. 4–1, which shows all the shielding sections.

The thermal shield, a gamma-absorbing layer of metal(s) next to the reflector tank, contains copper tubes through which cooling water is circulated. In the CP-5, there are $3\frac{1}{2}$ in. of lead; in the MITR, there are 2 in. of steel, $1\frac{1}{2}$ in. of lead, and 2 in. of steel. The small quantity of heat produced in the concrete does not require a cooling system.

The shield is pierced by many openings for experimental facilities. To shield the facilities and provide maximum flexibility for changing and modifying experiments while the reactor is running, experimental facilities generally have shutter arrangements used for cutting out most of the radiation when desired. Shutters are usually rotating or sliding plugs of high-density material built into the shield. In the MIT reactor, a neutron shutter can be provided by a water tank which can be drained to permit

FIG. 4–8. Large top shielding plugs for a heavy-water research reactor. Each hole in these large plugs is filled with a small plug during operation. Seventeen of the holes are for fuel elements, one for a regulating rod, and the remainder for experimental facilities. (Courtesy of Argonne National Laboratory.)

the passage of neutrons. This technique is particularly effective for vertical facilities.

Blowers pull air from within the concrete shield structure and the experimental facility tubes and exhaust it to the atmosphere at a distance from the operating area to prevent contamination of the area.

The heavy-water system must be shielded for personnel safety. The equipment is in a basement room with a thick concrete ceiling. Approximately 2 ft of concrete is enough to shield against the radiation from activated impurities in the water and from the N^{16} produced by oxygen activation. The heavy-water activity dies out rapidly, so that the system is readily accessible immediately after reactor shutdown.

4–2.5 Control rods. The two U. S. heavy-water research reactors each have a single regulating rod along the edge of the core in the reflector region where the rod has a small reactivity worth. This permits fine control of the power level. From 4 to 6 combination shim-safety rods are used for shutdown safety and for reactivity changes due to burnup and fission-product buildup. These rods are partly withdrawn during operation and are adjusted from time to time to compensate for reactivity changes

Drive Motor
Magnetic Clutch
Ball-Nut Screw Unit
Spring
Shaft
Shield Plug
Information Train
Shaft
Signal-Arm Control Rod
Shock Absorber

FIG. 4–9. Semaphore-type shim-safety rod with its rod drive unit on a test stand external to the reactor. This is the type used in the CP-5 reactor. (Courtesy of Argonne National Laboratory.)

which cannot be controlled with the fine regulating rod. When a quick reactor shutdown is demanded, all the shim-safety rods are driven into the core in a fraction of a second (0.3 to 0.5 sec).

Cadmium in blade form or as a hollow cylinder is the neutron-absorbing material employed for both types of rods. The cadmium is covered with aluminum and weld-sealed to prevent contact with the water and to make the rod rigid. The CP-5 rods are hollow. MIT reactor rods, which are open cylinders, are operated much like those in light-water reactors, that is, with an aluminum guide tube extending into the core tank, an armature connected to the top of the rod, and a fail-safe electromagnetically coupled rod-drive mechanism. In addition, a shock absorber arrests the motion of the rod after its drop. The entire assembly can be removed, tested, and replaced as a unit. With vertical-acting rods of the light-water reactor type, part or all of the rod-drive mechanism must be directly above the rod. Rack and pinion rod-drive mechanism is used. A seal must be provided for the sliding shaft entering the top of the reactor tank to prevent the escape of the helium blanket gas.

The rotating semaphore-blade control rod used in CP-5 lends itself to heavy-water reactors because of the spacing between the elements. This

FIG. 4–10. Argonne Research Reactor (CP-5). This is the reactor shown in a sectional drawing in Fig. 4–1. The square thermal-column exit and the round irradiation ports on each diagonal face indicate the height of the reactor above floor level. The two rectangular openings above the thermal column and to each side of the lighted bulb on the core face contain drive units for the shim-safety rods. (Courtesy of Argonne National Laboratory.)

type of rod extends diagonally through the core when in its "in" position, and rotates upward about a pivot point above and outside the core, so that when fully withdrawn it is in a horizontal position above the core (Fig. 4–9). This rod does not require additional tank height for operating space but does not give linear reactivity response. This type keeps the mechanisms to the side and above the area of the experimental facilities, leaving the top of the reactor available for additional experimental facilities and for fuel-element handling.

The semaphore rod requires a pivot bearing within the reactor tank and a drive rod extending through the tank wall. There is a seal for the rotating shaft. The design of the drive shaft and the method of coupling it to the rod must permit displacement in all directions, since there will be differential heating and expansion of the metal parts in the reactor and differential expansion between the metal parts and the concrete shield through which the driving rod passes. Heating in the rotating drive shaft itself is caused principally by gamma-ray absorption in the steel. The aluminum reactor tank expands as it is heated from room temperature to the operating temperature of the reactor, and this expansion lifts the rod pivot bearing upward. These displacements are permitted by the proper spline-shaft connections.

Drive units for semaphore rods are compact, since only rotary motion is required; the units are above the level of the core. Since radiation toward the drive units passes horizontally through the shield, it can be recessed at this level to accommodate the mechanisms without reducing its effectiveness. This results in a clean, smooth-faced shield structure. A magnetic coupling connects the drive unit to the shaft and, as the unit rotates, a spring is compressed. The combination of gravity acting on the blade and the compression of the spring causes the rod to be inserted rapidly when the magnetic coupling is disengaged. Two drive mechanisms may be seen near the center of the photograph in Fig. 4–10.

4–2.6 Reactor cooling system. The CP-5 cooling system illustrates the features required for a heavy-water facility. The primary coolant system contains heavy water which is cooled by light water flowing in the secondary cooling system. The shield is cooled by a light-water circulating system. In addition, there are two helium loops, one for purging the region above the heavy water in the reactor tank and the other for maintaining an inert atmosphere in the graphite-containing reflector tank.

Heavy water is introduced near the bottom center of the reactor tank into the inlet plenum formed by the core support plate. This inlet plenum distributes the heavy water to the various fuel elements. The water flows upward through the fuel elements and overflows into the moderator and reflector region. It is drawn from this region of the reactor tank at 100 to 120°F by a centrifugal pump, enters the main heat exchanger, and is returned to the tank. A regulating valve controls the flow and a flowmeter measures the flow rate.

In both reactors an overflow pipe connects directly to a storage tank which can hold all the heavy water in the system. The overflow controls the heavy-water level in the reactor tank, which is filled from the storage tank by means of a centrifugal pump. Some heavy water is bypassed through micrometallic or ceramic filters to remove particles, and then through a resin column to demineralize the water. A dump system permits enough heavy water to be rapidly drained to remove the top reflector from the core, thus providing a measure of shutdown control. The principal function of this control is to secure the reactor against unintentional criticalities during extended shutdown periods. The system has a quick-acting dump valve and a limited-volume dump tank. A centrifugal pump returns heavy water to the reactor tank.

FIG. 4–11. Part of the heavy-water handling system for the CP-5 reactor. Most components are stainless steel or aluminum. All valves except a regulating valve are manually operated. This equipment is in a basement room in the reactor building. (Courtesy of Argonne National Laboratory.)

The dump and regulating valves are remotely operated from the control room; all other valves are manually controlled. The heavy-water piping is designed and the valves oriented so that the system will drain completely. Figure 4–11 depicts part of the heavy-water plumbing shown as line drawings in Fig. 4–1.

The reactor system contains about $7\frac{1}{2}$ tons of heavy water, which is circulated at the rate of several hundred gallons per minute. Heavy-water pressure is kept higher than that of the light water because it is less costly to lose some heavy water by leak to the light-water coolant system than to allow the entire volume of heavy water to be diluted with a small quantity of light water.

For normal operation, the heat capacity of the system is sufficient to take care of fission-product heat after reactor shutdown, so shutdown cooling is unnecessary. For operation above 2 Mw, there is danger of the fuel elements melting if the heavy water is lost from the system. To provide emergency cooling in this situation, a spray system is incorporated into the core. This system can operate for a limited time from a heavy-water reservoir and continue operating on light water if further cooling is required, or it can operate entirely on light water because heavy water lost from the system will already be contaminated and emergency light water can do no further harm.

With careful design and operation, loss of heavy water can be kept low. In 10 years of CP-3 operation, losses averaged less than 1% a year. Over this period, the heavy-water concentration changed from 99.85 to 99.65%, the remainder being light water. The CP-5 has surpassed CP-3 in low loss and low dilution. Heavy water can become diluted when ordinary water is accidentally admitted to the system or when heavy water is allowed to come in contact with air, permitting an exchange between the heavy water and the normal water vapor in the air.

The CP-5 light-water secondary cooling system consists of a loop with a centrifugal pump which circulates the water through the heat exchanger to the cooling tower and back to the heat exchanger. The system is connected to the process water supply to make up losses in the cooling tower. If the cooling-tower capacity is large enough, it can be utilized to reduce the heavy-water temperature below normal operating level. Because the reactor has a large negative temperature coefficient, this extra cooling will provide additional reactivity control for overriding transient xenon poison.

The thermal shield (the steel and lead layers next to the reflector tank) is cooled by a separate cooling loop. This cooling loop uses a centrifugal pump to circulate the water through the cooling coils in the shield, through a heat exchanger, and back to an elevated tank. The tank provides a head of water for emergency cooling if power fails. Since heat produced in the shield is not great, water from the heat exchanger in the shield cooling system is cooled by passing the makeup water for the main cooling tower through it.

A helium system supplies gas to the region above the heavy water in the reactor tank. Helium also minimizes the entrance of air when the system is opened for fuel element changes. The helium is circulated through an external system at a low rate (4 cfm is sufficient for 1-Mw operation). This external system includes a variable-volume tank to permit volume changes in the system, and heaters and a catalyst chamber for recombining the dissociated deuterium and oxygen (approximately 0.02 liter/min at 1 Mw). The recombined heavy water is collected in a tank in the helium circulating system and drained back to the heavy-water storage tank.

A second helium system provides a supply of helium to fill the reflector region and a variable-volume storage tank to permit expansion of the gas in the reflector tank. Helium in this tank provides a medium for heat conduction from the graphite to the reflector tank on one side and to the core tank on the other, and retards chemical reactions. Helium consumption amounts to 1000 ft^3 or more per month, depending on the tightness of the system.

4–2.7 Instrumentation. Nuclear instrumentation of heavy-water reactors is almost identical to the instrumentation of light-water reactors discussed in Chapter 3. Ionization chambers are the chief source of information on nuclear behavior. Fission counters and BF$_3$ counters may also be used. The ionization chambers are used with vibrating-reed electrometers, logarithmic amplifiers, and/or galvanometers to indicate power level. Logarithmic signals are differentiated to give period signals. A certain number of the power-level and period signals are connected to reactor trips which will shut the reactor down if preselected levels are exceeded.

Frequently the conditions of an experiment must be maintained within prescribed limits to prevent damaging the reactor or contaminating the operating area. In these cases the instruments monitoring the conditions can be connected to alarms or to the reactor scram system.

Temperatures and pressures are measured at several points in the heavy-water system. The flow rate is determined by measuring the pressure across an orifice or venturi in the circulating loop. The flow rate in CP-5 is also measured in each element by a float in the element tube (see Fig. 4–2). This float is connected to the armature of a differential transformer. The heavy water within the element support tube will be at a level different from that of the surrounding heavy water, depending on its velocity up through the fuel element. Thus the level of the float as shown by the differential transformer signal will be a measure of the heavy-water velocity through that particular element. The temperature of the heavy water is usually measured with thermocouples in the element support tube and in the external parts of the system. The temperature rise in the heavy water through the reactor tank is combined electrically with the flow rate to produce a signal proportional to the reactor thermal power, which is indicated on meters and recorders.

A sight glass connected to the heavy-water tank gives a positive indication of the heavy-water level. This level is also measured electrically by using a float connected to a differential transformer.

Many temperature indicators in the system are connected to alarms to alert the operator to abnormal conditions. For example, low-temperature alarms on both the heavy-water and the secondary light-water cooling systems alert against freezing. Light-water freezes at 32°F but heavy-water freezes at approximately 39°F; temperatures near this level must be prevented. It is also customary to place leak detectors at all valves, pumps, and gasketed joints in the heavy-water loop. These detectors consist of a metallic grid insulated from a metal plate, with a voltage between the two. A little heavy water will short the grid to the plate and energize a signal in the control room to alert the operator.

Temperatures and pressures in the two helium systems and the thermal-shield cooling system are also measured with standard instruments.

Periodically, a sample of the water is removed to be analyzed for hydrogen content by mass spectrography.

4–2.8 Experimental facilities. The reactor core in a heavy-water reactor is not as accessible as that in a light-water reactor. Consequently, all experimental facilities must be designed and built into the system when the facility is constructed. To give flexibility, facilities provided are numerous and varied. The sectional drawings of Figs. 4–3 and 4–4 and the photographs of Figs. 4–10 and 4–12 show some facilities available and in use at the U. S. heavy-water research reactors.

FIG. 4–12. Experimental equipment grouped about the CP-5 reactor. The reactor is on the left. The horizontal holes are utilized principally for beam work, the vertical holes for irradiations. (Courtesy of Argonne National Laboratory.)

One or two thermal columns are made an integral part of the facility. In the MITR there is a 6-in.-thick removable split lead curtain between the graphite core reflector and the graphite in the thermal column. The thermal column is about 5 or 6 ft square for the first few feet of its length near the core. The last 2 ft or so consist of a shield plug of lead or other heavy metal and a neutron-absorbing material. In this shield is a central hole, 1 to 2 ft square, with a separate plug, that can be used for small experiments. The entire shield can be removed and the region stacked with graphite or used for a large experiment. Access to the top and sides of the thermal column increases its total usefulness. The graphite in the thermal column can be removed so that experiments can be inserted within the column, or more intense (although less thermalized) beams obtained. The MIT thermal column has a lead gamma shutter available at its inner end for use during shutdown changes.

From 8 to 17 horizontal beam holes are provided, as well as a few through-ports. They approach the core as closely as possible—if a large core tank is used, the beam holes penetrate the tank; if a small tank is used, the beam holes merely extend to the surface of the tank. It is possible to vary the intensity and energy spectrum of the neutrons at a particular beam hole by changing the fuel element arrangement. The horizontal beam ports range from 4 to 12 in. in diameter. They are fitted with shutters, either rotating plug or vertical, for reducing the radiation intensity so that experiments may be changed while the reactor is operating.

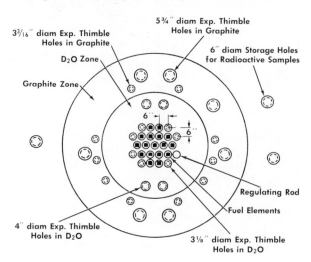

Fig. 4–13. Location of fuel elements and vertical experimental facilities in the CP-5 reactor. The unoccupied element location may be used for experimental facilities. Use of cylindrical fuel elements permits experiments to be located on the centerline of these elements, where there is maximum fast flux.

Several through-holes penetrate the core tank or pass tangent to it. Usually one or two of these are permanently equipped with rapid insertion and removal irradiation devices such as the pneumatically driven "rabbit." The through-holes are from 2 to 6 in. in diameter. A number of vertical experimental ports are also provided (Fig. 4–13).

Since the fuel elements are widely spaced in the core, vertical irradiation facilities can be located within the core itself. In addition, unused spaces for fuel elements can be adapted to experimental purposes. When cylindrical fuel elements are used, as in CP-5, it is possible to have irradiation ports (providing high fast-neutron flux) in the center of the elements. This can be done in MTR type elements by removing some of the center plates.

The bottom of the heavy-water reactor can be utilized for research by passing tunnels beneath it, as at the CP-5, or by constructing a room beneath it, as at the MIT reactor. This room, directly under the reactor, has a bismuth gamma-ray shutter and a water-filled-tank neutron shutter to control the radiation level; it will be used for medical research and for other purposes.

4–2.9 Fuel-loading procedure. The fuel-loading procedures and facilities used in these reactors differ slightly from those required for light-water reactors because a closed system must be maintained. For access, the top shield has removable small plugs (slightly larger in diameter than the elements) above each element. Since the top shield is in two layers, there are separate small plugs in each layer.

After two matching plugs have been removed, the element is withdrawn into a lead shielding cask, weighing from 7 to 10 tons, on the top of the reactor shield structure. Once the element is within the cask, water may be circulated through it to continue cooling, if necessary. If the element is left in the core after shutdown (for 1 hr after 2-Mw operation or 8 hr after 10-Mw operation), water cooling in the cask is not necessary. Spent elements are lowered into a pit of water which serves as shielding (and is sometimes used as a gamma irradiation facility) until they are shipped for reprocessing. New elements are only very slightly radioactive. However, a new element is loaded into the core from the shielding cask placed over a refueling hole in the reactor shield, thereby preventing radiation streaming from the radioactive core.

4–2.10 Heavy-water research reactors using natural uranium and low-enrichment fuels. Heavy water, because of its favorable moderating properties and extremely low thermal-neutron absorption, can be used with natural uranium to form a reactor. Reactors of this type are larger than enriched-uranium reactors, have a much higher critical mass, and operate at much higher power for a given thermal-neutron flux. Solid

TABLE 4–2

HEAVY-WATER REACTORS USING FUELS OF
VARIOUS ENRICHMENTS

Reactor	Enrichment, %	Power, Mw	Uranium, kg	U^{235}, kg	Thermal-neutron flux, $n/(cm^2)(sec)$
CP-5	90	1	1.87	1.68	3×10^{13}
NRX	Nat.	40	9550	68	7×10^{13}
CP-3	Nat.	0.3	2700	19	1×10^{12}
CP-3′	90	0.3	4.2	3.8	4×10^{12}
MITR	90	1	1.83	1.75	2×10^{13}

uranium fuel rods about 1 in. in diameter and 10 ft long are located in a grid on approximately 6-in. centers. This uranium is clad with aluminum or other metal of low cross section to prevent corrosion of the fuel and resulting contamination of the coolant. Cooling may be achieved by circulating the heavy water through a heat exchanger, as is done with the highly enriched fueled heavy-water reactors, or by use of annular spaces next to the fuel elements through which a gas or light-water coolant may flow.

Slightly enriched (1 to 20%) uranium fuel may also be used. This compromise between natural and high enrichment results in critical masses close to those of the highly enriched system.

Table 4–2 gives information on three reactors using highly enriched fuel, and two using natural fuel. The CP-3′ was the CP-3 modified for highly enriched uranium. The contrast in critical masses and thermal fluxes for the same power is clear.

4–3. PHYSICS CHARACTERISTICS

Heavy water is less effective than light water in slowing down fast neutrons, but the neutron absorption cross section of heavy water is far less (approximately 1000 times) than light water. These differences in nuclear properties result in differences in the reactor systems.

4–3.1 Nuclear properties of heavy water. Because of deuterium's low scattering cross section (as compared with hydrogen) neutrons in heavy water travel greater distances between collisions, with a correspondingly greater probability of escaping from a reactor core of given size. Also, the greater mass of the deuterium atom results in less energy loss per collision. These two factors are responsible for heavy water's poorer moderating ability compared with light water. However, neutrons make many more scattering collisions in heavy water (as compared with light water) before being absorbed, and therefore have a much higher probability of being usefully absorbed in fuel or in experimental devices.

The distance a neutron travels in slowing down to thermal energies in heavy water is about twice that in light water. The heavy-water reactor core must therefore be larger to reduce fast-neutron leakage. However, the thermal-neutron absorption is so low that the amount of fuel and structure in a heavy-water core will be less than in a corresponding light-water core. Because fuel and structural materials displace water and thus increase the slowing-down length in light-water reactors, the actual difference between heavy- and light-water systems is considerably less than the factor-of-two difference between the two moderators.

In heavy-water moderated systems the much longer thermal-neutron diffusion length causes the reactor to respond more slowly to large changes in reactivity. This effect is heightened by the photoneutron production in deuterium. Gamma-ray photons above the threshold energy of 2.21 Mev can be absorbed by a deuterium nucleus, which then emits a neutron [(γ, n) reaction]. Photons of the required energy are released in the process of fission and in the decay of the fission products. Reactor operation is affected in two ways: (1) there is a larger fraction of delayed neutron emitters, causing the heavy-water reactor to respond more slowly to reactivity changes (thus increasing safety), and (2) the photoneutron production is an effective neutron source for reactor startup. A source of gamma photons might be initially introduced into one of the reactor's experimental holes; then, after the reactor has been operated for a period, the gamma rays from fission products will produce enough photoneutrons for reactor startup.

4–3.2 Critical mass. The critical mass of a heavy-water moderated reactor is less than that of a light-water moderated reactor of the same power. Because of the extremely low neutron-absorption cross section of the heavy water, a large fraction of the neutrons are absorbed in the fuel. Indeed, absorption in the moderator is so low that practically all the neutrons are absorbed in the fuel or structural material. The lower cross section of the moderator permits the fuel to be more dilute, but requires the use of a larger core with a lower surface-to-volume ratio to reduce the neutron leakage.

Enriched heavy-water reactor cores are about 2 ft in diameter compared with about 1 ft in diameter for a light-water core of the same height and of comparable power. At the same time, the critical mass in the heavy-water reactor is approximately half that in the light-water reactor, and the thermal-neutron flux will be approximately twice as much. Typical fuel loadings are shown by the fuel requirements for the CP-5. The minimum critical mass is 1.2 kg; 1.68 kg are required for 1-Mw operation of a clean core. This is increased to 2.11 kg for 4-Mw operation, primarily because greater surface area is needed to remove the additional heat. After a year of 1-Mw operation, a uranium loading of 2.38 kg is required to overcome fuel depletion and fission-product poisoning.

4–3.3 Neutron flux. For a given power, the heavy-water reactor has higher thermal-neutron flux than any other type. The heavy-water reactor also provides large volumes of flux for experimental purposes and a relatively high leakage flux for beams and experiments. The good reflecting properties of heavy water and graphite produce a rather flat neutron distribution flux across the core. At points distant from the fuel element the ratio of thermal-neutron to fast-neutron flux is large. However, by inserting experiments within cylindrical fuel elements or by taking beams from near the surface of a fuel element, a fast-neutron flux approximately equal to the thermal flux can be obtained.

Figures 4–14 and 4–15 give the radial thermal-neutron flux distribution and the cadmium ratio for a gold foil measured at the core midplane of the CP-5 reactor operating at 2 Mw. Figures 4–16 and 4–17 show these same quantities for axial traverses at several radii, while Fig. 4–18 shows the flux through an isotope hole beneath the core tank. Figure 4–19 shows the locations at which the measurements given in Figs. 4–14 through 4–18

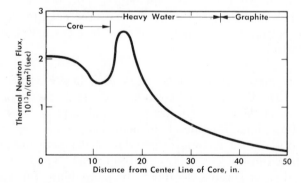

Fig. 4–14. Radial distribution of thermal-neutron flux in the CP-5 reactor at the core midplane for 2-Mw operation. The flux is directly proportional to the power. The dashed line in the core region shows flux distribution when the central element is left out. This is sometimes referred to as the "heavy-water thermal column." All points taken within the core region were at the centers of fuel elements; points between elements have higher flux.

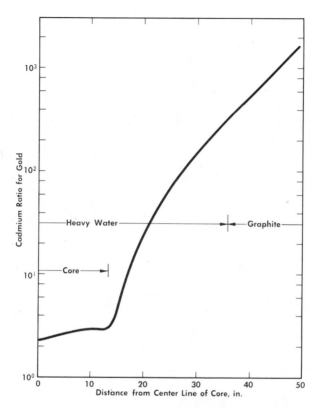

Fig. 4–15. Radial variation of the cadmium ratio for gold at the midplane of the CP-5 reactor (line A-A in Fig. 4–19). The points within the core were taken at the centers of fuel elements.

were made [1]. These plots are typical of highly enriched uranium heavy-water moderated research reactors. The flux values shown in Figs. 4–14, 4–16, and 4–18 are approximately proportional to the reactor power; there will be local changes due to burnup, added elements, and changing shim-rod positions. Figures 4–14 through 4–17 show how uniform the flux is in the core region. The large region of relatively high flux in the reflector and the degree of thermalization of the neutrons can also be seen in these figures.

The gamma-ray flux per unit neutron flux from a heavy-water research reactor is lower than that of a light-water reactor because of the low power per unit flux. However, the gamma-ray intensity near the core is comparable to that found in light-water reactors and higher than that in graphite research reactors. Figure 4–20 shows the gamma-ray intensity in the CP-5 measured along line C-C in Fig. 4–19 while the reactor is operating at 2 Mw.

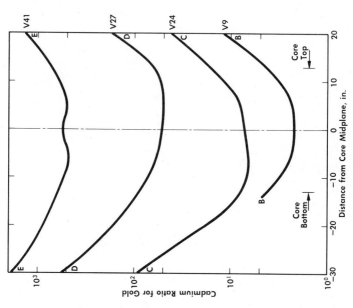

Fig. 4-17. Axial variations in the cadmium ratio for gold for the CP-5 reactor. The location at which these data were taken are shown in Fig. 4-19.

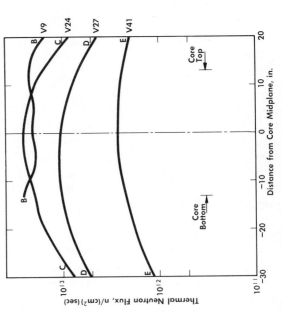

Fig. 4-16. Axial thermal-neutron distributions at various radii for the CP-5 reactor at 2 Mw. The locations at which these data were taken are shown in Fig. 4-19.

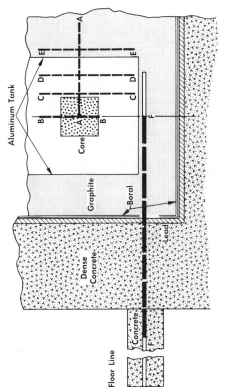

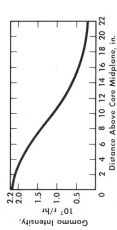

Fig. 4–19. Section through the CP-5 reactor, not to scale, showing the locations at which the data shown in Figs. 4-14 through 4-18 were obtained. These locations (also shown in Fig. 4–3) are (1) line B-B, Position V-9, (2) line C-C, Position V-24, (3) line D-D, Position V-27, and (4) line E-E, Position V-41.

Fig. 4–20. Gamma-ray intensity near the CP-5 core operating at 2 Mw. These data were obtained along line C-C shown in Fig. 4-19.

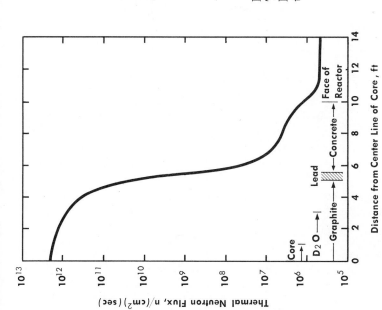

Fig. 4–18. Thermal-neutron flux along a line beneath the reactor core tank. The location at which these data were taken is shown in Fig. 4-19. These data were obtained with the reactor operating at 2 Mw.

4–3.4 Excess reactivity requirements. Anything that changes the neutron balance of a heavy-water reactor will have a relatively large effect on its reactivity because of the low critical mass and the large fraction of neutrons absorbed in the fuel. This is particularly true of fission-product poisons, fuel burnup, and experiments where these compete with the uranium fuel for neutrons. Therefore their absorption relative to uranium, or their poison effect on the core, will be greater than in other types of reactors.

In general, the temperature coefficient of reactivity will be significantly greater in heavy-water reactors than in light-water reactors. The exact amount will depend on the detailed design of each reactor; an exact comparison is difficult to make. Typical excess reactivity requirements of a heavy-water reactor are shown in Table 4–3. The 6 to 8% excess reactivity necessary for operation increases the fuel requirement of the CP-5 from 1.2 to 1.68 kg of U^{235}.

At 1-Mw operation, no provision is made to override the xenon poison that increases immediately after a reactor shutdown. At this power level its effect is not large, and the normal excess reactivity in the shim and regulating rods is sufficient to accommodate the maximum xenon poison that can occur. At 2 Mw the problem is a little more serious, with 5 to 6% reactivity needed to override the peak xenon concentration. Fuel loading may be increased to provide this reactivity, or shutdown periods can be limited so that the xenon concentration will not have time to build up so high, particularly after excess reactivity has been lost through fuel burnup. At still higher powers the problem becomes increasingly serious, and loading and control provisions must be made to take care of it.

TABLE 4–3

EXCESS REACTIVITY REQUIREMENTS FOR THE CP-5
HEAVY-WATER REACTOR (2-Mw)

Item	Reactivity, $\%\,\dfrac{\Delta k_{eff}}{k_{eff}}$
Temperature rise from room to operating temperature (approximately 25°C)	0.8
Equilibrium xenon poison (2-Mw operation)	3.5
Fuel burnup (30 to 40% maximum, 15 to 25% average)	1 to 2
Experiment requirements	1 to 2
Total excess reactivity required	6 to 8

4–3.5 Control requirements. Changes in the operating condition of heavy-water reactors produce greater reactivity changes than in light-water reactors. However, the control rods or blades have a higher reactivity worth in a heavy-water reactor than in a light-water reactor. Each safety or shim element is worth 4 to 8%; thus only one or two are needed to overcome the 6 to 8% excess reactivity required for operation. However, for safety, four to six shim-safety rods are incorporated in a heavy-water research reactor.

Since the reactivity of a shim-safety rod is so great, a small motion of one changes reactivity significantly. Therefore, a rod of lesser worth is desired for fine regulation. A vertically driven regulating rod in the reflector region with a worth of less than 0.5% $\Delta k_{\mathrm{eff}}/k_{\mathrm{eff}}$ provides fine control in both the CP-5 and the MIT reactors.

The neutron lifetime in a heavy-water reactor is long: approximately 20 times that in a corresponding light-water reactor. Therefore, for a given large reactivity change, the power rises much more slowly in a heavy-water reactor than in its light-water counterpart. Because of the slower power increase for large reactivities, the heavy-water reactor is considered safer than the light-water type, and the requirements on the speed of response of the control system are correspondingly less stringent. However, the control rods for a highly enriched heavy-water moderated system are physically small and can be inserted fully in 0.3 to 0.5 sec. The high worth of the reflector offers an additional means of control. The top reflector can be removed (leaving the elements covered for cooling) to reduce reactivity about $3\frac{1}{2}\%$. These factors add up to an extremely safe reactor.

4–3.6 Shielding requirements. The shielding problem in the heavy-water reactor is generally less than that encountered with other types of reactors. The low power per unit flux results in a low gamma-ray production, and the efficient reflector system reduces neutron leakage. Consequently, it is possible to use 2 to 4 in. of lead to cut down the intensity of the core gamma rays and $\frac{1}{4}$ in. of Boral to reduce thermal neutrons by a factor of 10^4, thus limiting capture gamma-ray production in the remaining part of the shield. The layer of several feet of high-density concrete external to the next-to-the-core materials reduces the radiation intensities far below biological tolerances. Consequently, experimental background radiation is also of low intensity.

4–4. OPERATIONAL CHARACTERISTICS

4–4.1 Fuel cycles. The fuel cycles for a heavy-water research reactor are very flexible. They depend on the power level at which the reactor is operated, the loading pattern, and fuel loading per element. Usually only a few of the elements are replaced at a time, to keep the average burnup in the core lower than the maximum burnup in particular elements. When the CP-5 operates at 4 Mw, four elements are replaced monthly; a complete core change is accomplished in 4 or 5 months. The MIT reactor staff plans to replace one element per month for 1-Mw operation; approximately 19 months will be required for a complete core change. These fuel changes are made at scheduled shutdowns. In another scheme, operations are started with the required fuel mass, and elements are added to maintain reactivity. At the end of a year all elements are replaced except those which were added last and hence have suffered little burnup. (The burnup attained in heavy-water reactors is 30 to 40% of the U^{235}.)

Usually fuel is shipped for reprocessing at less frequent intervals than fuel elements are changed in the core. For the CP-5 operating at 4 Mw with replacements of four fuel elements monthly, shipments for reprocessing are made semiannually. This schedule requires a 7.5-kg inventory of fuel which must, of course, be considered in planning operations.

4–4.2 Operating cycles. Operating cycles for the heavy-water research reactor can be set by research requirements. The average experiment may require a 5-day around-the-clock schedule with shutdowns on weekends, or it may require more continuous operation. Changing fuel elements will interrupt the research; these changes can be infrequent, one per month or at even longer intervals.

4–4.3 Ease of startup and shutdown. For the CP-5 and the MIT reactors operating at from 1 to 2 Mw of thermal power, there are no major problems in starting up and shutting down. The temperature changes in the system are slight, and either reactor can be started up at any rate considered safe. Likewise, they can be shut down almost instantaneously. The natural circulation within the reactor tank and heavy-water loop and the heat capacity of the system will take care of the heat produced by fission products after shutdown.

At higher powers, 4 Mw and above, the fission-product heat after shutdown becomes significant, and many hours of cooling may be required.

4–4.4 Reactor stability. In operation, the heavy-water reactor is quite stable, a characteristic necessary for accurate physics measurements. Automatic control will hold the power within $\pm 1\%$ of the desired value. Closer control can be obtained if greater accuracy is needed, or the intensity of the beams and fluxes at experiments can be monitored.

Daily variation in temperature at the cooling tower can cause temperature changes at the reactor, resulting in variation in the position of shim rods and, therefore, in flux distribution. The operating temperatures of the heavy water can be held quite constant and these variations minimized by controlling either its flow in the primary system or the flow of light water to the cooling tower. In one reactor the light-water coolant is maintained within $\pm 1°F$ of the desired value, which in turn holds the heavy-water temperature constant. In the CP-5 no attempt is made to control daily variations in temperature; the variations result in changes in regulator-rod and perhaps shim-rod positions, but the resulting changes in flux distribution and the effect on the experiments are within acceptable limits.

A long-term drift in the position of the shim rods and in flux distribution is caused by burnup of fuel and production of fission products. Sharp changes in flux distribution occur when fuel elements are added or replaced. Most experiments are not affected by these changes.

4–5. Summary

4–5.1 Special characteristics. The two U. S. heavy-water highly enriched fueled research reactors are like light-water research reactors in many respects. Their sizes are comparable and both types use water for moderating and cooling. They have similar shielding requirements and use similar or identical fuel sections. However, there are also significant differences between heavy-water and light-water reactors. The heavy-water reactor requires a closed system to prevent loss or dilution of the expensive heavy water. The neutron absorption in the water is low and the thermal utilization in the core is high, resulting in a low critical mass, a low fuel inventory, a large accessible volume for experiments and for control purposes, and a reflector region having a relatively high flux for experiments and for neutron beams.

The core is not as accessible in a heavy-water reactor as in light-water systems; therefore the experimental facilities must be designed into the system initially. The facilities are likely to be greater in number than in a typical light-water reactor; in other respects they are quite similar.

4–5.2 Advantages. The principal advantage of a heavy-water reactor is its high thermal-neutron flux per unit power. This in turn results in low power, low gamma-ray flux, low fuel burnup, and long fuel cycles for a given thermal-neutron flux. The core has a relatively large experimental volume, with high thermal-neutron flux regions between fuel elements and in the reflector for experiments or for obtaining external beams.

The heavy-water reactor permits some selection of the neutron spectrum for use in an experiment. Within a cylindrical fuel element, the fast-neutron flux is slightly higher than the thermal-neutron flux, while between the elements and in the reflector region the thermal flux is ten times the fast flux. If fast-neutron flux beams are required, a fuel element can be placed close to a beam tube. If a thermal-neutron beam is required, the lattice location near the beam tube can be left vacant.

The heavy-water reactor operates at low temperature, hence corrosion is not a serious problem.

The safety and simplicity of the system permit the continuous uninterrupted operation so important for research, and makes possible operation by a small crew. The small crew, low burnup of uranium, and low power consumption for operating the facility (80 kw electrical for 1-Mw operation) result in low over-all operating costs for a heavy-water facility.

Since heavy water does not activate significantly, approximately 2 ft of concrete is sufficient shielding to protect personnel from radiation from the heavy-water circulating system. This radioactivity decays rapidly after shutdown, so that the system is immediately accessible.

4–5.3 Disadvantages. The principal disadvantage in the heavy-water system is the high cost of the heavy water, \$28/lb. Approximately 6 to 8 tons of heavy water are required for a reactor system using highly enriched uranium, and the high cost necessitates a more expensive plumbing system to prevent its loss, contamination, or dilution. Special care is required in handling the heavy water, although with proper design and procedures this disadvantage can be minimized. There is also neutron production even at shutdown because of the (γ, n) reaction in the heavy water.

REFERENCES

1. Data for Figs. 4–14 through 4–20. W. McCORKLE, Argonne National Laboratory, personal communication.

CHAPTER 5

HOMOGENEOUS REACTORS*

5-1. General Description

The term "homogeneous," as used in this book, refers specifically to the aqueous homogeneous type of research reactor frequently called "water boiler."

Usually the core of the homogeneous reactor is a stainless-steel sphere, about 1 ft in diameter, which contains a uranium salt in water solution, (uranyl sulfate and uranyl nitrate solutions have been used). Since a natural uranium-water system cannot be made critical, the uranium employed is enriched in the 235 isotope. Typical isotopic concentrations vary from about 14.5% to more than 90% U^{235}. Typical fuel loadings range from 580 to 1250 g of U^{235}, depending on the power level, core size, and reflector.

The fuel solution is cooled by water circulating through coils inside the core. Normally this cooling keeps the solution temperature below about 80°C and, since the operating pressure is near atmospheric, no actual boiling occurs. The name "water boiler" was prompted by the bubbling which results from the evolution of hydrogen and oxygen produced by decomposition of the water by fission fragments.

A fuel-handling system associated with the core adds fuel solution to the core and recovers solution that is expelled by accidental operation above design power. Means are also provided for recombining the hydrogen and oxygen evolved in operating at relatively high power and returning the water to the core. In low-power systems, the gases are collected for disposal. Since mixtures of these gases constitute an explosion hazard, precautions are taken to keep the mixture below the explosive concentrations. In addition to hydrogen and oxygen, the radioactive fission gases xenon and krypton are evolved from the fuel solution, hence it is necessary to shield the gas-handling system and prevent the uncontrolled escape of the these gases.

The core is surrounded by a graphite neutron reflector approximately 2 ft thick (beryllium oxide was used in some of the first homogeneous reactors). A concrete shield around the reflector protects personnel against radiation.

The reactor is controlled by neutron-absorber rods usually containing boron or cadmium. There are passages or thimbles for these rods in the

---

* By W. S. Hogan.

TABLE 5–1

HOMOGENEOUS REACTORS THAT HAVE BEEN OPERATED
IN THE UNITED STATES

Name of reactor	Location	Power, kw	Criticality date
Water Boiler Neutron Source (WBNS)	Atomics International, Santa Susanna Mountains, California	0.001 to 0.002	1952
Livermore Reactor	University of California, Livermore, California	0.5	1953
Raleigh Research Reactor I	North Carolina State College, Raleigh, North Carolina	10	1953 (replaced by RRRII)
Raleigh Research Reactor II	North Carolina State College, Raleigh, North Carolina	0.5	1957
Armour Research Reactor	Armour Research Foundation, Chicago, Illinois	50	1956
Lopo	LASL,* Los Alamos, New Mexico	<0.001	1944 (replaced by Hypo)
Hypo	LASL, Los Alamos, New Mexico	5.5	1944 (replaced by Supo)
Supo	LASL, Los Alamos, New Mexico	25	1951

* Los Alamos Scientific Laboratory.

core or an adjacent reflector. Ion chambers and fission chambers monitor
the neutron-flux level and reactor period. The homogeneous reactor has
the inherent safety features of large negative temperature and power
coefficients.

In general, these reactors have various experimental facilities such as
thermal columns and beam tubes. The radioactive fission gases (neutron-

free) may be used as a gamma-irradiation source. Thermal-neutron fluxes from 10^7 to 10^{12} n/(cm^2)(sec) are available, depending on the power. The powers of existing reactors of this type range from 1 watt to 50 kw.

This chapter describes in some detail the features mentioned above. Illustrations and examples are representative of the particular feature under discussion. Frequent reference will be made to the reactors listed in Table 5–1, which lists water-boiler research reactors that have been operated in the United States.

5–2. DESIGN FEATURES

This section contains a qualitative description of the characteristic features of homogeneous research reactors.

5–2.1 Core and fuel-handling system. Typical homogeneous research reactor cores are stainless-steel (type 347 or 316) spheres about 1 ft in diameter. At present the only exception is the Raleigh Research Reactor, North Carolina State College, which has a cylindrical core with hemispherical bottom. Lines carrying the fuel solution and the cooling coils are also of stainless steel. Figures 5–1 and 5–2 show two typical homogeneous-reactor cores.

For purposes of illustration, the core and fuel-handling system of the homogeneous reactor operated by the Atomic Energy Commission's

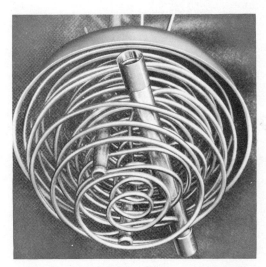

Fig. 5–1. Core details of the Super Power Water Boiler Reactor (Supo). This is the third version of the first water-boiler reactor, Lopo, which was put in operation at Los Alamos Scientific Laboratory in 1944. (Courtesy of Los Alamos Scientific Laboratory.)

Fig. 5–2. The core of Raleigh Research Reactor I. The core is a right-circular cylinder of type-347 stainless steel, $10\frac{7}{8}$ in. OD and $10\frac{5}{8}$ in. high. Cooling for 10-kw operation is provided by four coils, each $\frac{1}{4}$ in. OD by 7 ft long. (Courtesy of North Carolina State College.)

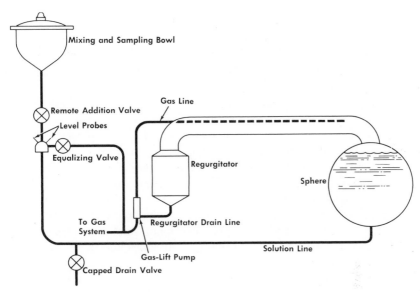

Fig. 5–3. Schematic diagram of the fuel-handling system of the Livermore Research Reactor.

Livermore, California, laboratories will be discussed. A flow sheet for the fuel-handling system is shown in Fig. 5–3.

The reactor core was fabricated by welding two type-316 stainless-steel spun hemispheres. The sphere has a $12\frac{1}{2}$-in. OD and a minimum wall thickness of 0.063 in. Its "glory hole," or central exposure facility, is a type-316 stainless-steel tube $1\frac{1}{4}$ in. in OD with a $\frac{1}{16}$-in. wall welded through the sphere along a horizontal diameter. A $\frac{3}{16}$-in. stainless-steel tube connects the core to the mixing and sampling bowl located outside the graphite reflector. The mixing bowl (Fig. 5–3) has a volume of about 3 liters and is also made of type-316 stainless steel. Fuel can be added to the core by gravity feed from the bowl through stainless-steel valves. The equalizing valve and T-joint in this line allow the solution to be drained from the core by gravity. The cooling coil is a helix 160 in. long, made of $\frac{5}{16}$-in. OD type-316 stainless-steel tubing. The coil is designed to give a fuel-solution temperature of 40°C at a power level of 2 kw; the normal power level is 0.5 kw. Distilled water at a minimum temperature of 7.2°C is circulated through the coil at a maximum rate of 1.3 gpm. A $2\frac{1}{2}$-in.-OD pipe is attached to the top of the sphere, and encloses the cooling water and sweep-gas lines. This line ends at a 2-liter reservoir (labeled "regurgitator") which collects any fuel solution expelled from the core due to solution expansion during a power excursion. This solution is slowly returned to the core by the gas-lift pump, which operates continuously when the gas-handling system is functioning.

Two electrical probes reporting high and low points indicate height of fuel in the lines to the mixing bowl.

5–2.2 Reflector and shield. All water-boiler research reactors in the United States now use graphite as the reflector material. Some earlier models, no longer in existence, employed beryllium oxide as the principal reflector. Beryllium oxide is a better reflector than graphite in that it gives a lower critical mass, but it introduces a source of neutrons by a (γ, n) reaction in beryllium. This source delays reactor shutdown and affects startup. The principal shielding material is concrete (dense concrete in some cases) with lead and a good thermal-neutron absorber as necessary. The Livermore Reactor has about 4 ft of timber with 1 in. of borated paraffin as the top shield. Five inches of lead and 0.03 in. of cadmium surrounding the core give additional shielding. Openings are provided in the shield and reflector for beam tubes and in the shield for a thermal column.

The 50-kw homogeneous reactor operated by the Armour Research Foundation employs a typical shield and reflector design (Figs. 5–4 and 5–5). The reflector and thermal column are composed of layers of high-purity graphite blocks forming a rectangular prism about $6\frac{1}{2}$ by 5 by 5 ft which is enclosed in a steel tank. The graphite has a density of 1.67 g/cm^3

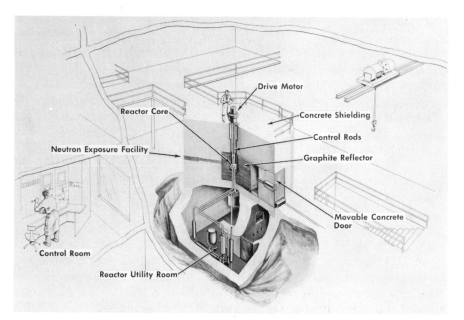

Fig. 5–4. Artist's cutaway drawing of the Armour Research Reactor showing the general arrangement of the facility. (Courtesy of Atomics International.)

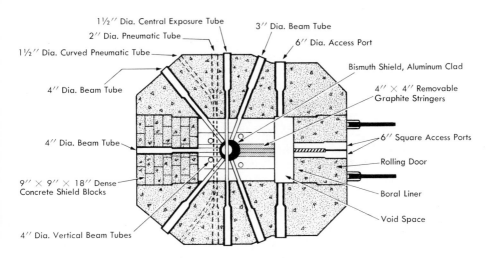

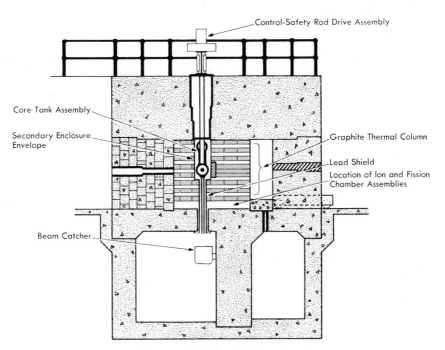

FIG. 5–5. Sectional views of the Armour Research Reactor. Plan view shows the beam tubes and thermal column extending from reactor core through the concrete shield. The control- and safety-rod system extends upward from core into the reactor room, and piping leads from the core into a subpile room, which contains the fuel- and gas-handling systems. (Courtesy of Armour Research Foundation.)

and a boron content of less than 0.1 ppm. The biological shield surrounding the reflector is about 5 ft thick and made of dense concrete. The shield is a monolithic structure except for the portion directly opposite the thermal column and its access door, which consists of dense concrete blocks, as shown in Fig. 5–5. The heavy concrete is composed of hematite ore, mill scale, colemanite, Portland cement, and water, and has a density of about 3.5 g/cm^3.

Each beam-tube facility is equipped with a graphite reflector plug and a dense concrete and steel shielding plug inserted when the facility is not in use. An aluminum-clad bismuth shield is next to the core behind the thermal column, to reduce the gamma flux.

Obviously, the amount of shielding required in aqueous homogeneous reactors depends on the power level of the installation. For example, a water boiler operating at 1 watt may use only a 2-ft thick concrete block shield, while a water boiler designed for a 50-kw power level will require 4 to 5 ft of dense concrete. Materials, other than concrete and lead, that are suitable for reactor shielding include boron-impregnated hydrocarbons, Boral (a boron carbide-aluminum matrix clad with aluminum), cadmium, baryte and colemanite, and water.

5–2.3 Instrumentation. Instruments for homogeneous research reactors supply much the same kind of information required by other reactors. It is necessary to have an indication of such information as power level, period, gamma flux at various places, coolant temperature, flow rates, liquid levels and control-rod positions. Different sets of neutron-detection instruments are usually required for different flux levels.

Typical instrumentation for a homogeneous reactor includes boron trifluoride (BF_3) proportional counters, fission chambers, and ionization chambers to indicate power level and reactor period. Usually, thermocouples measure coolant, catalyst, and core-solution temperatures, while ionization chambers measure gamma-radiation levels in the shield near the core and in the evolved gases. In addition, equipment is included to determine the core liquid level and pressure, coolant and gas-flow rates, control-rod positions, electrical conductivity of the cooling water, and the composition of the evolved gases. Signals from the instruments are fed to the control panel or console.

Figure 5–6 is a block diagram representing the essential features of the instrumentation of the Livermore Reactor. The three BF_3 proportional counters are outside the 5-in. lead shield which surrounds the core. From startup to about 50 milliwatts, they indicate neutron-flux level and period. The three gamma-compensated ion chambers supply the same information from 50 milliwatts to normal operating power. Reactor-shutdown signals are set off when any of the detectors indicates too high a power level or too short a reactor period. Scram signals are also caused by high pressure in the gas system, low gas-flow rate, a high hydrogen concentration, and too high or too low a core temperature. As indicated in Fig. 5–6, a number of temperatures are measured, as are system pressure, fuel-solution level, and electrical conductivity of the cooling water.

Two gamma-ray ionization chambers are within the concrete shielded enclosure called the "cave," which houses all reactor components except the control panel and cooling system. These chambers can measure radiation levels up to 2000 r/hr.

5–2.4 Control rods. Control rods and associated equipment for homogeneous research reactors are essentially the same as for the other reactors considered in the previous chapters. In addition to the rods, the components include drive motors, linkage between motors and rods, rod position indicators, rod channel guides, and shock absorbers. This reactor type may use rods in either the core or the reflector, or in both.

The Water Boiler Neutron Source (WBNS) has four control elements: two safety rods, and a coarse and a fine regulating rod. The rods move horizontally into the reflector adjacent to the core. The safety rods, made of two $\frac{1}{4}$-in. strips of Boral attached to aluminum channels, resemble a 4-in. I-beam about 3 ft long. These rods are held out of the reflector by a trigger mechanism which, when released, pulls them into the reflector through a metal counterweight arrangement. Over the last 6 in. of travel, wedges on the control rods come in contact with spring-backed brake shoes to give a shock-absorber action. The coarse regulating rod is similar in construction to the safety rods but has cadmium sheet as the neutron absorber. The fine regulating rod is a 1-in.-diameter steel pipe in which varying amounts of cadmium can be inserted. Both rods are driven by reversible motors through a rack-and-pinion arrangement.

The Livermore Reactor has a control-rod arrangement similar to that used by the WBNS. The rods are stainless-steel sleeves, $37\frac{1}{2}$ by $3\frac{3}{4}$ by $\frac{1}{2}$ in., packed with boron carbide. Their motion in the reflector is actuated by a counterweight and shock-absorber system, much as in the WBNS. The reactor at Armour Research Foundation uses four control elements operating vertically in re-entrant thimbles in the core. The elements are stainless-steel tubes containing boron carbide. The drive mechanism is a rack-and-pinion type, actuated through a gear reduction mechanism by an electric motor. Figure 5–7 is a photograph of the rods and of the drive mechanism located above the top shield of the reactor. The Supo at the Los Alamos Scientific Laboratory has three cadmium-aluminum-sandwich rods in the reflector and two rods containing sintered B^{10} in the core. The Raleigh Research Reactor uses two boron-carbide filled steel tubes in the core. Figure 5–8 is a photograph of the rod drive mechanism for this reactor.

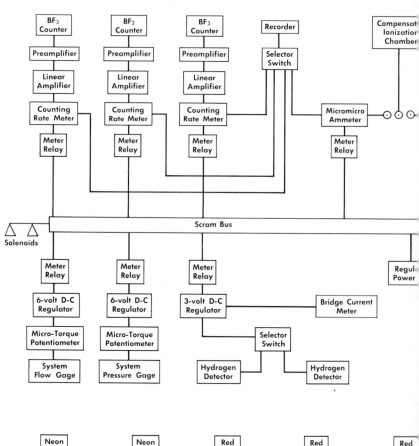

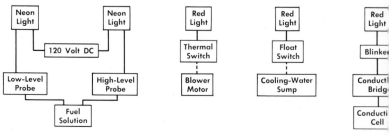

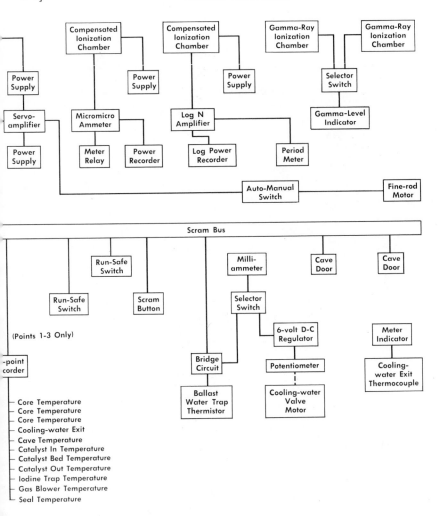

FIG. 5–6. Block diagram of Livermore Reactor instrumentation. Signals which initiate a scram are relayed to the scram bus. Other signals are indicated at the console by meters or lights.

FIG. 5–7. Control rods and mechanism for the Armour Research Reactor. (Courtesy of Armour Research Foundation.)

FIG. 5–8. The Raleigh Research Reactor control mechanism. The control-rod flanges and shock absorbers can be seen over the support plate below. The rods are lifted by motor-driven electromagnets to facilitate rapid shutdown. (Courtesy of North Carolina State Laboratory.)

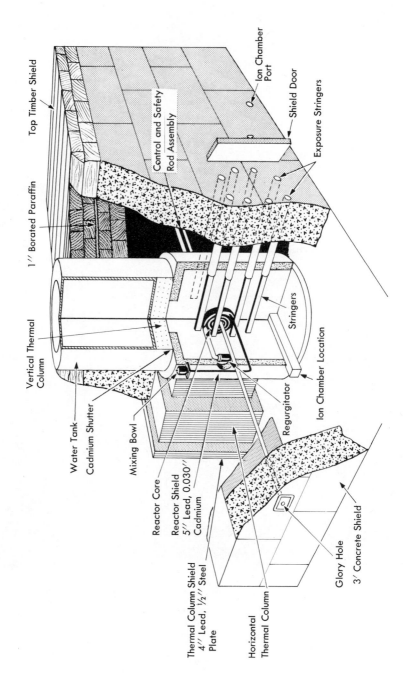

Top Timber Shield

1″ Borated Paraffin

Control and Safety
Rod Assembly

Ion Chamber
Port

Shield Door

Exposure Stringers

Vertical Thermal
Column

Water Tank

Cadmium Shutter

Mixing Bowl

Reactor Core

Reactor Shield
5″ Lead, 0.030″
Cadmium

Thermal Column Shield
4″ Lead, ½″ Steel
Plate

Horizontal
Thermal Column

Regurgitator

Stringers

Ion Chamber Location

Glory Hole

3′ Concrete Shield

FIG. 5–9. Isometric view of the Livermore Reactor.

5–2.5 Experimental facilities. Typical experimental facilities for homogeneous research reactors include beam tubes, a central exposure tube or glory hole, thermal columns, pneumatic tubes, and a gamma-irradiation facility using the gaseous fission products as a pure gamma source.

The Armour Research Reactor experimental facilities that give access to core radiation are listed in Table 5–2. The general arrangement can be seen in Figs. 5–4 and 5–5.

TABLE 5–2

EXPERIMENTAL FACILITIES OF ARMOUR RESEARCH REACTOR

Facility	Quantity	Size
Horizontal beam tube	1	4 in. in diameter (6-in. hole in shield)
Horizontal beam tube	2	4 in. in diameter
Vertical beam tube	4	4 in. in diameter
Horizontal beam tube	2	3 in. in diameter
Straight pneumatic tube	1	2 in. in diameter
Curved pneumatic tube	1	2 in. in diameter
Central exposure tube	1	$1\frac{1}{2}$ in. in diameter
Horizontal thermal column	1	5 ft square
Column access port	4	6 in. in diameter

The tube facilities consist of steel sleeves extending through the concrete shield and aluminum thimbles piercing the reflector near the core. The thermal column has nine removable horizontal graphite stringers in its center, and a space for exposures between the outside end of the column and the inner face of the movable concrete door. Evolved fission gases are piped to the recombiner tank in the subpile room. Facilities for exposure to this pure gamma source are provided from this room into the exposure and valve rooms.

Figure 5–9 is an isometric cutaway view of the Livermore Reactor and associated equipment showing the experimental facilities and shielding

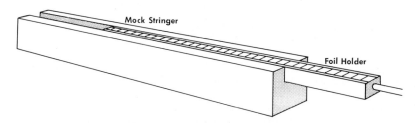

FIG. 5–10. Mock stringer bar simulating those used for foil exposures in the Livermore Reactor.

The exposure stringers are graphite bars 4 by 4 in. square by 36 in. long. Figure 5–10 shows a mock stringer. This reactor has a water tank on top of the vertical thermal column, which serves as an additional exposure facility.

5–2.6 Cooling and gas-handling systems. The cooling system of the Armour Research Reactor illustrates the general features of these systems in homogeneous reactors (Fig. 5–11).

In the core, the distilled water coolant flows through a 10-loop coil of $\frac{1}{4}$-in. stainless-steel tubing. It leaves the core at 110°F at the rate of 12 gpm and joins the 95°F, 2-gpm stream from the recombiner heat exchanger. The combined stream enters the main heat exchanger at 109°F, where it is cooled to 80°F and then returns to the core and recombiner. The secondary coolant in the main heat exchanger is ordinary tap water.

Flow-meters monitor the flow to the core and recombiner, and a 5-gal surge tank smooths out pressure variations in the primary loop. A conductivity cell is used to measure the purity of the primary coolant. The

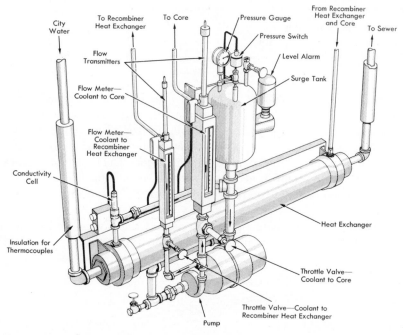

FIG. 5–11. The cooling system of the Armour Research Reactor. The primary-coolant pump circulates distilled water through the core cooling coils and recombiner heat exchanger and then to the main heat exchanger, where heat generated in the reactor is transferred to the secondary coolant. (Courtesy of Atomics International.)

pump in the primary loop is a constant-speed centrifugal type designed to deliver 14 gpm against a pressure of 50 psig.

Normally, the secondary loop is completely free from radioactivity, but it is continuously monitored. If activity should appear, the loop is automatically closed off from the water supply and sewage system. A leak from the radioactive primary loop would contaminate the secondary loop.

Cooling systems for other homogeneous reactors are similar to the one described. A variation is refrigeration of the cooling water of the Livermore Reactor.

Figure 5–12 is a schematic of the gas-handling system for the Supo Reactor at Los Alamos. The reactor is normally operated at a power of 25 kw.

The circulating carrier gas (air) carries the gases produced in the core through the reflux condenser, where water and acid vapor are removed (along with any solution spray present) and returned to the core. The air then goes through a stainless steel wool trap where residual entrained liquid is removed before the air enters the blower. From the blower, the air flows to one of two interchangeable catalyst chambers containing platinized alumina pellets. This chamber recombines the hydrogen and oxygen into water vapor. At a reactor power of 25 kw, the catalyst bed reaches a temperature of 465°C.

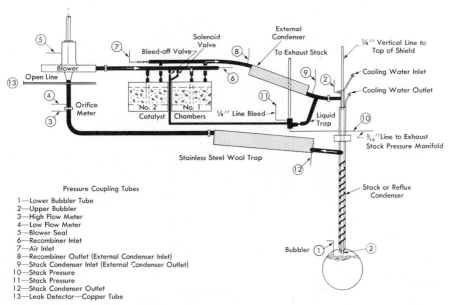

Fig. 5–12. Schematic diagram of gas-handling system for Supo. (Courtesy of Los Alamos Scientific Laboratory.)

The external condenser reduces the gas temperature to approximately that of the gas leaving the reflux condenser. The circulation rate is about 100 liters/min, which keeps the hydrogen concentration below the explosive limit at all points of the system. The recombiner assembly is in the shield above the core and reflector.

The WBNS Reactor at Atomic International (power about 1 watt) collects all gas in a stainless-steel gas-accumulator tank, with a volume of about 40 liters. When enough of the core gases have been collected, a neoprene-rubber bag within the tank is expanded with helium to force the gases into a disposal tank for removal from the system (Fig. 5–13).

The Armour Research Reactor uses a wet-gas handling system (Fig. 5–14). Oxygen at about 12 psia serves as a sweep gas. It enters the core assembly above the solution level, picks up the decomposition gases, and dilutes their hydrogen content to about 1% by volume. The sweep gas and its burden then go through the entrainment eliminator, which serves as a reflux condenser and returns entrained solution to the core, and joins with the outlet water from the recombiner pump (which circulates the recombiner-tank water). The resulting stream is forced through a nozzle into the recombiner tank. The gas drifts to the catalyst-bed intake, where it passes through another entrainment eliminator and on to the platinized-alumina catalyst bed. Water in the recombiner tank covers the catalyst

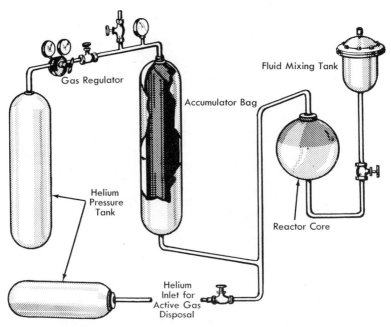

Fig. 5–13. Fuel- and gas-handling system for WBNS.

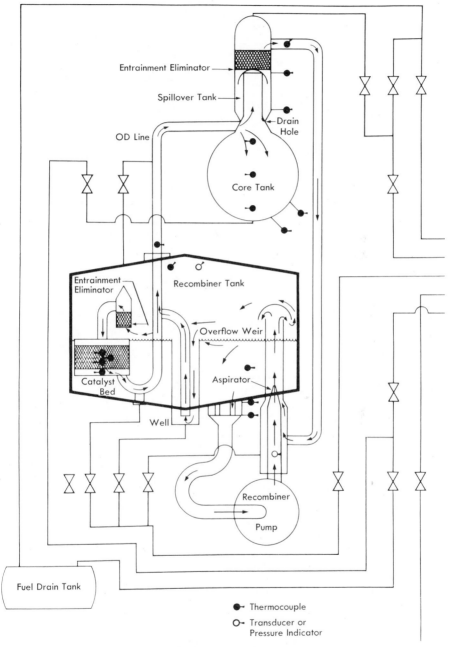

Entrainment Eliminator

Spillover Tank

OD Line

Drain Hole

Core Tank

Entrainment Eliminator

Recombiner Tank

Overflow Weir

Catalyst Bed

Aspirator

Well

Recombiner Pump

Fuel Drain Tank

●– Thermocouple

O– Transducer or Pressure Indicator

Fig. 5–14. Flow diagram of the gas-handling system for the Armour Research Reactor.

TABLE 5–3

FUEL LOADINGS IN HOMOGENEOUS REACTORS

Reactor	Core geometry	Fuel enrichment, %	Core solution	Core temperature, °C	Reflector	Power, kw	Zero-power mass, g	Operating mass, g
WBNS	Sphere	90	Uranyl nitrate		Graphite	0.001–0.002	633.9	638
Livermore	Sphere		Uranyl sulphate	~14	Graphite	0.5	687	694.2
RRR II (North Carolina State College)	Cylinder with one hemispherical end	90	Uranyl sulphate	~40	Graphite	0.5	766.5	775.7
Armour	Sphere	88.14	Uranyl sulphate	~40	Graphite	50 (design)	1170*	1248*
Supo	Sphere	88.7	Uranyl nitrate	~85	Graphite	25	777	870
Lopo	Sphere	~14.5	Uranyl sulphate	~39	BeO and graphite	<0.001	580	580
Hypo	Sphere	~14.5	Uranyl nitrate	~85	BeO and graphite	5.5	808	896.6

* The somewhat large critical mass of the Armour Research Reactor is due in part to a large amount of structural material in the core and a large reflector void directly above the core which contains the reflux condenser and other equipment.

bed at a constant level, and absorbs the heat of recombination. Excess water flows over the weir. Water in the well is also kept at a constant level by maintaining a constant pressure difference between the recombiner tank and the gas line. Excess water in the well is forced into the return-gas stream and cools the stream to about 90°F.

5–3. PHYSICS CHARACTERISTICS

This section will discuss experimental results pertaining to the physics of homogeneous reactors.

5–3.1 Critical mass. Homogeneous reactors have the lowest critical mass of any reactor type, and the variation in critical mass from reactor to reactor is not large. Operating fuel loadings range from 580 to 1250 g of U^{235}. Since homogeneous research reactors currently in operation have similar core geometry, reflectors, and enrichment, the most significant factors causing fuel-loading differences are core temperature, power level, amount of structural material in the core, and reflector geometry. Higher temperature and higher power mean larger fuel loadings. The presence of a glory hole and beam tubes and the nature of the experiments can alter the loading required for criticality. Table 5–3 lists fuel loadings for the five homogeneous research reactors currently operating in the United States, with some parameters affecting them. Information on Lopo and Hypo, early models of the Los Alamos Supo Reactor, is included.

5–3.2 Flux distribution. Since all homogeneous research reactors operating in the United States today are based on the Los Alamos design (although most utilize sulphate instead of nitrate solution), the energy distributions of the neutron flux should be similar. However, such items as the location of control rods relative to beam tubes, etc. can cause a perturbation in flux level and distribution.

Figure 5–15 shows the thermal-neutron flux distributions and the indium-foil cadmium ratios in the glory hole and tangent hole of the Supo reactor. The latter quantity is a measure of thermal to total flux. Figure 5–16 shows the neutron-energy spectrum from the Los Alamos water boiler, both at the surface and after moderation through 1 ft of graphite and 8.5 in. of bismuth. Thermal-neutron distribution in the graphite stringers of the Livermore Reactor is shown in Fig. 5–17. Generally speaking, flux depressions are caused by voids, foreign materials, and the presence of control rods. Figure 5–18 illustrates the neutron-flux distribution in the horizontal thermal column of the Livermore Reactor along the centerline of the column.

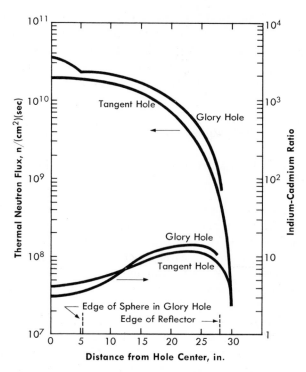

FIG. 5–15. Thermal-neutron fluxes and cadmium ratios in glory hole and tangent hole of the Supo.

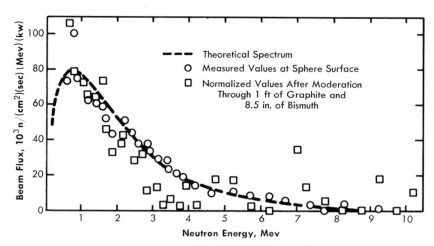

FIG. 5–16. Nuclear-track determination of neutron spectrum from the Supo.

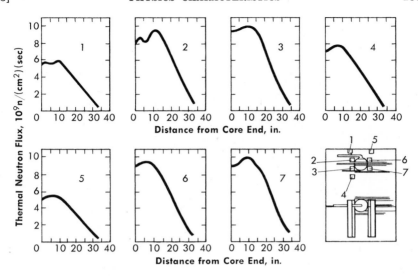

FIG. 5–17. Thermal-neutron distribution in graphite stringers of Livermore Reactor. The last diagram shows the location of the stringers and control rods with respect to the core.

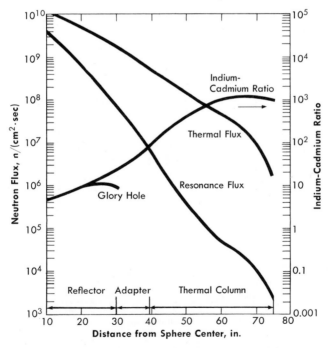

FIG. 5–18. Neutron distribution in horizontal thermal column of the Livermore Reactor.

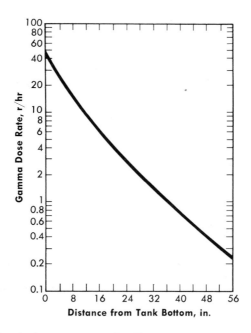

FIG. 5–19. Vertical gamma-ray distribution in water tank above the Livermore Reactor.

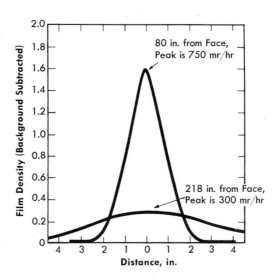

FIG. 5–20. Horizontal thermal-column gamma-ray beam profiles in the Livermore Reactor. These measurements were made with a $3\frac{1}{2}$ in.-square graphite bar, the $2\frac{1}{2}$-in. adapter plug, the 2-in. reflector plug, and the 1-in. OD lead plug removed. The cadmium shutter was in place.

TABLE 5–4

MAXIMUM THERMAL-NEUTRON FLUX VALUES FOR FIVE
HOMOGENEOUS REACTORS

Reactor	Thermal-neutron flux, ϕ_{th}, n/(cm^2)(sec)	Power, kw
WBNS	8×10^7	0.001 to 0.002
Livermore	2×10^{10}	0.5
RRR II	$\sim 2 \times 10^{10*}$	0.5
Supo	9.3×10^{11}	25
Armour	$\sim 1.2 \times 10^{12*}$	50 (design power)

* Estimated; reactor not yet operated at design power.

Figure 5–19 illustrates the gamma distribution along the vertical center-line of the water tank above the Livermore Reactor, and Fig. 5–20 shows the gamma-intensity profiles at two points in the horizontal thermal column. Thermal-neutron flux values available at normal operating powers in the five operating homogeneous research reactors are listed in Table 5–4.

5–3.3 Shielding characteristics. Shielding characteristics of homogeneous research reactors differ somewhat from one system to another. As noted in Article 5–2.2, power level is an important factor in determining shielding requirements. Although many different materials meet shielding requirements in specific applications, reflectors of concrete, lead, and graphite are common to all existing systems.

Attenuations through shielding materials are a strong function of the incident spectrum. Although the neutron and gamma spectra are similar for all the homogeneous systems, the relative locations and amounts of shielding materials differ from system to system, so that it is difficult to predict an attenuation factor for one system from measurements on another.

Illustrative measurements of pertinent distributions in the shield of the 500-watt Livermore Reactor are given in Fig. 5–9. Figure 5–21(a) shows the slow-neutron flux in the glory hole through shielding materials, Fig. 5–21(b) shows the indium-cadmium ratio, and Fig. 5–21(c) the relative gamma activity in the same location. Figure 5–22(a) and (b) show, respectively, the thermal-neutron flux attenuation through the concrete and the gamma spectrum outside the concrete. The neutron flux was measured in a concrete cylinder placed in a stringer hole, and the gamma spectrum was measured at one corner of the shield at the west end. Figure 5–23 gives similar information for the top timber shield.

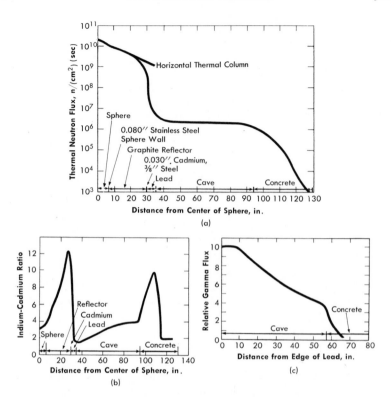

Fig. 5–21(a) Thermal-neutron flux in glory hole of the Livermore Reactor.
(b) Indium-cadmium ratio in glory hole of the Livermore Reactor. (c) Relative
gamma activity in glory hole of the Livermore Reactor.

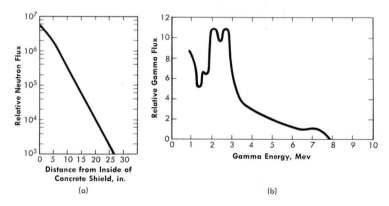

Fig. 5–22(a) Thermal neutron attenuation in concrete shield of the Livermore Reactor. (b) Gamma spectrum from concrete shield of the Livermore
Reactor.

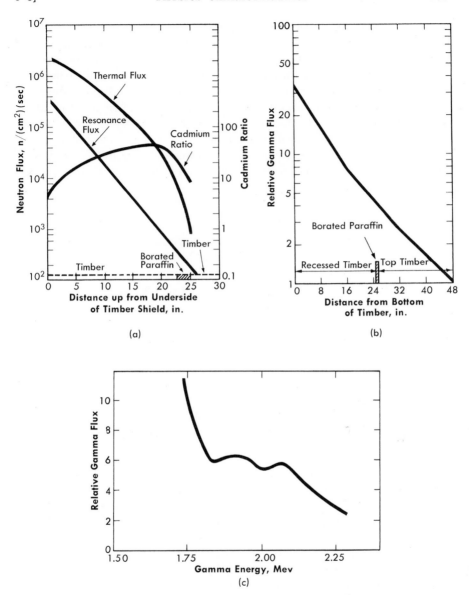

Fig. 5–23(a) Thermal neutron attenuation in top timber shield of the Livermore Reactor. (b) Gamma attenuation in top timber shield of the Livermore Reactor. (c) Gamma spectrum in top timber shield of the Livermore Reactor.

5–3.4 Excess reactivity requirements. Important factors influencing homogeneous reactor excess reactivity requirements for operating above zero power are temperature, power, and reactivity worth of experiments. Since homogeneous reactors have negative temperature coefficients of reactivity, higher temperatures require more reactivity. Power affects the temperature, the fission-product poisons, and, most important, the rate of bubble formation due to decomposing water. Since fluxes are relatively low, and since the gaseous fission products are evolved continuously from the core solution, excess reactivity requirements to overcome fission-product poisoning are considerably less severe in water boilers than in most other reactors.

TABLE 5–5

EFFECT OF REFLECTOR VOIDS ON REACTIVITY IN THE
LIVERMORE REACTOR

Stringer	Distance from center of core, inches	Reactivity loss, $\% \dfrac{\Delta k_{eff}}{k_{eff}}$
1 and 5	17.2	0.004
4	13.6	0.014
6	10.1	0.035
2	10.1	0.052
3	8.9	0.079
7	8.9	0.076

Table 5–5 shows the measured loss in reactivity due to $1\frac{1}{2}$-inch-square voids in the graphite stringers of the Livermore Reactor, along with the minimum centerline distances from the void to the center of the sphere.

The excess reactivity for operation above zero-power is directly dependent on the fuel loading which can be varied. These reactors have mass coefficients of reactivity in a range about 0.04%/g of U^{235}. On the basis of this estimate and reported differences in zero-power critical mass and operating fuel loadings, the excess reactivity ranges from about 0.2 to 4%. It should be kept in mind that normally only a fraction of this is available at full-power operation.

5–3.5 Control requirements. As mentioned in Article 5–2.4, homogeneous research reactors are controlled by about four absorber rods in the core or reflector, or in both. Usually, one of these rods is a shutdown rod and is not used during normal operation. The reactivity worths of the

TABLE 5–6

EFFECT OF DIFFERENT ABSORBER MATERIALS IN
SUPO CONTROL RODS

Material	Comments	Equivalent U^{235}, g	Estimated reactivity, $\% \dfrac{\Delta k_{\mathrm{eff}}}{k_{\mathrm{eff}}}$
Cadmium	0.015-in. cadmium 18 in. long wrapped on 0.595-in.-OD brass tube with $\frac{1}{16}$-in. wall; inside length of tube was $17\frac{3}{4}$ in.; weight of cadmium, 71.7 g; weight of brass tube, 183.3 g	39	1.3
Cadmium	0.015-in. cadmium wrapped on $\frac{1}{2}$-in. polystyrene rod	39	1.3
Cadmium plus paraffin	Above brass tube filled with 46.5 g of paraffin	26	0.87
B_4C	Density of B_4C, 1.33 g/cm^3; weight of B_4C, hand tamped, 73.3 g	53.3	1.8
B_4C plus cadmium	Same cadmium sleeve as above	58	1.9
B^{10}	95.5% B^{10} material in above brass holder; 68 g of B^{10}	68.5	2.3
B^{10}	Same as above	73.5	2.4
B^{10}	92.5 g of B^{10} tamped into brass holder as above, but $18\frac{1}{8}$ in. long inside	78.5	2.6
B^{10}	Sintered 95.5% B^{10} plugs 0.555 in. in diameter; overall length, 17.9 in.; B^{10} density, 1.73 g/cm^3; actual weight of B^{10}, 116.5 g; encased in $\frac{5}{8}$-in.-OD stainless-steel tube with $\frac{1}{32}$-in. wall.	80.2	2.67
B^{10} plus cadmium	Same rod as above plated with about 0.003 in. cadmium (these are actual rods in use)	82.2	2.74

TABLE 5–7

CONTROL-ROD WORTHS FOR WBNS

Rod	Reactivity, $\% \dfrac{\Delta k_{eff}}{k_{eff}}$
Coarse control $\left(\begin{array}{l}\text{2 cadmium strips} \\ \frac{1}{4}\text{ in.} \times 40\text{ in.}\end{array}\right.$	1.05
East safety $\left.\begin{array}{l}\text{2 Boral strips} \\ \frac{1}{4}\text{ in.} \times 40\text{ in.}\end{array}\right)$	1.45
West safety (same as above)	1.17
Coarse control and both safeties	3.27

TABLE 5–8

CONTROL-ROD WORTHS FOR THE LIVERMORE REACTOR

Rod	Reactivity, $\% \dfrac{\Delta k_{eff}}{k_{eff}}$
Safety No. 1	1.4
Safety No. 2	1.2
Fine rod	0.67
Coarse rod	1.40
All rods	4.00

rods depend primarily on rod geometry, location, and material. The large negative temperature and power coefficients inherent in the reactor tend to minimize the control-rod movement required for stable full-power operation.

A series of safety and operation tests demonstrated the self-controlling features of water boiler reactors. (See Chapter 7.)

The reactivity of a number of control rods was measured in the Los Alamos water boiler. Results are tabulated in Table 5–6. Control-rod reactivity (worth) may vary slightly with core temperature, fuel concentration, etc. Table 5–7 lists rod worths for the WBNS Reactor and Table 5–8 lists rod worths for the Livermore Reactor. The discrepancy between the sum of individual values and the measured total is due to interference (shadowing) effects between rods.

5–4. OPERATIONAL CHARACTERISTICS

This section deals with the operational characteristics of homogeneous research reactors, as contrasted with operating and maintenance problems covered in Chapter 12. Reactor operations performed prior to full-power normal operation are discussed in Chapter 11. A number of items which might be classed as operational characteristics, such as rod worths and flux levels, have been covered in previous sections and will not be discussed here.

5–4.1 Effect of power level on operation. The primary effect of increasing the power level in a water boiler is the increase in rate of gas production and evolution. Associated with the increased gas production is a loss in reactivity and some increase in the heat-transfer coefficient between the core solution and the cooling coil. A free space at the top of the core allows thermal expansion of the liquid and provides room for the foam or froth from the gas bubbles. Figure 5–24 shows, for the Supo Reactor, the variation of liquid and froth levels with power and temperature. Gas-evolution rates have been measured. The WBNS Reactor produces hydrogen at the rate of about 1 liter/watt-hr; the Supo Reactor forms 13 liters/min of all gases at 30 kw.

One of the problems related to gas evolution is the reaction affecting the nitrate or sulphate in the system. In operating Hypo (an early version

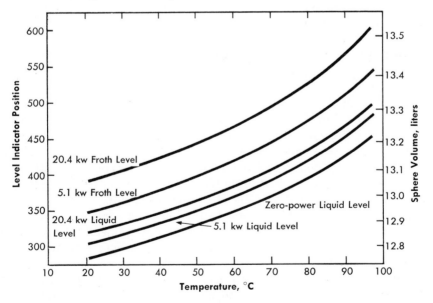

FIG. 5–24. Supo froth and liquid levels for different powers and temperatures.

of Supo), it was found that the uranyl nitrate was being converted into basic nitrate and nitrogen was being carried off with the gases evolved. This phenomenon increased the reactivity of the reactor. To correct it, changes were made to eliminate possible traps for precipitation products, and both acid and water were added to the core, rather than water alone. In the Supo model, fuel of higher enrichment is used; the resulting decrease of nitrogen in the core makes the problem less severe. In the Raleigh Research Reactor I, which used a uranyl-sulphate solution, cooling the core solution caused fuel to be precipitated by a reaction between hydrogen peroxide and the uranyl ion. Adding $CuSO_4$ and $FeSO_4$ to the solution catalyzes the decomposition of the peroxide and allows the precipitate to be dissolved. After operation at 10 kw and 80°C it was found that the solution could not be cooled below about 40°C without forming the precipitate.

The Armour Research Reactor, which uses uranyl sulphate, has copper and ferrous sulphate in the solution. At operating powers of 10 kw, there has been no trouble with fuel precipitation.

Raleigh Research Reactor I exhibited corrosion difficulties after being in operation somewhat less than 2 years. It was found that chlorides in the catalyst bed that were carried by the purge airstream to the core caused the corrosion.

Raleigh Research Reactor II does not use a gas recombiner, but employs a holdup and dilution system before releasing the gases. This system limits continuous full power to 500 watts and continuous operating time at this power to about 2 hr.

5–4.2 Temperature and power coefficients of reactivity. The temperature coefficient of reactivity has been measured in all water boilers in operation. In the Livermore Reactor, a value of -0.027% $\Delta k_{eff}/k_{eff}$ per °C was obtained between 50 and 100°F. Figure 5–25 shows the effect of temperature on reactivity (temperature coefficient) in the Supo Reactor. The Armour Research Reactor, which has a relatively high fuel concentration, has a temperature coefficient of -0.03% $\Delta k_{eff}/k_{eff}$ per °C. The response of water boilers to sudden reactivity changes has been studied in both operating systems and experimental reactors constructed especially for such studies (see Chapter 7). It was determined for the Supo Reactor that the reactivity decrease immediately following a sudden increase was mainly due to bubble formation rather than to a temperature rise, but as bubbles had time to leave the core, the effect of temperature increased in relative importance.

There have been similar transient experiments with the Livermore Reactor. In one experiment, the coolant flow was stopped after an equilibrium power of 500 watts had been established. The reactor power was

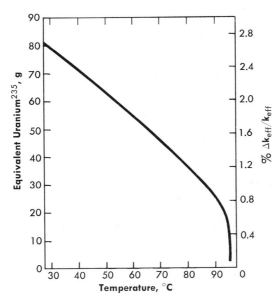

FIG. 5–25. Effect of temperature on reactivity in Supo at 5-kw operation.

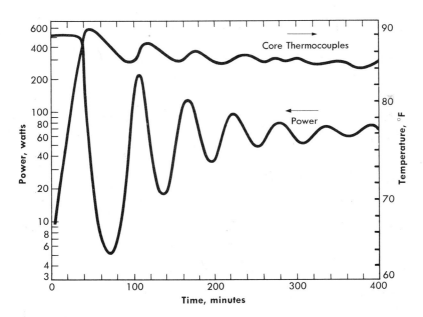

FIG. 5–26. Power-temperature vs. time oscillations for the Livermore Reactor. In this test, the coolant flow was stopped after the reactor had reached an operating power of 500 watts.

TABLE 5-9

SUMMARY OF THE CHARACTERISTICS OF EXISTING U. S. HOMOGENEOUS RESEARCH REACTORS

Reactor	Maximum thermal flux, n/(cm²)(sec)	Normal operating power, kw	U^{235} loading, g	Uranium salt used	Control rods	Maximum core temperature, °C	References
WBNS	8×10^7	0.001–0.002	638	Nitrate	Four Boral in reflector		AECU-2900, ARCD-3860, NAA-SR-839
Livermore	2×10^{10}	0.5	694.2	Sulphate	Four boron carbide in reflector	14	LRL-136, LRL-148, LRL-149, LRL-151, LRL-152, LRL-154
Raleigh II	$\sim 2 \times 10^{10}$	0.5	775.7	Sulphate	Two boron carbide in core	40	AECU-2900, AECU-1986
Supo	9.3×10^{11}	25	870	Nitrate	Five: two sintered B^{10} in core; three cadmium sheet in reflector	70	AECD-3045, AECD-3287, AECU-2900; Geneva Conference Paper 488 (1955)
Armour	$\sim 1.2 \times 10^{12}$ at 50 kw	50 (design) 10 (current operating)	1248	Sulphate	Four boron carbide in core	40	

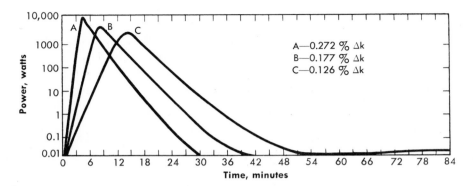

FIG. 5–27. Power vs. time in transient experiments on the Livermore Reactor.

allowed to oscillate freely for several hours (Fig. 5–26). In a second series of tests three different amounts of excess reactivity were introduced and the power time-dependence observed (Fig. 5–27). The excess reactivities introduced were 0.126, 0.177, and 0.272% $\Delta k_{eff}/k_{eff}$.

In general, homogeneous research reactors have negative temperature coefficients of about 2.5×10^{-4} $\Delta k_{eff}/k_{eff}$ per °C, and negative power coefficients which vary somewhat depending on the operating condition.

5–4.3 Stability of operation. In some experimental work involving the use of a research reactor, it is essential that power fluctuations be small. Problems encountered in achieving stable operation are peculiar to the particular reactor involved. In Supo, to attain stability of 0.1% or better, the power level must be limited to 25 kw. This limitation appears to be due to the capacity of the recombination system. Power levels above 30 kw increase the hydrogen concentration to above 9% in the circulating gas and raise the catalyst bed equilibrium temperature above 500°C. It is believed that this combination causes the hydrogen and oxygen to ignite in the catalyst bed and produce small power fluctuations for which the automatic power-level control cannot compensate.

For sensitive measurements in the WBNS Reactor, such as cross-section measurements by the danger-coefficient method, it is necessary to minimize any extraneous reactivity changes while the measurements are being made. One method is to operate at a low power level (about 0.2 watts) to minimize temperature and power coefficient effects. Even at this power level, slow changes in reactivity have been observed. These are thought to be caused, in part, by a slow heating of the solution by the absorption of fission-product energy and by a buildup of dissociated gases in the solution. It should be noted that the rate of reactivity change varies from time to time, and is not always negative. The effects of these reactivity drifts can be further lessened through use of proper experimental techniques to average out reactivity drifts.

In the Livermore Reactor, a pressure change above the core solution can cause a change in solution level in the core. This effect is a function of the volume of air trapped in the filling line. If danger-coefficient measurements are made with the gas system in operation, the automatic control system limits reactivity changes caused by the pressure fluctuation to $\pm 0.0018\%$ $\Delta k_{eff}/k_{eff}$.

In general, for experiments requiring a high degree of stability the reactor is operated at somewhat less than design power.

5–5. Summary

The advantages of the homogeneous reactor over other types include simplicity of design, relatively low cost, low fuel inventory, continuous removal of gaseous fission products, no fuel-element handling, and inherent safety due to large negative temperature and power coefficients. Important disadvantages are the relatively low neutron fluxes, problems associated with fuel precipitation, potential danger of leaks, and power limitations for stable operation.

The most prominent special characteristic of the homogeneous reactor is the decomposition of water by fission fragments. This phenomenon results in negative power coefficients of reactivity, chemical instabilities in the core solution, and necessity for the use of gas-handling and gas-recombining equipment.

The water-boiler design has operated for several years and has proved to be a useful, reliable research reactor. Table 5–9 summarizes the characteristics of the five water boilers currently in operation as research reactors in the United States.

CHAPTER 6

GRAPHITE REACTORS*

6-1. GENERAL DESCRIPTION

Only a few moderating materials are suitable for use with natural uranium fuel. Of these, only graphite was available in quantities sufficient for reactor use in the early days of atomic energy development, and so it was used as the moderator in the first research reactors constructed in the United States. The use of graphite not only offers the designer of research reactors availability, but also a large volume of nearly uniform neutron flux that is ideal for extensive experimental facilities, and the additional advantage of relatively stable operation.

These advantages are offset, however, by the large physical size and critical mass required by the use of natural uranium fuel. Also, the size and the potential for experimentation require a large operating staff, and the capital investment is high. To date only the Federal Government has underwritten construction of such installations in the United States. Only two graphite-moderated research reactors (Table 6-1) are operating in this country: the Brookhaven Research Reactor and the Oak Ridge Graphite Reactor (X-10). Other reactors, built for experimental and production purposes, are available for only a limited amount of classified research.

TABLE 6-1

GRAPHITE RESEARCH REACTORS OPERATING IN THE
UNITED STATES

Name and location	Power, kw	Reference
Oak Ridge Graphite Reactor (X-10), Oak Ridge National Laboratory, Oak Ridge, Tennessee	3,500	"Peaceful Uses of Atomic Energy," Vol. II, pp. 353–371
Brookhaven Research Reactor Brookhaven National Laboratory Upton, Long Island, New York	28,000	"Peaceful Uses of Atomic Energy," Vol. II, pp. 281–294

* By F. J. Jankowski and W. S. Hogan.

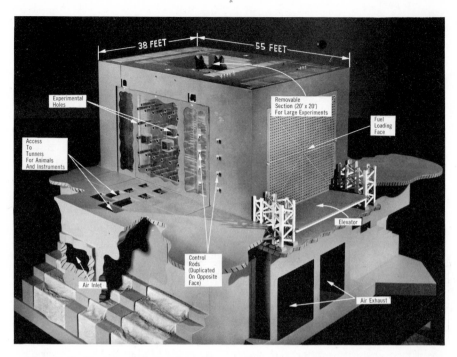

Fig. 6–1. Features of the Brookhaven Research Reactor are shown in this cutaway model. Other graphite reactors have similar features shown in the figure but may be changed in detail. (Courtesy of Brookhaven National Laboratory.)

Graphite-moderated reactors are constructed of graphite blocks stacked on a bed plate to form a self-supporting cube about 20 ft on each side, not including shielding. The cube is pierced by many holes for fuel, coolant flow, control rods, and experimental facilities. The central region is loaded with uranium slugs to form the core; the unfueled region surrounding the core acts as a reflector. Figure 6–1 is a view of a model of the Brookhaven Research Reactor, and Fig. 6–2 shows an experimental face of the reactor. The reactor is fueled with natural uranium aluminum-canned slugs about 1 in. in diameter and 4 in. long. The critical mass is about 33 tons of uranium. The fuel is inserted by pushing fuel assemblies into the holes through the graphite.

Both the Brookhaven and X-10 reactors are air-cooled (graphite reactors used for producing plutonium are water-cooled). Large volumes of air are drawn through the reactors at low pressure and discharged from stacks.

The Oak Ridge X-10 operates at 3.5 Mw, while the Brookhaven Research Reactor operates at 28 Mw, certainly not limiting powers. The

FIG. 6–2. Brookhaven Research Reactor, showing a few of the many experiments supported by a single graphite reactor. (Courtesy of Brookhaven National Laboratory.)

Brookhaven Research Reactor has a thermal-neutron flux of 5×10^{12} n/ $(cm^2)(sec)$. The gamma flux is 1.6×10^{12} photons/$(cm^2)(sec)$ or, assuming an average gamma-ray energy of 1 Mev, approximately 3×10^6 r/hr. Because they are large, graphite reactors have large volumes in regions of moderately high flux for many experimental facilities. In addition, fuel holes can be used as irradiation ports.

No additional natural uranium graphite-moderated research reactors are planned because of extremely high cost per unit of flux. However, performance of graphite reactors can be improved considerably by replacing the natural uranium with highly enriched fuel. This change, completed at Brookhaven, reduces the fuel loading appreciably and increases the neutron flux almost ten times. It is also planned to use enriched fuel in the X-10.

6–2. DESIGN FEATURES

The graphite used in reactors is known as "reactor-grade" or "normal reactor-grade" graphite. It has a density of approximately 1.67 g/cm^3. It is made by partially recrystallizing at high temperature a mixture of petroleum coke fillers and coal tar pitch binders. The petroleum cokes are calcined and ground or milled to the particle size desired. Most reactor graphite is available in the form of extrusions about 4 by 4 in. in cross section baked at 2500 to 2800°C. The material has a crystalline structure in which the long axis of the crystals runs parallel with the direction of extrusion.

Graphite is useful as a moderating material because it slows down neutrons and has an extremely small absorption cross section for thermal neutrons. It also has good physical properties for reactor construction, such as high thermal conductivity and resistance to thermal shock. Its oxidation in air at high temperature and its permeability to gases and liquids limit its use. However, proper treatment can make graphite less permeable.

If graphite is irradiated for a long period at room temperature (30°C), the strength may double and the thermal conductivity decrease as much as fifty times. In addition, the linear expansion can be as great as 3% and there can be as much as 500 cal of stored energy per gram. This stored energy is sufficient to raise the temperature of the graphite from 30 to 1200°C. However, if the graphite is irradiated at 150°C, instead of 30°C, there is tenfold reduction in the changes; for example, the magnitude of linear expansion is reduced to a few tenths of a percent. Even so, the Brookhaven Research Reactor, which, like the X-10, operates with minimum graphite temperature between 130 and 250°C to avoid radiation damage, has been observed to change $\frac{21}{32}$ in. in height at a reflector hole in one of the coolest regions of the graphite after an irradiation of 5 × 10^{20} nvt.

Radiation damage in graphite is lessened by operation at high graphite temperatures; the maximum graphite temperature in the structure is then limited either by the fuel element design or graphite oxidation. In the BNL reactor, the graphite temperature limit, established with respect to oxidation rates, is 250°C. Since these reactors are of the once-through type cooling, there is in each a low-temperature graphite zone, which is in contact with the cool inlet air. Radiation damage in these areas depends upon the power density. In the X-10 reactor, this low-temperature zone is at one end of the reactor where the power density is low; therefore, radiation damage has been negligible. In the BNL reactor this region is adjacent to the vertical central gap, which is the region of highest power density. Here radiation damage is a serious operating problem, as indicated by the growth previously quoted.

Radiation effects can be alleviated to a great extent by periodic annealing, i.e., by heating the graphite by chemical or nuclear heat to a temperature of approximately 300°C. Such annealing operations result in the removal of the low-temperature stored energy (below 300°C), a substantial shrinkage of graphite growth, and, if the frequency of annealing is one to three times per year, the energy stored above 300°C is accumulated at a reduced rate.

6–2.1 Reactor core and reflector. In graphite research reactors the core and reflector are a single unit, a cube about 25 ft on a side constructed by stacking thousands of graphite bricks and stringers (blocks of various shapes). The core is the inner part of the cube containing the fuel, and the outer part serves as the reflector. Considerable flexibility is possible in loading fuel and inserting experiments. Other core configurations, for example cylindrical or spherical, could be used.

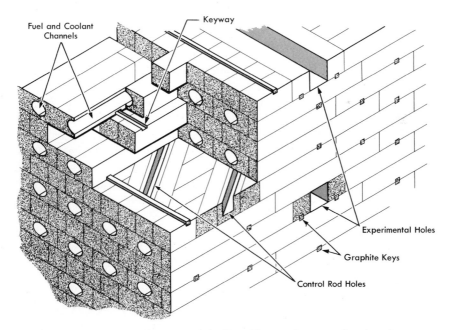

Fig. 6–3. A cutaway drawing of the Brookhaven Reactor showing the arrangement of the graphite stringers. The stringers are keyed together to make a self-supporting structure. The fuel elements are fitted into cylindrical holes formed by machining half cylinders into two adjacent stringers. (Courtesy of Brookhaven National Laboratory.)

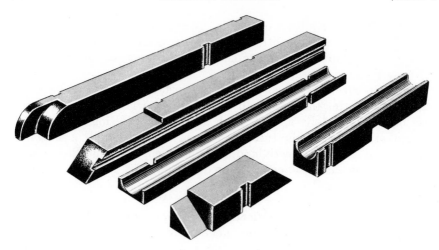

FIG. 6–4. Typical graphite shapes used to form a graphite research reactor core.

The graphite structure forming core and reflector is pierced by many holes, parallel to one of the axes, to provide fuel element locations and coolant flow paths. The holes not used for fuel are plugged with graphite to increase reflector effectiveness and to keep the coolant from flowing through them. The sizes and shapes of the holes are determined principally by fuel element dimensions and coolant flow requirements. Fuel holes are spaced to give the best neutron economy; the optimum spacing is about 8 in. between centers.

The cube forming the core and reflector has holes in other directions for control rods and experimental facilities. Figure 6–3, an isometric view of a graphite lattice, shows the principal features of a core reflector.

The graphite, usually 4 by 4 in. in cross section, is used in lengths up to 4 ft (Fig. 6–4). The pieces, designed to permit expansion and radiation growth, are machined and fitted together. Since the graphite and fuel weigh many tons, the reactor must have a strong base.

6–2.2 Fuel element design. Both U. S. graphite research reactors were designed for natural uranium fuel. The X-10 Reactor at Oak Ridge still uses it; the Brookhaven Research Reactor has been converted to highly enriched fuel.

Natural uranium. Natural uranium rods about 1 in. in diameter have been used as the fuel elements for the U. S. graphite research reactors. The diameter is determined by physics considerations, since the value of k_∞ is a function of rod diameter. The fuel, in slugs or elements 4 to 12 in. long, extends the full length of the reactor. Usually, uranium extruded in the gamma phase is used. This form is preferred because it does not elongate on temperature cycling as much as rolled uranium, and in large

FIG. 6–5. This view shows aluminum clad uranium fuel elements being loaded into the X-10 graphite reactor. (Courtesy of Oak Ridge National Laboratory.)

quantities it is cheaper than the rolled metal. It is extruded oversize and machined to the proper dimensions.

Natural uranium fuel oxidizes badly in air if unprotected, causing uranium and its fission products to enter the coolant stream. When the uranium oxidizes, usually to U_3O_8, the expansion of the element restricts the coolant flow, thus bringing about further heating and more rapid oxidation. It is necessary to bond the jacket to the fuel. Thicknesses of the jacketing materials vary, but a representative value is about 0.030 in. For a reactor producing low power per element, the uranium may be jacketed with aluminum and loaded into the reactor (Fig. 6–5). At higher powers, better cooling is required than can be obtained from a simple cylindrical element lying in a channel. Finned tubes have been used because they offer larger heat-transfer surface and also center the element in the channel to allow better air flow (Fig. 6–6).

Fuel element ruptures are detected by monitoring for fission-product activity in the downstream coolant system or by monitoring each element individually. A combination of these methods is sometimes used, as described in Article 6–2.6.

Enriched uranium. When the U. S. graphite research reactors were built, not enough highly enriched uranium was available for use as fuel.

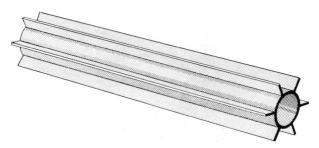

Fig. 6–6. A finned aluminum tube for holding the uranium slugs for a fuel element in a higher powered graphite reactor. The fins space the element in the coolant channel and provide additional cooling surface.

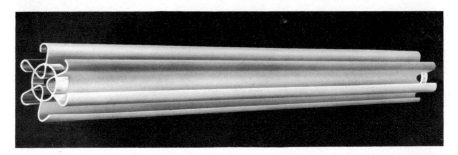

Fig. 6–7. Fuel element containing highly enriched uranium for the Brookhaven Research Reactor. (Courtesy of Brookhaven National Laboratory.)

Indeed, the fact that natural uranium could be used and that graphite was relatively cheap and abundant led to the decisions for this type of reactor. Now that highly enriched uranium is available, the research reactor at Brookhaven has been changed over to use it. The fuel elements are a plate type, each plate containing about 5 g of U^{235} in an aluminum matrix clad with aluminum. The plates, approximately $2\frac{1}{4}$ in. wide, 24 in. long, and 0.060 in. thick, are bent along the central axis of the long dimension on approximately a $\frac{1}{8}$-inch radius to a 60° angle. Both long edges of the plate are also bent on the same radius. Three plates are welded to a thin ring at each end to form the 2-ft-long element shown in Fig. 6–7. Eight elements will be used in each fuel channel of the reactor.

There are several advantages gained from using highly enriched fuel in graphite reactors. In the Brookhaven Reactor, the required mass of U^{235} decreases from 385 kg contained in natural uranium to 50 to 57 kg in the enriched elements. The central neutron flux increases from $5 \times 10^{12} \text{n}/(\text{cm}^2)(\text{sec})$ at a power of 28 Mw in the natural uranium loaded core to 2 to $3 \times 10^{13} \text{n}/(\text{cm}^2)(\text{sec})$ at 20 Mw for the highly enriched core. Operation at lower power and the lower resistance to air flow with the new fuel elements require less pumping power, which results in significant savings in electricity. Also, fuel elements are less likely to rupture, so there is less chance of contaminating coolant air or the cooling water in which the discharged elements are stored. All these factors result in simpler operation and improved performance. However, the experimental facilities will be smaller.

6–2.3 Shielding. A thin, high-density shield is desirable for a graphite research reactor for two reasons: (1) A graphite reactor has a large surface area to be shielded; keeping the shield thin helps to reduce foundation requirements and decrease cost. (2) A thin shield minimizes the length of irradiation ports for neutron-beam work, allowing experiments to be placed closer to the reactor core face and thus to receive more intense beams. (This is the more important reason for high-density shields.)

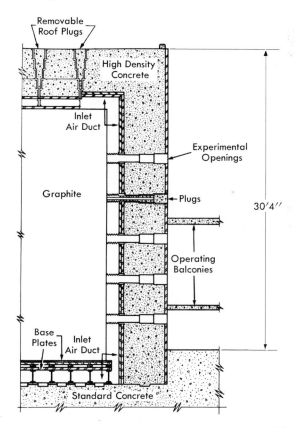

Fig. 6–8. Vertical section through the shield of the Brookhaven Reactor. This section shows many of the features of the shield and reactor support base for a typical graphite reactor.

A typical shield for a graphite research reactor consists of three sections. The first, next to the reactor, prevents heat flow from the core to the other sections. The next part, a shield designed to absorb gammas from the core, requires a high-density material. (This is usually of steel or iron, since materials of higher density are too expensive.) In absorbing gammas, this section of the shield may produce a significant amount of heat and require cooling. The third section of the shield is made of high-density concrete to absorb mostly neutrons. To provide for coolant flow, an open space is left between the reflector and the shield on two or more sides of the core. (See Fig. 6–8.)

The vertical faces of the shield must be penetrated by a number of ports for fuel loading and experimental facilities. These holes have steps (changes in diameter) to prevent radiation streaming into the work areas when the shielding plugs are inserted. Above the reactor, shielding can be a solid unit with experimental holes (X-10), or it can be made in removable sections (Brookhaven). The latter arrangement permits access to the reflector surface for building thermal columns and for other experimental purposes.

6–2.4 Cooling system. Graphite research reactors are cooled by low-pressure air making one pass through the core. The air is drawn through by blowers that produce negative pressure within the core, preventing coolant gas leakage into the working area. The rate of coolant flow through the reactor is adjusted to keep the uranium temperature below certain limits. The coolant air is drawn in at surrounding air temperature, which may go as high as 90°F in the summer. The air leaves the reactor at about 360°F; fuel element jacket temperature is about 660°F. Individual fuel channels can be orificed so that coolant temperature rise will be about the same in each. Auxiliary cooling may be required to prevent the hot outlet air from coming in contact with and damaging the shield.

Fiber glass or asbestos paper filters are used in the coolant stream on each side of the reactor. On the inlet side, the filters prevent dust from entering the core and reducing reactivity or becoming radioactive. The filter on the outlet side removes radioactive particles and minimizes activity before release to the atmosphere. Argon in the air becomes radioactive on its pass through the reactor and is not removed by the particle filters. Consequently, the cooling air is discharged through a high stack at a safe distance above the facility and is diluted in the atmosphere. Stacks are from 200 to 400 ft high.

Pumping requirements depend on the coolant channel, the system, the fuel element, the amount of heat to be removed, and the temperature at which the element operates. The X-10, operating at 3.5 Mw, pulls 120,000 ft^3/min of air through the reactor by means of two blowers of 900 hp each. The cooling system of the Brookhaven Research Reactor has five blowers

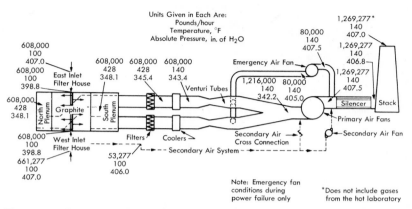

Fig. 6–9. Coolant air flow diagram for the Brookhaven Reactor. This diagram shows all the components which might be required in a graphite reactor, along with the conditions of the coolant at several points. The secondary air system is used to prevent the shield from becoming heated.

of 1500 hp each. Aproximately 5000 kw of electricity is needed to force 300,000 ft^3/min of air through the reactor and remove the heat at 28-Mw operation. It is expected that about 2000 kw will be required when the Brookhaven Research Reactor is fueled with highly enriched uranium.

Brookhaven personnel have increased the efficiency of the cooling system and reduced pumping power by equipping the reactor with a center inlet for the air which is removed at each end of the reactor. This shortens the path of the air through the reactor while increasing the cross-sectional area for air flow. Air velocity reaches 40 mph in the main duct and hundreds of miles per hour in the fuel channels.

Figure 6–9, a schematic of the cooling system for the Brookhaven Research Reactor, shows air flow, temperature, and pressure at several points.

6–2.5 Fuel-loading equipment. The two shield faces opposite the fuel element channels have a pattern of holes identical to that of the core. Through these ports fuel elements are charged and discharged. Figure 6–10 shows the charging face of the X-10. The fuel elements are manually loaded through the hole in the shield and pushed into the core by means of a ramrod. The ramrod is calibrated so that each element may be positioned correctly. To remove elements, the ramrod pushes them through the core into a chute which leads down into the water canal (Fig. 6–11). In an alternate method, the elements are withdrawn into the space between the core and the shield at the loading face, and lowered into the canal. The canal water shields personnel against fission-product activity and cools the element.

FIG. 6–10. The loading face of the X-10 Reactor, showing the elevator for reaching the loading positions; fuel is being inserted. (Courtesy of Oak Ridge National Laboratory.)

Since a great many elements are handled, some fuel elements can be expected to rupture and contaminate the canal. Previously in the Brookhaven Research Reactor, 33 fuel slugs were in a single aluminum jacket 11 ft long. This element was cut apart in the canal to separate the slugs for shipment. In the process, the ends of the slugs were exposed, thus further contaminating the water; activity in the canal water has been

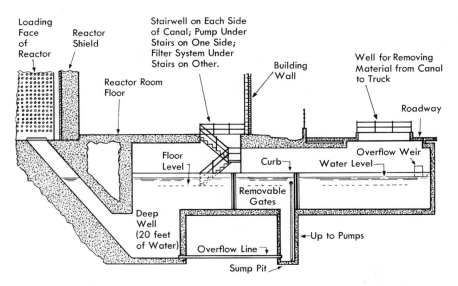

Loading Face of Reactor

Reactor Shield

Stairwell on Each Side of Canal; Pump Under Stairs on One Side; Filter System Under Stairs on Other.

Building Wall

Well for Removing Material from Canal to Truck

Reactor Room Floor

Roadway

Floor Level

Curb

Water Level

Overflow Weir

Removable Gates

Deep Well (20 feet of Water)

Overflow Line

Up to Pumps

Sump Pit

FIG. 6–11. Vertical section of the canal system at the Brookhaven Reactor. This canal is used for holding the spent fuel elements until they decay sufficiently to permit shipment.

measured at 2.8×10^{-8} curie/ml. When enriched elements are used, much less contamination is expected.

To reduce radioactivity, canal water can be circulated through a demineralizer and immediately returned to the canal, or can be used for such purposes as cooling experiments in the reactor before it is returned to the canal. In the latter case it must be pumped to a standpipe or elevated tank, where it is held on standby in the event water from the demineralizer is cut off.

If experimental samples taken from the fuel element channels are extremely radioactive, they can be discharged into the canal in the same manner as the fuel elements.

6–2.6 Control rods. Safety and shutdown rods are provided in graphite reactors to reduce the power quickly and to maintain the reactor at a subcritical level. Shim rods are used to compensate for long-term changes in coolant temperature, experiments in the core, fission-product poison buildup, and uranium burnup. The regulating rods hold the power constant during short intervals and also are used to change power level.

The large size of the graphite reactor requires a control rod design different from that of other research reactor types. The most commonly used control rod for graphite reactors is a steel bar approximately 2 in. square, containing about 1.5% boron by weight. These rods are approxi-

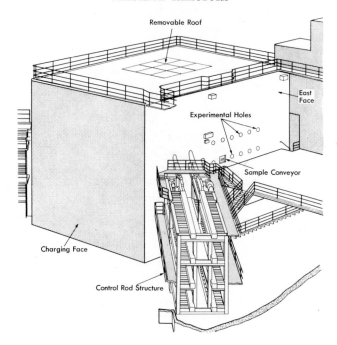

FIG. 6–12. Isometric view of the Brookhaven Reactor, showing the control rod drives and their locations. (Courtesy of Brookhaven National Laboratory.)

mately the same length as the core. They are usually driven horizontally, either perpendicular or diagonal to the fuel element direction to free the face of the core for experimental facilities. The rods are moved by rack-and-pinion gears, and are supported on tracks or rollers outside the core (Fig. 6–12). Since the rod steel becomes radioactive, the section withdrawn must have lead shielding. (Figures 6–1 and 6–3 show the locations of control rods in a graphite reactor.)

Another design, consisting of a hollow steel section lined with cadmium, usually requires a larger cross-sectional area for operating into the core. Either type may be inserted into a vertical core channel as a safety and shutdown rod. They are horizontally driven, and can serve any of the purposes for which rods are required. While a rack-and-pinion drive could be used with a vertical rod, a cable-and-drum arrangement requires less height for operation. This is the type currently employed.

A primary requirement of the drive mechanism is that the rod be inserted into the core rapidly on shutdown signal or power failure. In cable-and-drum drives for vertical rods a magnetic clutch engages the drum; it disengages on power failure or a shutdown signal, allowing the rod to fall by gravity in approximately 1 sec.

Two hydraulic drives for horizontal rods are now in use. Ordinarily, electric pumps supply the hydraulic pressure. If power fails, there are two methods of driving the hydraulic motors. In one, pressure is maintained by weights on a piston. The hydraulic system is interlocked so that if, in the event of leakage, the level in the cylinder falls below a predetermined value the rods are inserted. The other hydraulically driven unit has a continuously rotating flywheel. On power failure, the flywheel has sufficient energy to insert the rods fully. In the cylinder system, a normally open valve is employed to control the oil flow. In the flywheel system, a variable-flow valve serves the same purpose.

Rod drive speeds are higher than for other reactor systems because of the length of the rod and because each rod has a relatively small reactivity worth. Rod speeds vary from 1 to 6 in/sec for hydraulically driven shim-safety rods and up to 1 ft/sec for safety rods. All these rods have quick shutdown speeds, ranging from 1 sec for gravity drop to 4 sec for full insertion by hydraulic motors. The regulating rods, positioned manually or automatically to maintain constant reactor power, are driven by electric motors and have no fast-insertion feature. These rods are driven at speeds comparable to those of the shim rods, that is, 4 to 6 in/sec; they also have a slow speed (approximately 100 times slower) for fine adjustment.

The number of rods required depends on the excess reactivity to be controlled and the reactivity worth of each rod. More than the minimum number are provided, for spares in the event that some rods become stuck. There are from 5 to 14 shim and safety rods, and two or more regulating rods for operating flexibility.

Additional emergency shutdown schemes are provided for graphite reactors because accident or earthquake could so distort the core that control rods might fail to operate properly. One such device consists of a hopper of boron-steel balls with a manual release valve. When released, the poison balls roll into tubes within the core and cause shutdown. A second shutdown mechanism consists of trichlorobenzene under pressure, which can flow into the core after diaphragms are punctured by a manually operated control.

6–2.7 Instrumentation. Much of the instrumentation for graphite research reactors is similar to that for other reactors. For example, the neutron detection system, rod position indicators, and radiation monitoring systems do not vary greatly from those of other reactor systems. Therefore, instrumentation will be described only briefly, with emphasis on the differences.

Neutron-pulse counters with count-rate meters are used for low-level detection work and reactor startup. These detectors are retracted as the neutron flux increases. The reactor is usually critical by the time these detectors are retracted completely, and other detectors such as ion chambers are indicating. The neutron-sensitive ion chambers are used for reactor control and for startup. The type which can be adjusted electronically to indicate primarily neutron level (as opposed to indicating both gamma and neutron intensity) is preferred and can be used over six or more decades, depending on the electronic instrumentation accompanying the chamber. Signals from several of the ion chambers are fed into logarithmic amplifiers whose output signals are then differentiated to give reactor period signals. The neutron level and the period on which the neutron level is rising are used for reactor control.

Obviously, research reactor operations should not be interrupted unnecessarily. Instrument failures as a frequent cause of shutdown can be mitigated by requiring for shutdown the receipt of scram signals from two or three instruments measuring the same item. This increases the reliability of the system without significantly lessening safety.

Fuel element failure in a natural uranium fueled graphite reactor is a potential major hazard and must be guarded against. Therefore, several devices for detection of element failure are included in the instrumentation. In one method, part of the exhaust coolant air is diverted for a few seconds from the main stream to a holdup tank, where the gas activity is monitored with an ion chamber for fission-product activity above normal.

In the higher-powered, higher-temperature graphite reactors, a more positive leak-detection system may be necessary. This can be provided by pressurizing each element with helium and connecting the element to a pressure measuring system. In addition to leak-detecting, the helium prevents or retards uranium chemical reactions and acts as a good heat-transfer medium between the uranium slug and the metal jacket or cladding. A low pressure, such as 1 psig, is applied to the element. Any leak will be indicated by a drop in pressure. To simplify the system, several elements can be connected to a common manifold which can be monitored for pressure change. When a pressure change is noted the elements can be tested individually for pressure drop to determine which is causing the difficulty. The helium leak-detection system gives an early alarm on leaking elements, thus preventing a contamination of the core and cooling system.

The coolant system must be adequately instrumented, since any loss of coolant flow could increase core temperature and rupture elements, with serious consequences to the whole facility. Coolant system instrumentation designed to prevent malfunctions and to quickly locate the source of failure in the coolant system measures temperature and pressure at the following points: outside air, before and after inlet filters; at the inlet plenum; at the outlet plenum; before and after the outlet filters; before and after the air coolers (if such are included in the system); before and after the blowers; before and after the noise silencers (if included in the system); and at the top of the stack. The total air flow can also be measured by a venturi in the main air duct or by a pitot tube. The temperature and flow of the cooling water are measured if used in the system.

Coolant measurements which might feed signals into the emergency shutdown system are pressure drop across the core, outlet-gas temperature, and ratio of power to coolant flow.

In addition to these precautions, background radiation at several points in the building is continuously measured and recorded, even though negative pressure is maintained in the reactor to prevent contamination. The activity of the canal water is also monitored (see Chapter 3).

Reactor power can be measured by calibrated neutron flux level detectors (rod shadow effects must be taken into account) or by a heat balance (requiring suitable averaging) on the system. The heat balance can be determined automatically by an electronic unit and the power displayed on a meter or recorder.

Many temperatures are measured in and about a graphite reactor. Since fuel element rupture is the most probable hazard to the system, as many as 100 fuel element surface temperatures are monitored. A number of these temperature readings are fed into the emergency shutdown system. In normal operation the highest heat flux is near the center of the reactor, but the hottest point will be downstream in the direction of coolant flow (Fig. 6–13). Therefore, it is important that fuel element temperatures be measured in this region. However, since the buildup of xenon poisoning, shim rods, or the insertion of experiments into the core

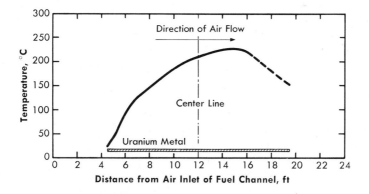

FIG. 6–13. Temperature traverse through a fuel channel in the X-10 Reactor, showing that the peak temperature is downstream from the reactor center. (Courtesy of Oak Ridge National Laboratory.)

may shift the power distribution (and thus the temperature distribution) temperature should be measured throughout the core.

Graphite temperature is also measured, but is not usually fed to the emergency shutdown system. Appreciably fewer points need be measured than in the case of fuel elements, since the graphite temperature is less critical.

6–2.8 Experimental facilities. The graphite research reactor always contains a very large number of experimental facilities (see Figs. 6–1, 6–2, 6–3, 6–8, and 6–12). These must be built into the system.

The channels for fuel also may be used as experimental facilities. They extend the length of the reactor and are about 2 in. in diameter. Coolant flow through the channel can be controlled by orificing, or be stopped entirely by plugging part of the hole with graphite. Within the core region only a limited number of fuel channels can serve experimental purposes. However, at the edge of the core or in the reflector region many coolant channels are available for experiments. These unused fuel channels are normally filled with graphite to increase reflector effectiveness and to force the coolant through the fueled channels. The graphite plugs can be removed to make room for experiments and coolant flow is allowed when necessary.

Channels identical to and parallel to the fuel channels but midway between them are also used. This places the experiment at the point of local thermal-flux peaking. If not in use, these channels are plugged with graphite. Coolant flow can be regulated as required.

Graphite research reactors have many 4 by 4-in. holes (usually 30 to 50) penetrating to the midplane of the core, or passing completely through the core. These holes have the same cross section as the standard graphite pieces used in constructing the core. If desired, the holes can be plugged entirely or can be filled with graphite stringers penetrated by smaller holes. The 4 by 4-in. holes may be either horizontal or vertical, but are always perpendicular to the fuel channels so that the free faces of the core can be used for obtaining beams of neutrons or for inserting experiments. Frequently, several of the holes have permanent apparatus for experiments which are performed frequently, e.g., a slot for foil irradiation. Holes must be so spaced on the reactor face that experiments will not interfere with one another. In the Brookhaven Research Reactor, the holes are 3 ft apart horizontally and 4 ft apart vertically.

It is desirable to provide at least one large opening into the core. This hole can be plugged with graphite when not in use. The Brookhaven Research Reactor has a 1-ft square hole paralleling the fuel elements and penetrating to the center of the core. Neutron beams have been obtained up to 100 ft from the surface of the core. This facility is used in conjunction with the fast chopper.

Another facility installed on graphite reactors comprises one or more tunnels passing close to the bottom surface of the core. These are used for large experiments, such as irradiating animals or large instruments. The tunnels are horizontal, in order to interfere as little as possible with the other facilities and with the shield design. Tunnel dimensions vary from 1 by 1 to 2 by 2 ft. Irradiation windows face the core at the midpoint of the tunnel. A conveyor or miniature rail car is required to move experiments into position.

A sample conveyor, useful for irradiating miscellaneous small samples, may be used with one of the experimental facilities. The conveyor at Brookhaven has 430 graphite sample holders which make a continuous loop through the core. These sample holders go through a duct of 2 by 3-in. cross section. Samples can be loaded while the reactor is operating and can be irradiated for a controlled length of time.

As with the side faces, the core top can be equipped with fixed irradiation ports, beam holes, and thermal columns, as in the X-10 at Oak Ridge. At Brookhaven the top provides a flexible facility, since sections of the shield on top can be lifted with the crane. The Brookhaven top shield has a 20-ft-square section made of 4-ft-square removable blocks. In these locations thermal columns can be constructed or large irradiation experiments performed. Of course, sufficient biological shielding must be added around the experiment to compensate for that lost by removing the blocks.

In addition to facilities discussed above, thermal columns and pneumatic tubes are also available in graphite research reactors.

6–3. PHYSICS CHARACTERISTICS

6–3.1 Critical mass. Factors influencing fuel loadings in graphite research reactors include enrichment, cladding material, coolant, size of coolant passages, fuel element geometry, lattice spacing, core and reflector geometry and size, power level, operating temperatures, and excess reactivity requirements for experiments. The two graphite research reactors in the United States are quite similar in most of these features except power level, although, as previously noted, the Brookhaven Reactor is now modified to use highly enriched fuel (see Article 6–6.2).

The Oak Ridge X-10 is a 24-ft cube of graphite; the fueled region forms the core, and the remainder of the graphite forms the reflector. The critical mass for this reactor is 30 tons; the loading was increased to 54 tons to provide the necessary excess reactivity.

The Brookhaven Research Reactor is a 25-ft cube of graphite. The fuel element arrangement is such that the active core length is always 22 ft. The other two core dimensions can be modified by altering the loading pattern. The minimum critical mass was found by loading an approximate cylinder 14.83 ft in diameter, producing a critical mass of 33 tons of natural uranium. The actual operating mass for the reactor is over 60 tons and is varied according to the needs of the experiments.

The enrichment change in the Brookhaven Research Reactor decreases the critical mass to approximately 50 to 57 kg of U^{235}.

6–3.2 Flux distribution. The magnitude and distribution of thermal-neutron flux are the primary interests in research reactors. For a graphite research reactor the flux distribution calculated from simple theoretical considerations very closely approximates the actual distribution. In an operating reactor, flux distribution is affected by the presence of rods, experiments, and accumulation of fission-product poisons. These factors require measuring of the neutron flux in the region of interest at various times. Figure 6–14 gives the measured thermal-neutron flux distribution across the core of a graphite reactor. The asymmetry noted may be due to the presence of control rods or experiments. The reflector causes perturbation in the flux distribution near the core reflector interface; however, this is very slight compared with the flux peaking observed in water-moderated systems.

The graphite reactor may be considered as being made up of unit cells, that is, a region may be associated with each individual fuel rod. To obtain a smooth curve for the flux distribution, as indicated in Fig. 6–14, the flux must be measured at the corresponding point in each of the unit cells. If the detailed flux distribution is measured within a unit cell local variations will be found; the thermal-neutron flux is found to dip in the uranium and peak in the graphite far from the uranium. For a detailed flux distribution this local variation must be superimposed upon the over-all core flux distribution.

The peak flux in the graphite reactor fueled with natural uranium is almost directly proportional to the power per unit volume of core, al-

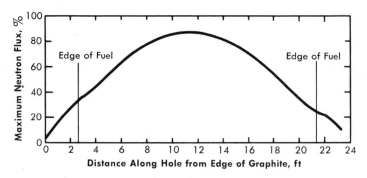

FIG. 6–14. A typical thermal-neutron flux traverse through the X-10 Reactor on a line perpendicular to the fuel elements.

though it is also dependent on the details of the lattic structure, such as moderator-to-uranium and aluminum-to-uranium ratios.

Fast flux is not utilized to a large extent in graphite reactors and therefore fast-flux intensities are not usually quoted. However, Brookhaven has published some approximate fast-flux data showing that the flux above the U^{238} fission threshold is about 10% of thermal, and that the resonance flux as measured by cobalt activation is about 8% of the thermal-flux intensity. This gives a total fast flux above the cadmium cutoff of about 18% of thermal flux.

The gamma flux in reactors is of interest because it will cause gamma heating in experiments within the core and may contribute to radiation damage to materials. An approximate relation applicable to graphite research reactors gives the gamma intensity in roentgens per hour at a given point as approximately equal to the square root of the thermal flux measured at the same point in neutrons per square centimeter per second. Calorimetric measurements in the Brookhaven Research Reactor give values of the gamma flux approximately 50% higher than those given by this approximation; however, these measurements are subject to the same uncertainties as in the approximate relation.

6–3.3 Shielding requirements. The general problem of shielding a reactor has been treated in Chapter 2. The differences in shielding a graphite research reactor mainly involve mechanical and structural problems.

The intensity of both the neutron and gamma fluxes at the outer surface of the reactor shield must be kept low to protect personnel and to keep the background level low enough to permit accurate research work. The specification chosen for the Brookhaven shield was 45 mr per 40-hour week. This was but 5% of the acceptable weekly tolerance in existence at the time of choosing this value, and is still far below the revised acceptable tolerance. Also, the Brookhaven shield performs better than its specifications.

The shielding problem in a graphite research reactor is not as severe as in some other types because of the relatively low power density. The average neutron or gamma photon traverses many feet of graphite with a fair probability of encountering other fuel elements before it can escape from the reactor. The radiation intensities through graphite research reactor shields have been low enough that radiation heating within the shield has not been a serious problem. Cooling of the inner surface of the shield by incoming air has proved sufficient.

Approximately 300 curies/hr of A^{41} are discharged from the Brookhaven facility. The intensity of this radiation from other reactors would depend on the mass flow of air, the time in the reactor, and the power at which the reactor is operating. This radioactive coolant gas must be shielded as it passes from the reactor to the discharge stack. Here ordinary concrete serves the purpose.

6–3.4 Excess reactivity requirements. As pointed out in Article 6–3.1, the core, like that of any research reactor, must be designed with a certain amount of excess reactivity to accommodate the temperature rise from room to operating condition, to overcome fission-product poisoning (primarily Xe^{135}), to provide for experiments that decrease reactivity, and to permit a certain amount of control. The excess reactivity provided to overcome each of these factors in the two existing U. S. graphite research reactors is given in Table 6–2. Note that the use of natural uranium in these systems limits the amount of excess reactivity available.

Because of the large core volume in a graphite system, individual experiments usually have small effect on core reactivity; in addition, the fluxes have been lower in graphite systems than in heavy-water and light-water types, so that the xenon poisoning has been less serious. These factors make it possible to operate the graphite reactor with less excess reactivity than that required in some other types. The graphite reactor's large size and relatively low pumping capacity limit the rate of change of temperature and, consequently, the amount of reactivity and rate of reactivity change due to the temperature coefficient of reactivity.

The burnup of uranium is not a serious factor in graphite natural uranium research reactors. The effect is minimized by rotating the elements so that those most nearly burned up can be placed in a position of lower reactivity worth. A second means of minimizing the effect is to arrange a loading schedule so that only part of the loading is replaced each time. A further factor is that plutonium is formed in the natural uranium fuel, partially replenishing the burned out U^{235}. It is possible to allow burnup of approximately 10% of the U^{235} atoms before the elements must be removed for reprocessing.

TABLE 6–2

EXCESS REACTIVITY REQUIREMENTS

Factor	Excess reactivity required, %	
	X-10	Brookhaven
Temperature	0.4	0.8
Xe^{135}	0.2	0.74
Experimental purposes	0.5	0.75
Control	0.3	0.75
Total	1.4	2.3

6–3.5 Control requirements. The reactivity worth of a control rod varies from 0.2 to 0.6% and depends on the size and location of the rod, the concentration of the neutron absorber in the rod, and the size of the reactor core. Since the excess reactivity requirements are small, it is possible to use a relatively small number of rods. Graphite research reactors are generally constructed with rods having a total reactivity worth approximately twice the excess reactivity built into the core, to provide a safe margin of shutdown.

The rods used for control are similar to the rods used for shutdown; however, the drive mechanisms may be different.

The demand on the control system of graphite research reactors is less than with other types. Reactivity changes occur rather slowly, and because of the great mass and limited coolant flow of the reactor, temperatures cannot change quickly. There is a flux depression at fuel channels and an increase in flux when a fuel channel is unloaded for an experiment. Also, any single experiment represents a very small change in reactivity and precludes the possibility of suddenly adding a large amount of reactivity by removing the experiment. A further factor decreasing the demand on the control system is the relatively long neutron lifetime in the reactor. With natural uranium fuel this is approximately 1.5 msec. This neutron lifetime is expected to increase to about 6 msec with highly enriched fuel.

6–4. Operational Characteristics

6–4.1 Fuel cycles. Research reactors fueled with natural uranium have low specific powers (11 kw/kg in the X-10, 70 kw/kg in the Brookhaven facility), permitting long fuel-irradiation times. The time between fuel changes will depend on the power of the reactor and the reactivity loss that can be overcome by the control system and by loading changes (power density at the edge of the core is about 35% of the maximum). Brookhaven reports from 10 to 20% burnup of the U^{235} atoms. These burnups result in fuel element irradiation lifetimes of from 2 to 7 years. In this time some elements will fail because of radiation damage and must be replaced. However, these are small in number compared with the total loading.

In research reactors using highly enriched fuel, the critical loading will be much less but the permitted burnup will be much higher, approximately 40%. This will result in fuel cycles from one-fourth to one-half as long as those of. the same reactor fueled with natural uranium. However, because of the much reduced total mass and the low probability of fuel element rupture, the entire operation is simplified with the highly enriched fuel.

6–4.2 Operating cycles. Shutdowns are required periodically with a graphite research reactor to permit changing and inserting experiments, changing the fuel loading, and routine system maintenance. Such shutdown periods can be spaced for the convenience of the research, usually at intervals of 7 to 10 days. The shutdown may be a few hours or as long as half a day.

6–4.3 Ease of startup and shutdown. It is relatively easy to start up and shut down a graphite research reactor. Before startup, the coolant system must be put into operation by starting the blowers and the water-cooling heat exchangers (if these are in the system), and checking the instrumentation for proper functioning of all units. Following this it is necessary only to withdraw control rods until the reactor is on an increasing period, and then to continue to adjust the position of the control rods until operating power is reached.

For safety, the rate at which power is increased is limited to periods above 15 or 20 sec. However, other considerations may be important in determining this rate. For example, at Brookhaven it has been found that fuel elements rupture much less frequently if they are not subjected to a temperature rate of change greater than 2°C/min. The startup is controlled by varying the position of the control rod to stay within these temperature limitations. During shutdown the rate of change of fuel element temperature is controlled by adjusting the rate of coolant flow.

6–4.4 Stability. The stability referred to here is the stability of the power and neutron flux from the point of view of the experimenter, who desires to have a constant neutron flux. (This is only achievable within certain limits.) Most research reactors are controlled by automatic instrumentation which must see a change in power before a correction can be made. However, a good controller will hold the power constant to $\pm 0.5\%$.

Further variations in reactor power are induced by temperature changes in the intake air which affect the core temperature distribution and the average core temperature, resulting in control rod movement and changes in flux distributions. This air temperature will reach a maximum in the afternoon of a normal day and a minimum sometime near midnight or later. If precise data are required it is best for experiments to be done during a period when the temperature variations are small, or to use some monitoring instrument for normalizing the data obtained.

Another source of variation arises from the fixed facilities incorporated in the reactor. Most graphite research reactors have a certain number of such fixed facilities as irradiation ports, rabbits, and foil slots, that can be used without shutting the reactor down. Inserting and removing samples causes flux variations in the reactor, particularly near the sample being moved. This effect can be minimized by scheduling irradiations so as to have a minimum interference with experiments and to locate the more sensitive experiments at long distances from the facilities most likely to cause variations. In addition, regulating rod movements will cause some change in the flux distribution.

All the effects noted above are relatively small, probably smaller than in other kinds of research reactors. In general, the graphite research reactor is quite stable and capable of producing good experimental results.

6–5. SUMMARY

6–5.1 Special characteristics. The graphite research reactor is characterized by its large size and the many research facilities provided in the design. The reactors now use natural uranium fuel which must be clad or canned to prevent oxidation and the release of fission products. The higher-powered graphite reactors require more careful design and construction of the fuel elements to ensure that critical temperatures are not exceeded and that the elements can be properly cooled.

The graphite reactor can have one or several thermal columns, and usually 100 or more ports, holes, and channels for experimental purposes. There are usually provisions also for a large hole into the core, large irradiation areas adjacent to the surface of the core, and tunnels beneath or above the core.

The graphite research reactors currently in use in the United States are air-cooled. The complexity of the cooling system depends on the power of the reactor. The higher-powered reactors require large blowers, air ducts, filters, and stacks for dispersing the air, which contains radioactive argon, at a height such that personnel will not be endangered.

Provisions must be made for handling the spent fuel elements. This is done with a water-filled canal that shields the active elements and permits inspection and convenient storage while the activity of the fission products decays.

The substitution of highly enriched fuel for the natural uranium will increase the flux significantly (a factor of 6 in the Brookhaven Research Reactor) and reduce the critical mass, the problems involved in handling the fuel, and the probability of fuel element failure. It will also generally simplify the reactor operation. The new fuel element design will reduce power required for cooling.

6–5.2 Advantages. The principal advantage of the graphite research reactor is that it has a large volume and large surface areas, permitting a great many experiments to be conducted simultaneously. Another advantage is the accessibility of the fuel channels, which are available for a limited number of in-pile experiments.

The low power-to-volume ratio permits a relatively simple cooling system using air at low pressure. With these systems there are few corrosion or coolant-disposal problems.

The relative simplicity of construction and operation of the graphite research reactor and its relative slowness in response to changes make it an ideal type for research work requiring uninterrupted reactor operation at constant power.

6–5.3 Disadvantages. The major disadvantage of the graphite research reactor using natural uranium fuel is the high cost resulting from its large size.

A second disadvantage is its low power density, which means that a relatively large power is required to obtain a sufficiently high neutron flux, which results in large amounts of potentially hazardous fission products.

The graphite research reactor, even with the introduction of highly enriched fuel, has a high cost per unit flux. However, since more experiments can be accommodated, the cost per unit research project can be comparable with that of other reactor types with either highly enriched or natural uranium.

The large blowers required for the cooling system result in high power consumption. The first two reactors, CP-1 and CP-2, were made without provisions for cooling. They normally operated at 200 w, and were operated at 2 kw for short periods of time. These reactors have been dismantled.

The two principal reasons for initially choosing the graphite reactor as a research reactor, that is, the availability of natural uranium and suitable graphite in the necessary quantities and at low cost, no longer exist. Because of the size and cost of the facility and the high power per unit flux, it is doubtful whether new graphite research reactors will be constructed.

CHAPTER 7

REACTORS FOR TRANSIENT STUDIES AND
SPECIAL REACTORS*

7–1. Introduction

In 1953, the first of a continuing series of tests sponsored by the USAEC to obtain information on the performance and safety of water-moderated reactors began. These tests are divided into three general classifications:
(1) Borax (boiling reactor experiments).
(2) Spert (special power-excursion reactor tests).
(3) Kewb (kinetic experiments on water boilers).
Some of the work is not yet completed. This chapter discusses that part of the information thus far developed which applies to research reactors.

In general, the experiments were concerned with the kinetic behavior and stability of water-moderated systems, both heterogeneous and homogeneous. The Borax experiments of interest were carried out on a reactor core made from MTR-type fuel elements. Power transients were purposely introduced to permit study of the reactor behavior. The Spert tests extended the Borax work to obtain more detailed information. A different fuel-element design was used in the Spert tests, but the Kewb work was done on a homogeneous system similar to that covered in Chapter 5.

7–2. Borax Experiments

Of the four Borax reactors, by far the most significant in relation to research reactors were Borax I and II. Borax III was a prototype boiling power reactor which was operated to investigate the stability of such reactors under different operating conditions and problems arising from radioactivity in the turbine. Borax IV was also a power-reactor experiment, whose principal purpose was to test fuel elements made from mixed oxides of uranium and thorium. A series of tests on fuel-element failures, along with other experiments, are planned to conclude the Borax tests in 1958. A paper by J. R. Dietrich (Geneva Conference Paper, No. 481) presented at the 1955 Geneva Conference contains an excellent summary of the Borax I and II experiments. Most of the material presented here is taken from this paper. The results of these experiments are pertinent to the operation of tank and pool research reactors.

* By W. S. Hogan.

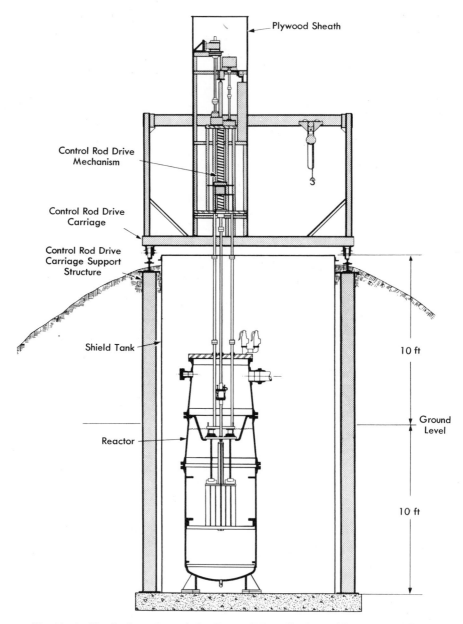

Plywood Sheath

Control Rod Drive
Mechanism

Control Rod Drive
Carriage

Control Rod Drive
Carriage Support
Structure

Shield Tank

Reactor

10 ft

Ground
Level

10 ft

FIG. 7–1. Vertical section of the Borax I installation. (Courtesy of Argonne National Laboratory.)

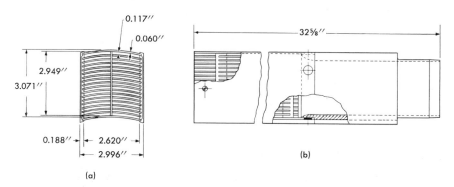

FIG. 7–2. Borax I fuel element, similar to MTR fuel element (see Chapter 3). (Courtesy of Argonne National Laboratory.)

7–2.1 Description of reactors. The important differences between Borax I and II lie in the core characteristics. Therefore only Borax I will be described in detail, but the differences in core characteristics will be given fully. Figure 7–1 is a vertical section of the Borax I reactor. The reactor tank was made of carbon steel lined with plastic for corrosion resistance. Provisions were made for operating the reactor at pressures up to 125 psig.

The core was built upon a lower grid plate into which 36 fuel assemblies or dummy plugs were placed. This arrangement provided about 7% excess reactivity above the clean cold condition. The reactor was just critical with 26 assemblies. The dummy plugs were made so that a reflector of almost pure water was directly adjacent to the active reactor core over most of its length.

The fuel assemblies (modified MTR type) each contained about 130 g of U^{235}. They were made from 18 aluminum-clad aluminum and uranium alloy plates 60 mils thick brazed into aluminum side plates to make boxes roughly 3 in. square (Fig. 7–2). The Borax II reactor used elements of identical outside dimensions, but each element contained only 10 fuel plates. Table 7–1 compares the core properties of the two reactors.

In operation, the reactor tank was filled with water to a height of 3 to $4\frac{1}{2}$ ft above the top of the core. This water constituted the reflector, moderator, and coolant. The shield tank was filled with water only when the reactor was shut down.

Borax I contained five cadmium control rods operated by drive mechanisms located in the housing above the shield tank and connected to them through spring-loaded magnetic couplings. The center rod was ejected from the core to allow the excess reactivity to initiate the transient, and the other four rods were dropped into the core to end the experiment. Each rod traversed the length of the core in about 0.2 sec.

TABLE 7–1

COMPARISON OF CORES USED IN BORAX I AND II

	Borax I	Borax II
Aluminum-to-water ratio in core	0.626	0.422
U^{235} content per fuel element, grams	138.6	93.4 or 157.3
Number of fuel plates per element	18	10
Plate spacing (between centerlines), inches	0.177	0.324

Measured reactivity loss with temperature increase, percent $\Delta k_{eff}/k_{eff}$:
    80 to 200°F
    80 to 280°F
    80 to 420°F
	
	0.82
	1.93
	—
		
		0.45*
		0.76*
		1.57*

Calculated loss of reactivity caused by replacement of 10% of core water by steam at 200°F, in percent $\Delta k_{eff}/k_{eff}$	2.4	1.0*
Effective neutron lifetime, 10^{-5} sec	6.5	7.5*

* These values apply when the reactor is loaded only with the fuel elements of comparatively low uranium content.

7–2.2 Experimental procedures. Transients (power excursions) were initiated in the Borax reactors by adjusting the water temperature to a desired value, making the reactor critical at low power (~1 watt), and then ejecting the center control rod out of the core. In nearly all cases the initial power was low enough and the rod ejection fast enough so that the rod was completely out of the core and the reactor on a stable period before the power was high enough to produce significant thermal effects. The power was allowed to rise until steam formation reduced the reactivity to below criticality, and the power, consequently, was reduced to a low value. After it became evident that the power had been limited by the formation of steam, the control rods were inserted to end the experiment.

The magnitude of excess reactivity supplied to the core could be varied by adjusting the number of fuel elements and the position of the 4 outer control rods. With these adjustments, the reactor could be made critical with the center control rod at any desired axial position.

7–2.3 Summary of results. The detailed behavior of the reactors in a specific experiment will not be presented here. Rather, experimental results will be summarized. To clarify what follows, it should be stated that for the results presented here the initial water temperature was either ~80°F or at the saturation level, although tests were started from other water temperatures.

In the Borax I experiments, once the power excursion had been checked by boiling, the specific power variation was dependent on the amount of excess reactivity and on the temperature of the reactor water. Figure 7–3 summarizes the behavior of the reactor for various amounts of excess reactivity when the reactor water is at the saturated condition. For low excess reactivities, corresponding to periods of 0.03 sec or longer, the power returns to a relatively steady value of about $\frac{1}{2}$ Mw after the initial power surge (top curve, Fig. 7–3). For periods in the range 0.02 to 0.03 sec, the first excursion was followed by a series of similar excursions of smaller amplitude (second curve, Fig. 7–3). For periods less than about 0.01 sec, enough water was expelled from the reactor tank to bring about perma-

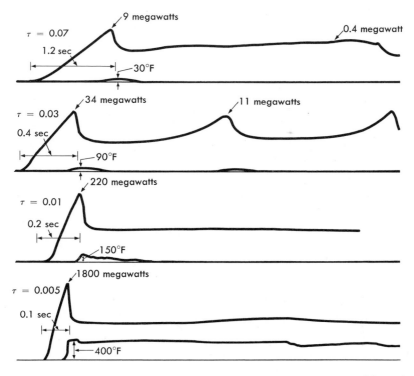

Fig. 7–3. Representative excursions at saturation temperatures with various excess reactivities in Borax I.

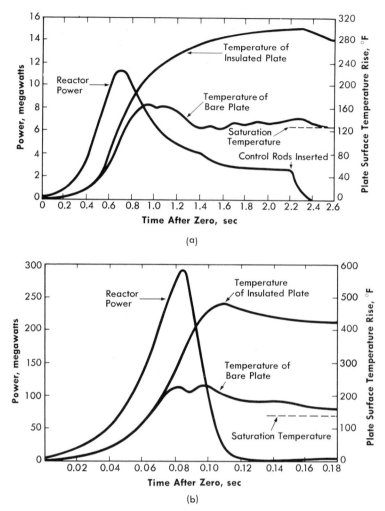

FIG. 7–4. Power and fuel-plate surface temperature rise during Borax I power excursions: (a) initial temperature at 80°F and period of 0.134 sec, (b) initial temperature at 82°F and period of 0.021 sec.

nent shutdown. When the period was in the 0.005-sec range, the qualitative behavior of the reactor power remained the same as for 0.01-sec periods, but the fuel plate temperature remained high for almost 1 sec after the power surge, and then decreased by small steps, as though the plate had been blanketed by steam for some time after the excursion.

The shortest period obtained in experiments of this type with the reactor water at the subcooled (~80°F) condition was about 0.013 sec. In all these subcooled cases, after the first excursion the reactor power

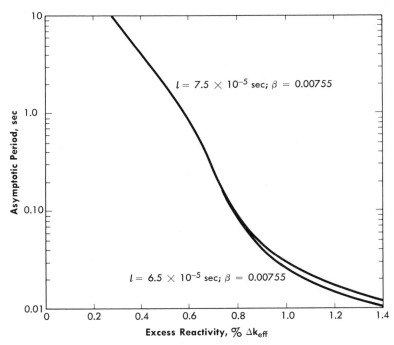

Fɪɢ. 7–5. Relation between excess reactivity and reactor period.

stabilized at a nearly steady value. Oscillation in the subcooled run was, in general, much less than in the saturated runs.

Figure 7–4 illustrates the typical behavior of Borax I in the subcooled cases. The insulated plate temperature curve is very nearly proportional to the time integral of the power, since this is the temperature history of a thermally insulated thermocouple. The plate temperatures were measured at or near the region of maximum neutron flux. It should be noted that the time relationship between peak power and peak temperature of the bare plate and the ratio of maximum temperatures of the bare and insulated plates will depend on the power density at the plate relative to the power density elsewhere in the core. It is interesting to note that in the run represented on the left in Fig. 7–4 reactor shutdown started before the temperature of the one plate which was instrumented had reached the saturation value, indicating that heat generation in the other plates was responsible for the initial steam formation or that some mechanism other than steam formation was aiding shutdown.

The total nuclear energy release of an excursion and the maximum fuel plate temperature attained are dependent on the excess reactivity added. The reciprocal of the stable reactor period will be used as a measure of the excess reactivity. The relation between the two is shown in Fig. 7–5,

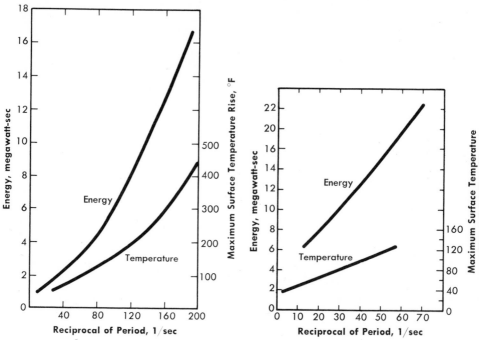

FIG. 7–6. Maximum temperature rise of fuel-plate surface and total energy release during power excursions of various exponential periods for Borax I at saturation temperature and atmospheric pressure.

FIG. 7–7. Maximum temperature of fuel-plate surface and total energy release during power excursions of various exponential periods for Borax I, at room temperature (approximately 80°F) and atmospheric pressure.

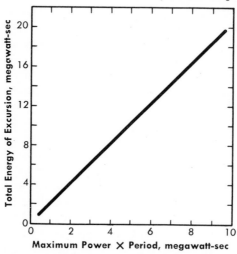

FIG. 7–8. Relation of total energy, maximum power, and period for water at both room temperature and saturation temperature in Borax I tests.

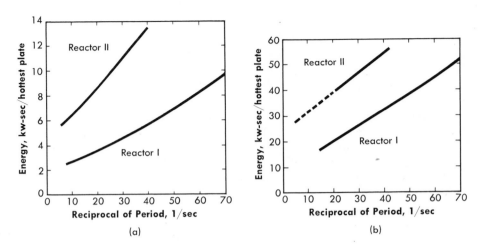

FIG. 7–9. Energy release of hottest fuel plate during power excursions in Borax I and II: (a) reactor water at saturation temperature and atmospheric pressure, (b) reactor water at room temperature and atmospheric pressure.

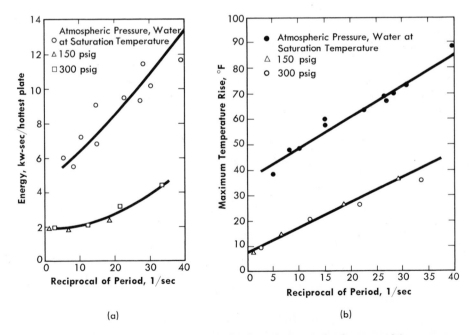

FIG. 7–10. Comparison of unpressurized and pressurized cases: (a) energy release of hottest fuel plate during power excursions at different pressures, (b) maximum fuel-plate temperature rise during power excursions.

where l is the neutron lifetime and β is the effective delayed neutron fraction. Figure 7–6 shows the total prompt fission energy release up to the time of the first minimum in reactor power and the maximum fuel-plate surface temperature as a function of reciprocal period for saturated temperature in Borax I. Figure 7–7 presents information for the subcooled (~80°F) runs. The total energy was found to be about twice the product of maximum power and stable reactor period. This is shown in Fig. 7–8.

Since the core sizes were different in Borax I and II, it is informative to compare energy per fuel plate. The comparison is given in Fig. 7–9 for fuel plates in the region of highest neutron flux. From Table 7–1 and Fig. 7–8, it can be seen that the energy release per unit volume of water is nearly identical for a given reactor period for both Borax I and II.

Figure 7–10 summarizes the Borax II results obtained for a pressurized core and compares them with those obtained at atmospheric pressure.

7–2.4 The destructive experiment. As a final Borax I experiment, about 4% excess reactivity was purposely introduced. The energy release was large enough and rapid enough to destroy the reactor, and because of damage to the instruments findings were not complete. The excursion melted most of the fuel plates, burst the reactor tank, and ejected most of the contents of the shield tank into the air.

The minimum period in this excursion was 0.0026 sec. Total nuclear energy released, as determined by calibrated cobalt foils in the core, was 135 Mw-sec. The maximum pressure reached was estimated to be greater than 10,000 psi. All the reactor fuel was found within a radius of 350 ft from the reactor. At the time of the experiment, wind velocity was 8 mph at ground level and 20 mph 250 ft above. Fifteen minutes after the experiment, the total beta plus gamma activity 0.8 mile downwind of the reactor was 5 mr/hr. At a point $\frac{1}{2}$ mile crosswind from the site, a dose rate greater than 400 mr/hr was indicated at the time of the excursion, but this decayed rapidly. The total dose at the $\frac{1}{2}$-mile point was less than 10 mr. There was no conclusive evidence that a chemical reaction between aluminum and water contributed significantly to the energy release. The nuclear energy release of this experiment was found to be consistent with that measured in similar experiments which did not reach destructive violence.

7–2.5 Discussion. The Borax experiments indicate a high degree of inherent safety in research reactors. In inferring the behavior of other reactors whose excursions would be limited by steam formation, the effect of thermal conductivity of the plates must be considered. For reactors with fuel plates of low thermal conductivity the inherent safety will probably not be as great.

The following is a brief summary of Borax I results most pertinent to research-reactor operation:

(1) Steam formation and consequent ejection of water from the core constituted an effective and fast-acting inherent power-limiting process that protected the reactor from the effects of large and instantaneous additions of excess reactivity.

(2) In the entire series of some 200 excursions, no inconsistencies were observed which could *not* be attributed to instrumental errors that arose from rather difficult experimental conditions.

(3) When the purposely caused excess reactivity was not removed by external means, the reactor would settle down to steady boiling ("chugging"), consisting of a sequence of power surges of nearly constant amplitude lower than the initial surge, or to a permanently subcritical state. This behavior depended on the amount of excess reactivity applied and should vary with reactor design.

(4) For a given period, the total energy release and the maximum fuel plate temperature increased with the amount of initial subcooling of the reactor water.

(5) The speed of the power-limiting process is indicated by the fact that during excursions the power rose from 10% of peak value to peak value and returned to 10% of peak value in from 3 to 4.5 exponential periods. The period is taken to be the asymptotic exponential period reached after the control rod is fully ejected, and maintained until shutdown starts. The total energy release of the excursion was roughly equal to the product of maximum power and two exponential periods.

(6) In the destructive experiment, there was no evidence that the power-limiting process differed qualitatively from that effective in other experiments. It was evident that the nuclear power release terminated at an early stage of the explosion. Motion pictures showed that the light flash emitted by the reactor as it reached high power ended before any material was ejected above the top of the shield tank. The flash lasted about 0.003 sec.

7–3. SPERT EXPERIMENTS

Information on the first Spert reactor is presented here; two more were under construction in April 1958. Spert I is a nonpressurized light-water moderated and reflected reactor using highly enriched fuel in plate-type elements. Spert II will be similar to Spert I but will be designed for operation up to 300 psi and 400°F; it will be used primarily to study how various moderators and reflectors influence transient behavior and safety. Spert III will be a high-pressure high-temperature reactor for transient and safety studies pertinent to water cooled and moderated power reactors.

Spert I differs from Borax I principally in fuel element design, as described in Article 7–3.1 below. The Spert program is an extension of the Borax experiments. A comparison of results follows.

7–3.1 Description of reactor. Figure 7–11 is a cutaway view of the Spert I reactor. The core is contained in a tank 4 ft in diameter and 10 ft high. The tank is filled to a height of about 2 ft above the core with water which serves as coolant, reflector, and moderator. As in Borax I, the outer shield tank is normally empty during operation. The five control blades are similar to those in Borax I. The central rod is used to start power excursions, and the four outer blades serve as shim-safety rods.

Spert I elements differ from those of Borax I in that stiffening members have been inserted between the plates (which are less than one-third the usual width) for extra strength. This construction divides each fuel

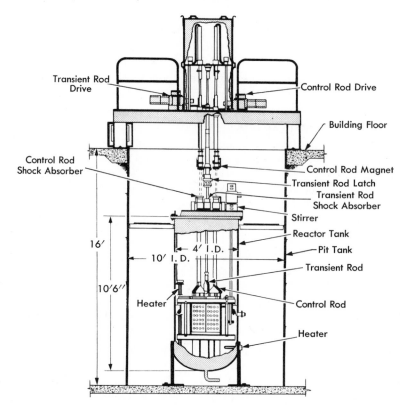

Fig. 7–11. Vertical section of the Spert I Reactor. Note the over-all similarity between this and Borax I (Fig. 7–1). (Courtesy of Phillips Petroleum Co.)

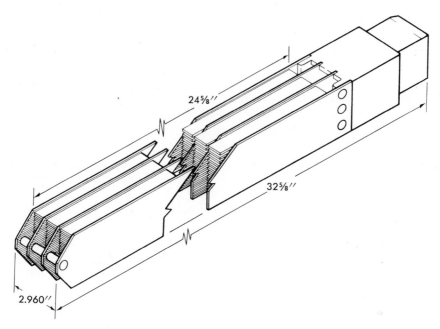

24⅝″

32⅝″

2.960″

FIG. 7–12. Spert I fuel subassembly. Note the stiffening members, not present in Borax I elements (Fig. 7–2). (Courtesy of Phillips Petroleum Co.)

element into three longitudinal subassemblies. Holes in the square end boxes at the bottom of the subassemblies are so positioned in the bottom grid plate as to permit water to flow into the end boxes from the channels between subassemblies. The corresponding channels were blocked in the Borax experiments. Each Spert I fuel assembly contains 51 fuel plates, totaling 168 g of U^{235} (Fig. 7–12).

Table 7–2 lists core characteristics of the Spert I reactor.

TABLE 7–2

CHARACTERISTICS OF THE SPERT I CORE

Critical mass at 18°C	3.86 kg U^{235} (23 fuel elements)
Excess reactivity at 18°C	4% (28 fuel elements)
Prompt neutron lifetime	5×10^{-5} sec
Reactivity loss, 20°C to boiling	1.05% ($\Delta k_{eff}/k_{eff}$)
Average void coefficient	-3.5×10^{-4}% ($\Delta k_{eff}/k_{eff}$)/cm³
Maximum void coefficient	-7.2×10^{-4}% ($\Delta k_{eff}/k$
Temperature coefficient at 30°C	-0.85×10^{-2}% (Δ
Temperature coefficient at boiling	-2×10^{-2}% ($\Delta k_{eff}/$

7–3.2 Experimental procedures. Procedures for initiating the transients in Spert I were similar to those used in the Borax tests. The critical position of the four outer rods was determined with the cadmium section of the transient (center) rod out of the core. This critical position was measured at a power level of about 200 watts to prevent any possible source effects. The reactor was then made subcritical by pulling the transient rod into the core. The reactor power was allowed to decay to a level of several watts, at which time the shim rods were withdrawn to predetermined positions for the transient. Ejection of the transient rod then made the reactor supercritical by an amount determined by the displacement of the shim rods above the critical position. As in the Borax experiments, these tests were at different initial reactor water temperatures.

In addition to tests in which the transient rod was ejected rapidly, several excursions were initiated by increasing the reactivity linearly with time. These tests were started with the reactor critical at a predetermined power level and with the water at 20°C in some tests and at boiling in others. Reactivity was increased by withdrawing the outer four rods at a fixed rate.

7–3.3 Summary of results. In Fig. 7–13, asymptotic reactor period is plotted against excess reactivity. Soon after ejection of the transient rod, the power rise becomes exponential with a period determined by the sudden reactivity increase. The power continues to rise until enough energy accumulates for the shutdown mechanism to cause an appreciable reactivity reduction. Reactivity then decreases until the power reaches its maximum. Since this maximum value is generally greater than the equilibrium power required to compensate for the excess reactivity, the

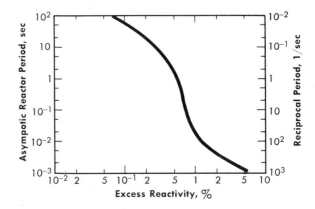

Fig. 7–13. Excess reactivity versus asymptotic reactor period (in-hour relation) for effective neutron lifetime of 50 sec using delayed-neutron data from Geneva Conference paper No. 831 (1955) by Keepin and Wimmett.

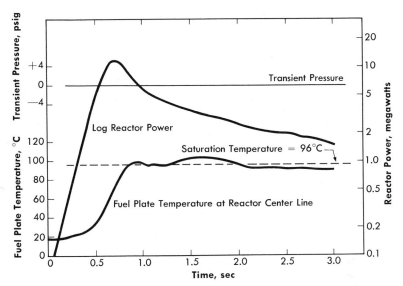

FIG. 7–14. Spert I transient test.   Conditions: reactor period, 110 msec; maximum power, 12 Mw; initial water temperature, 16°C; water head, 24 in. above core.

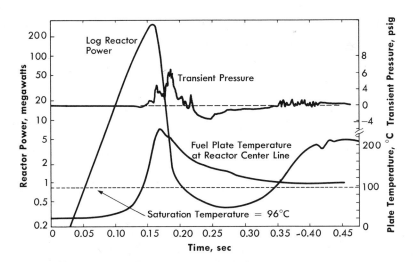

FIG. 7–15. Spert I transient test.   Conditions: reactor period, 16 msec; maximum power, 300 Mw; initial water temperature, 20°C; water head, 24 in. above core.

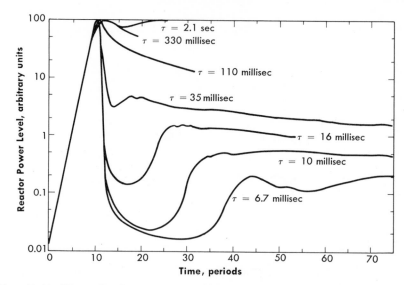

FIG. 7–16. Normalized reactor power as a function of transient period for Spert I. Conditions: initial water temperature, 20°C; water head, 24 in. above core. Periods plotted horizontally are asymptotic exponential periods.

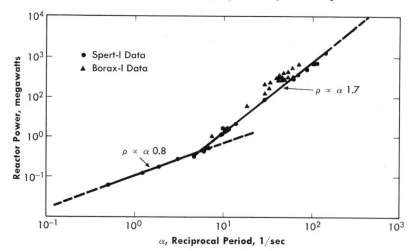

FIG. 7–17. Maximum reactor power vs. reciprocal period. Conditions: initial water temperature, 20°C; water head, 24 in. above core.

power decreases and approaches equilibrium either smoothly or in an oscillatory manner, depending on the particular reactor parameters (Figs. 7–14 and 7–15). Figure 7–16 shows the dependence of power behavior on reactor period. These curves have been normalized at their peak power.

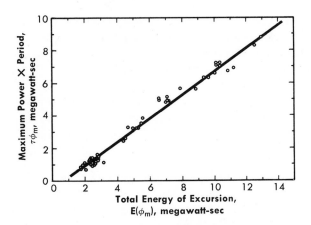

FIG. 7–18. Product of maximum reactor power, ϕ_m, and reactor period, τ, vs. energy released up to time of maximum power, $E(\phi_m)$, for Spert I.

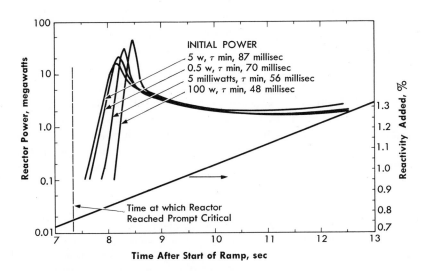

FIG. 7–19. Ramp rate tests for Spert I, showing reactor power behavior as a function of initial power level. Conditions: reactivity addition rate, about 0.1 %/sec; initial water temperature, 20°C; water head, 24 in. above core.

Figure 7–17 is a plot of maximum reactor power versus reciprocal period. Borax data are included for comparison. Figure 7–18 is a plot of the product of maximum power and period versus the total energy released up to the time of maximum power. As in the Borax tests, the relationship is approximately linear.

Results of a typical ramp rate (excess reactivity added linearly with time), starting with the water at 20°C, illustrate the effect of initial power level on power-time behavior (Fig. 7–19). As can be seen, no instabilities were observed, and in all cases the behavior after the initial power burst is relatively independent of the initial power level. The effect of water height above the core during the experiment may be important. In ramp tests with the reactor water boiling and with total reactivity additions somewhat larger than those of the 20°C tests discussed above, there were serious instabilities, and the power oscillations were divergent.

7–3.4 Discussion.   Most Spert I information is in agreement with Borax results.   Additional information regarding the shutdown mechanisms and the behavior of a reactor during ramp rate tests obtained from Spert I indicated that the temperature change in the moderator and radiolytic production of gas are important shutdown mechanisms. Indeed, it appears that these are the primary shutdown mechanisms for reciprocal periods less than 20 sec^{-1}, since the fuel-plate surface temperatures did not reach saturation during these runs until after peak power had been reached (see Fig. 7–14). The results of the ramp tests indicate that this type of reactor behaves in a stable manner if the water is subcooled.

7–4. KEWB Experiments

The KEWB (Kinetic Experiments on Water Boilers) experimental program was started in October 1954 to obtain and evaluate data on the dynamic behavior of aqueous homogeneous research reactors. A complete 50-kw research reactor was built near Los Angeles, California, and went critical in July 1956. Tests, while not yet complete, have yielded much information on how this reactor behaves when large amounts of reactivity are added.

7–4.1 Description of reactor.   A perspective view of the KEWB test reactor is shown in Fig. 7–20. The stainless steel sphere, 12.3-in. ID and with a minimum wall thickness of 0.22 in., contains 11.5 liters of uranyl sulphate (UO_2SO_4) solution (see Table 7–3). The reflector is a 56-in. cube of stacked reactor grade graphite bars. Heat is removed from the core by water circulating through 90 ft of stainless steel tubing ($\frac{1}{4}$-in. OD and wall thickness of 0.028 in.).

A 2-in. ID pipe leads from the top of the core to a 2-liter cylinder. Fuel expelled from the core during violent excursions rises into this chamber and later drains back into the core. The hydrogen and oxygen produced by radiolytic water decomposition rise through this overflow chamber and are swept to an external recombination system which returns water to the core.

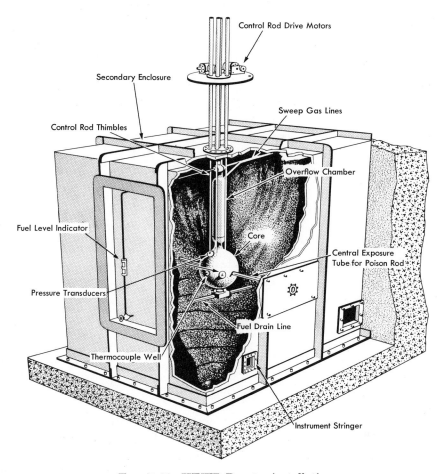

Fig. 7-20. KEWB Reactor installation.

Four symmetrically spaced control rods pass along the overflow chamber and enter the core vessel. These rods, made of boron carbide (B_4C), have a total reactivity of about 7% Δk. Another boron carbide rod of larger diameter, used to initiate power excursions, has a reactivity equal to the total of the other four rods. This large rod travels horizontally along a radius of the sphere.

The reactor instrumentation system includes equipment to record reactor power, internal core pressure, and solution temperature. Neutron-sensitive ionization chambers, coated with enriched boron, generate a current proportional to reactor power, which is first converted to a voltage and then amplified by an electrometer circuit. Pressures are detected by two transducers, one at the bottom of the core vessel and the other imme-

TABLE 7–3

PROPERTIES OF FUEL SOLUTION

1. Volume of fuel solution in core	11.5 liters
2. Mass of U^{235} in core	1929 g U^{235} 8.17 g-atoms
3. Mass of uranium in core	2059 g U 8.750 g-atoms
4. Concentration of U^{235} in solution	167.7 g U^{235}/liter 0.7137 M
5. Concentration of uranium in solution	179.9 g U/liter 0.7644 M
6. Hydrogen-uranium atomic ratio Hydrogen-U^{235} atomic ratio	137.9 147.8
7. Hydrogen ion concentration as determined with glass electrode	pH = 0.4
8. Density (25°C)	1.239 g/ml
9. Viscosity	1.830 centipoises (20°C) 0.902 centipoise (55°C)
10. Specific heat (20 to 24°C)	0.797 cal/(g)(°C)

diately above the normal fuel solution level. A change in pressure deflects the diaphragm to unbalance a bridge circuit. Iron-constantan thermo-couple junctions, protected from the corrosive action of the solution by a thin stainless steel sheath, measure fuel temperatures. Light-beam gal-vanometers are deflected by the different signals to produce continuous traces on moving photographic paper.

7–4.2 Reactivity coefficients. The temperature coefficient of reactivity was determined from 25 to 90°C at a core pressure of 68 cm of Hg. The coefficient is -0.016% Δk/°C at 25°C and increases slowly with temperature to -0.027 at 85°C and then increases rapidly to -0.032 at 90°C. A void coefficient of reactivity, calculated from the temperature coefficient and change of density with temperature, is -0.0039% Δk/cm^3.

Production rates of hydrogen and oxygen gases, resulting from dissocia-tion of water in the fuel solution, have been examined as a function of power (0.5 to 20 kw), pressure (27 to 68 cm of Hg), and temperature (17 to 90°C). Production was found to be independent of power. At 60 cm of Hg, gas production was affected only slightly by temperature and that by the lower temperatures; the value dropped from 14.0 liters/kwh at 30°C to 12.9 liters/kwh at 17.5°C; above 30°C the rate is constant. There is an essentially linear dependence of gas production upon pressure; the rate decreases from 15.4 to 13.7 liters/kwh as the pressure is increased from 27 to 68 cm of Hg.

7–4.3 Experimental conditions. Test results have involved the following parameters:

(1) Amount and rate of reactivity input.

(2) Initial core pressure.

(3) Initial core temperature.

Certain aspects of the reactor system, unchanged during the tests, and representing standard conditions for the experiments, are:

(1) No cooling water was circulated through the core.

(2) Void volume in the core was 2.1 liters.

(3) The gas recombination system was not utilized, and a ballast tank collected the hydrogen and oxygen gases produced during power excursions. The total gas phase volume of the system was 39.1 liters.

(4) The initial temperature of core solution was 25°C, except in those tests that were started at different temperatures.

(5) Initial core pressure was either 15.6, 43, or 71 cm of Hg.

(6) Initial reactor power was less than 1 mw.

(7) Excess reactivity in the core loading was maintained at approximately 4% Δk.

7–4.4 Summary of results. Reactivity has been systematically increased in transient tests on the KEWB-1 reactor, usually in steps. The maximum reactivity added to the reactor, 4% produced a stable period of 0.002 sec; it was initiated with a core pressure of 15 cm of Hg. Tests at initial core pressures of 43 and 71 cm of Hg have been carried as far as 0.004-sec periods. Pressures detected have never approached values that would cause permanent distortion or failure of the core vessel. Maximum pressures are the primary concern when considering safety aspects of homogeneous reactors, whereas damage to fuel elements is the principal concern in heterogeneous or solid-fuel reactors. The peak powers that resulted from tests with step input of reactivity are graphically presented in Fig. 7–21. The higher initial core pressures result in higher peak powers. Initial pressure is least important in the period region of 0.07 to 0.08 sec, but increases as the period decreases. The transients initiated at the higher pressures result in peak powers 50% greater when the period is 0.004 sec.

The power traces have been integrated to obtain the energy release associated with bursts. The data presented in Fig. 7–22 are based only on excursions starting from an initial pressure of 15 cm of Hg. The maximum

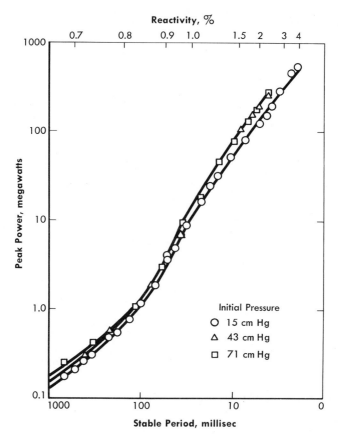

Fig. 7–21. Peak power vs. stable period and reactivity. Initial temperature of core was 25°C

energy release corresponds to a fuel solution temperature increase of only about 40°C. The maximum temperature reached, even at the low initial pressure, is insufficient to cause shutdown due to steam formation. The energy release in the largest excursion is equivalent to about 1.5 min of normal 50-kw operation.

For reactor periods longer than 0.030 sec, no pressure changes in the core vessel are detected. In all cases the pressure at the top of the vessel is the maximum observed. The data are presented in Fig. 7–23. It will be noted that "first" and "second" pressure pulses are plotted. Figure 7–24 shows records of linear and logarithmic power, pressure, and fuel solution temperature. A second transducer in the reflector, to check the radiation sensitivity of the device, has consistently shown radiation effects to be small (<5 psi equivalent) but measurable on the larger excursions.

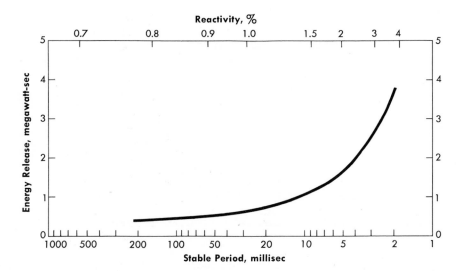

Fig. 7–22. Energy release in first burst vs. stable period and reactivity. Initial pressure in core vessel was 15 cm of Hg.

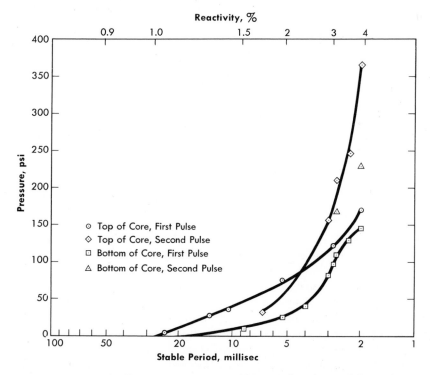

Fig. 7–23. Core pressures vs. stable period and reactivity.

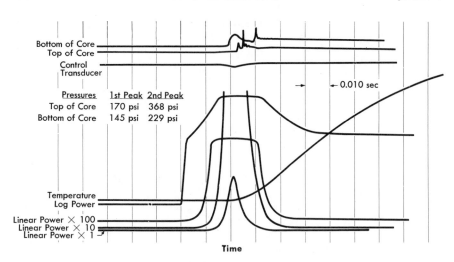

FIG. 7–24. KEWB transient test: peak power, 531 Mw; period, 1.97 msec; reactivity addition, 3.98%.

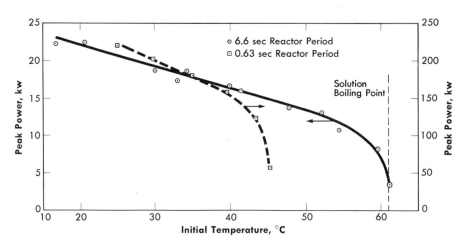

FIG. 7–25. Peak power vs. initial core temperature for reactivity additions of 0.4 and 0.7% and initial core pressure of 15.6 cm of Hg.

Information has been obtained on the effect of initial temperature on peak power for reactivity inputs of 0.4 and 0.7%. As the intial temperature is increased the maximum power for a given reactivity input decreases (Fig. 7–25). The initial pressure for these tests was 15.6 cm of Hg, which corresponds to a boiling point for the solution of 61°C. An increase in the initial temperature has a pronounced effect on maximum power, particularly in the slower transients, as the boiling point is approached.

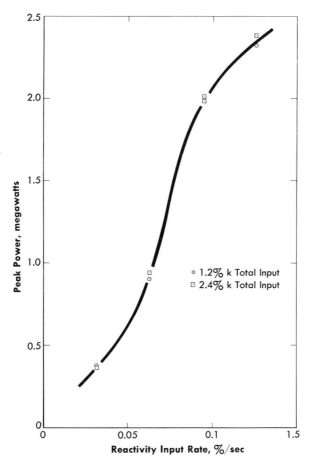

FIG. 7–26. Peak power vs. reactivity input rate with initial core pressure of 15.6 cm of Hg.

With larger reactivity input and initial temperature above 40°C the period is probably short enough and the energy generation so quick that localized heating in the central region of the core causes appreciable vapor formation. This would explain the more effective shutdown witnessed for transients caused by large additions of reactivity.

The most probable nuclear reactor accident is one in which reactivity is added gradually and continuously (ramp addition) rather than the step input tests reviewed above. Reactivity may be added by continuous withdrawal of control rods, increasing cooling capacity, flooding of a void in or near the core, etc. In the KEWB reactor the control rods were withdrawn to yield reactivity input rates per second of 0.032, 0.063, 0.095, and 0.126% until a total of either 1.2 or 2.4% Δk had been added to the reactor. These ramps were initiated with the reactor operating at less than 1 mw, the core solution at 25°C, and at a pressure of 15.6 cm of Hg. The power pulses resulting from these ramp inputs equal those of the same minimum periods resulting from step inputs. The power passes through a maximum and a minimum, and then increases slightly until the ramp is terminated. The power then decays slowly, and any small amplitude oscillations, sometimes produced while reactivity is still being added, immediately dampen out. The power level at the cessation of the reactivity input was usually between 25 and 40 kw; when cooling water was circulated through the core, the power was 160 kw. The results of the ramp tests are shown in Fig. 7–26.

7–4.5 Discussion. The KEWB experiments conducted thus far permit the following conclusions to be drawn regarding the nuclear safety of this reactor design:

(1) Radiolytic gas production, an inherent feature of this reactor, is an effective and dominant shutdown mechanism.

(2) Relatively thin core vessels can readily withstand power excursions of 0.002 and even shorter periods when initial core pressure is less than atmospheric.

(3) No inherent instability, resulting in divergent power oscillations, occurs during or following ramp insertion of reactivity. Similar conditions are known to produce instability in some heterogeneous reactors. Maximum power in such excursions depend on the rate at which reactivity is added rather than on the total added. Final power depends on the total amount of reactivity added and the rate of heat removal from the core.

(4) When the core is initially at room temperature, energy produced from a step input of reactivity, resulting in a period of 0.002 sec, is only 4 mw-sec, which is insufficient to cause boiling of the core solution.

(5) There appears to be a delay in formation of radiolytic gas bubbles which effect reactor shutdown.

(6) Increasing the initial fuel solution temperature reduces the peak power attainable for a given reactivity input; increasing the initial reactor pressure increases the peak power.

7–5. SPECIAL REACTORS

Classification of reactors by specific function can be misleading. The reactor systems discussed here as "special reactors" can be used to a limited extent as research tools and as isotope producers. These systems, however, are characterized by relatively low power, emphasis on safety in

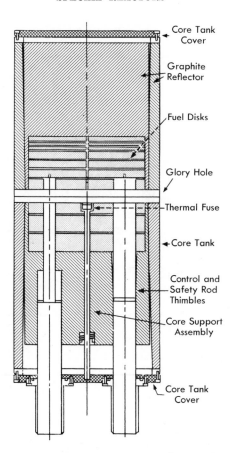

FIG. 7–27. Schematic of AGN-201 core and core tank. The core tank contains uranium-polyethylene core, safety fuse, and portions of the graphite reflector.

design, and simplicity coupled with low cost. Thus they are particularly suitable for university use in training programs.

A number of different reactor types are on the market as package units. Usually, the package includes the core, shielding, complete control and monitoring apparatus, and an operating console. Some training reactors now available are modifications of research reactors discussed elsewhere in this book. They will be mentioned only briefly. Two distinct reactor types have been developed and will be discussed more fully.

7–5.1 The solid homogeneous reactor. At least two different reactors in this category have been operated, the AGN-201 and TRIGA. The AGN-201 is described at length as representative of the type.

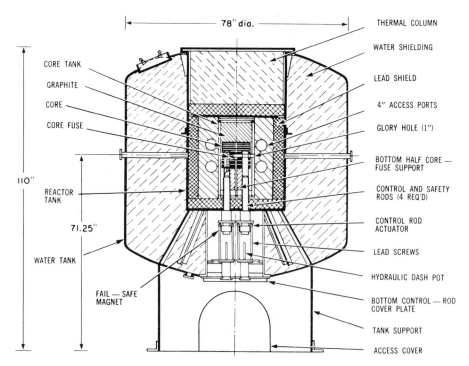

FIG. 7–28. Schematic of AGN-201, general view. This shows the location of reactor components. (Courtesy of *Nucleonics*.)

The AGN-201. The reactor core is made up of nine disks of UO_2-impregnated polyethylene, which serves as the moderator and fuel. The disks differ in thickness to allow for flexibility and control during assembly. The U^{235} enrichment is 20%; the operating fuel loading is 656 g of U^{235}. The assembled core is a cylinder 10 in. in diameter by $9\frac{1}{2}$ in. high (Fig. 7–27), surrounded by a graphite reflector 20 cm thick. A 10-cm thickness of lead outside the reflector is included for shielding. The core-reflector assembly is in an aluminum tank designed to contain any fission gases that might escape from the core, and is further contained in a steel tank 43.4 cm in radius. A steel tank $6\frac{1}{2}$ ft in diameter surrounds the other two tanks; the intervening space is filled with additional shielding of boric acid solution (Fig. 7–28). The region in the figure labeled "thermal column" is a removable tank that serves as a thermal column when filled with graphite, H_2O, or D_2O. In addition to the thermal column, there are four access ports and a central exposure facility.

Normal operating power for the AGN-201 is 0.1 watt, although it is possible to operate the reactor at 5 watts if additional shielding is provided. At the 0.1-watt power level, the maximum thermal-neutron flux is about

4.5×10^6 n/(cm^2)(sec). The flux in the thermal column is from 10^4 to 10^6 n/(cm^2)(sec), and the gamma intensity is about 40 r/hr. The reactor has about 0.2% excess reactivity and a prompt negative temperature coefficient of reactivity of about 3×10^{-4}% ($\Delta k_{\text{eff}}/k_{\text{eff}}$)/°C.

The reactor has two safety rods and two control rods containing U^{235}. Three of these rods are 1 in. in diameter and the fourth, the fine control rod, is half the diameter of the others. The coarse rods are worth about 1.3% in reactivity and the fine rod about 0.14%. A core fuse made of polystyrene containing 100 mg/cm^3 of U^{235} is designed to heat at a higher rate than the core and melt at about 100°C. This drops the lower half of the core-reflector assembly a few inches inside the core tank, making the assembly subcritical. The shielding provided is adequate to protect personnel in the event of a power excursion, and is more than adequate for normal operation. The control system uses two boron ion chambers and one BF$_3$ proportional counter to monitor power levels.

The TRIGA. This reactor core is made up of fuel elements consisting of an intimate mixture of 20% enriched uranium and zirconium hydride clad with aluminum. Approximately 70 such elements are submerged in a pool, with 16 ft of water over the core. The core is 35% water by volume. Temperature increases due to increase in heat generated in the fuel have an immediate (prompt) negative reactivity effect. This property is an inherent safety feature common to homogeneous reactors.

The Argonaut. The original Argonaut (Argonne's Nuclear Assembly for University Training) was designed and built at Argonne National Laboratory as a low-level supplementary reactor facility that would interest universities. Safety, flexibility, and low cost were primary considerations. Modified Argonaut-type reactors are available from several manufacturers.

The Argonaut* is a thermal heterogeneous reactor with an annular core region. The core-reflector assembly is of graphite, 5 ft by 5 ft by 4 ft high, containing an annular water tank 4 ft high, 3 ft OD, and 2 ft ID around a 2-ft cylinder of graphite serving as the internal reflector. The internal graphite is removable, and may be replaced by experiments if desired. The water annulus contains 12 clusters of 17 fuel plates, or a total of 204 fuel plates. Moderation is accomplished by graphite segments between the clusters and by water between fuel plates in each cluster. The graphite is waterproofed by spraying with aluminum. The fuel plates are $2\frac{27}{32}$ in. wide by 24 in. long by 0.096 in. thick, and are made of 40 w/o U$_3$O$_8$ dispersed in an aluminum matrix. The uranium is 20% enriched. Figure 7–29 shows a fuel-plate assembly.

Heat is removed by circulating water between the fuel plates, at about 6.5 gpm when the reactor is operating at maximum power. The cooling

---

* The term "Argonaut" will refer to the original version at ANL throughout this portion of the book.

FIG. 7-29. Argonaut fuel assembly. In operation, water between the plates and graphite between these assemblies provide moderation. (Courtesy of Argonne National Laboratory.)

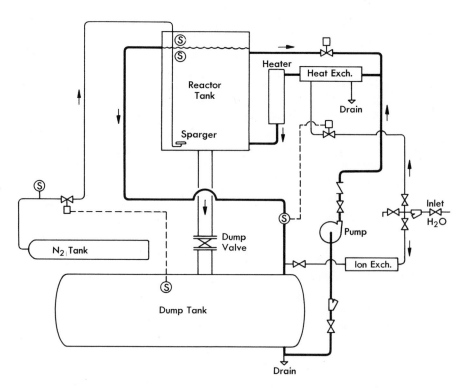

FIG. 7-30. Flow diagram of the Argonaut. The sparger is an auxiliary shutdown device whereby nitrogen can be bubbled into the core to reduce the moderator density.

system is composed of a stainless-steel centrifugal pump which delivers 20 gpm against a 14-ft head, a 34,000-Btu/hr stainless-steel single-pass shell-and-tube heat exchanger, a 3-kw heater for moderator temperature control, solenoid valves, strainers, check valves, piping, and a 275-gal dump and make-up water tank. Figure 7–30 is a flow diagram of the system.

The area directly above the graphite and core is shielded by a 5 ft square and 1-ft-high steel box filled with dense concrete. The shield has a removable plug over the central graphite region and a number of adjacent plugs for insertion of fuel assemblies.

A thermal column and 22 experimental ports are in the Argonaut. The maximum power level for short-time operation is 10 kw and the maximum thermal-neutron flux is 10^{11} n/(cm^2)(sec). The reactor has a negative temperature coefficient of about $1 \times 10^{-4}\%$ $(\Delta k_{eff}/k_{eff})/°C$.

The control elements are plates containing cadmium. Two separate emergency shutdown systems are provided. A line empties the core water into the dump tank and, simultaneously, a nitrogen system introduces bubbles into the core to reduce moderator density.

7–5.2 Other types of reactor. At least three other types of training reactors are on the market. These are similar in general design features to the pool, tank, and aqueous homogeneous reactors discussed in Chapters 3 and 5.

7–5.3 Subcritical assemblies for education and research. The subcritical assembly is a useful training tool. Universities are using a number of them. In general, these consist of a configuration of natural uranium fuel, a suitable moderator, and a neutron source. The assembly is designed so that it can operate only if a neutron source is present, and it is always at essentially zero power. Since no equipment is required for reactor control and little or no shielding is necessary, the subcritical assembly is both low in cost and versatile for training.

Two general types of subcritical assemblies are in use. One consists of natural uranium slugs with cladding arranged in a regular lattice array and immersed in water. This type is sometimes referred to as the "pickle barrel" reactor. The other type is graphite moderated, and is a small version of an X-10 reactor (see Chapter 6).

Experiments include those designed to familiarize students with basic detecting and measuring devices, investigation of the properties and behavior of particles and radiations, and experiments such as measurement of basic reactor parameters.

BIBLIOGRAPHY

Borax.

DIETRICH, J. R., *Experimental Investigation of the Self-Limitation of Power During Reactivity Transients in a Subcooled Water-Moderated Reactor*, USAEC Report AECD-3668, Argonne National Laboratory, 1954.

DIETRICH, J. R. Experimental Determinations of the Self-Regulation and Safety of Operating Water-Moderated Reactors, in *Proceedings of the International Conference on the Peaceful Uses of Atomic Energy*, Vol. 13. New York: United Nations, 1956. (P/481, p. 88)

DIETRICH, J. R., and D. C. LAYMAN, *Transient and Steady State Characteristics of a Boiling Reactor. The Borax Experiments, 1953*, USAEC Report AECD-3840, Argonne National Laboratory, February 1954.

ULRICH, A. J., *Results of Recent Analyses of Borax II Transient Experiments*, USAEC Report ANL-5532, Argonne National Laboratory, April 1956.

Spert.

FORBES, S. G. et al., *Instability in the Spert I Reactor, Preliminary Report*, USAEC Report IDO-16309, Phillips Petroleum Co., Oct. 10, 1956.

FORBES, S. G. et al., First Reports on Instability in Spert I, *Nucleonics* **15**(1), 41 (1957).

MONTGOMERY, C. R. et al., *Summary of the Spert I, II, and III Reactor Facilities*, USAEC Report IDO-16418, Phillips Petroleum Co., Nov. 1, 1957.

NYER, W. E. et al., "Experimental Investigations of Reactor Transients," IDO-16285, U. S. Atomic Energy Commission, Phillips Petroleum Co., Atomic Energy Division, 1956.

NYER, W. E. et al., Transient Experiments With the Spert I Reactor, *Nucleonics*, vol. 14, No. 6, p. 44, 1956.

SCHROEDER, F. et al., Experimental Study of Transient Behavior in a Sub-Cooled Water-Moderated Reactor, *Nuclear Science and Engineering*, vol. 2, No. 1, p. 96, The American Nuclear Society, Academic Press, New York, 1957.

WILSON, T. R., "The Spert II Reactor Facility Preliminary Design Report", IDO-16386, U. S. Atomic Energy Commission, Phillips Petroleum Company, Atomic Energy Division, 1957.

KEWB.

FLORA, J. W. et al., "Temperature Effect on the Reactivity of the California Research and Development Co. Water Boiler", USAEC Report LRL-148, Livermore Radiation Laboratory, June 1954.

HETRICH, D. L. et al., "Preliminary Results on the Kinetic Behavior of Water Boiler Reactors", NAA-SR-1896, U. S. Atomic Energy Commission, Atomics International, Canoga Park, California, 1957.

KASTEN, P. R., Reactor Dynamics of the Los Alamos Water Boiler, "Nuclear Engineering, Part I, Chem. Eng. Progr. Symposium Series", Vol. 50, 229 November 1954.

Kewb Staff, "Quarterly Progress Report—The Kewb Program", NAA-SR-1811, U. S. Atomic Energy Commission, Atomics International, Canoga Park, California, 1956.

PARE, V. K., "Experiments on the Kinetics of the HRE", U. S. Atomic Energy Commission, ORNL-2329, Oak Ridge National Laboratory, October 8, 1957.

REMLEY, M. E., "Experimental Studies on the Kinetic Behavior of Water Boiler Type Reactors", Second International Conference on the Peaceful Uses of Atomic Energy, U. S. Submission No. 756 (1958).

REMLEY, M. E. et al., "Program Review of the Water Boiler Reactor Kinetic Experiments", U. S. Atomic Energy Commission, NAA-SR-1525, Atomics International, North American Aviation, Inc., March 15, 1956.

REMLEY, M. E. et al., "The Kinetic Behavior of Water Boiler Type Reactors", NAA-SR-1618, U. S. Atomic Energy Commission, Atomics International, Canoga Park, California, 1956.

REMLEY, M. E. et al., "Program Review of the Water Boiler Reactor Kinetic Experiments", NAA-SR-1525, U. S. Atomic Energy Commission, Atomics International, Canoga Park, California, 1956.

WILSON, R. F., "Aqueous Homogeneous Type Reactors", Second International Conference on the Peaceful Uses of Atomic Energy, U. S. Submission No. 752 (1958).

AGN-201.

BIEHL, A. T. et al., Compact, Low-Cost Reactor Emphasizes Safety, *Nucleonics* **14**(9), 100 (1956).

Argonaut.

ARMSTRONG, R. H. et al., *Engineering, Construction, and Cost of the Argonaut Reactor,* USAEC Report ANL-5704, Argonne National Laboratory, March 1957.

ARMSTRONG, R. H. and C. N. KELLER, Argonaut-Argonne's Reactor for University Training, *Nucleonics* **15**(3), 62 (1957).

LENNOX, D. H., and B. I. SPINRAD, *A Generalized Reactor Facility for Nuclear Technology Training and Research, Interim Report on "Argonaut,"* USAEC Report ANL-5552, Argonne National Laboratory, March 1956.

CHAPTER 8

RESEARCH REACTOR SUPPORTING FACILITIES*

8–1. INTRODUCTION

The usefulness of nuclear energy as a tool for research depends not only on having the reactor experimental facilities to perform the desired type of irradiation, but also on having such supporting facilities as hot cells, radiochemistry and radioisotope laboratories, counting rooms, machine shops, instrument repair shops, and handling equipment necessary to obtain information regarding the effects of the irradiation. These facilities and their relationships with the reactor are of great importance in making the most effective use of a reactor installation.

Supporting facilities are dictated by the type of research planned for the reactor. For example, most irradiation experiments in biology and chemistry require the handling of materials of low specific activity; a laboratory similar to a conventional laboratory, but with provisions for some personnel shielding and radioactive storage, will usually suffice. On the other hand, experiments in metallurgy, such as studying the effects of radiation on reactor fuels and components, frequently involve such a high level of activity that the remote-handling facilities of a hot cell are required. Regardless of the type of research involved, counting rooms, instrument repair laboratories, and machine shops are required to maintain the proper operation of the reactor.

Here we shall not attempt to describe the detailed operation of the various supporting facilities, but rather shall point out the relationships between an operating research reactor and its hot cells, low-level radiation laboratories, and general laboratories. While some of the practices and equipment described may be considered standard, the use and location of these supporting facilities must be considered according to the needs of each installation.

8–2. HOT CELLS

A hot cell, or cave, is a closed, heavily shielded room within which operations can be performed remotely on highly radioactive materials. The facilities must afford protection from direct high-intensity radiation and also from minute quantities of airborne contamination. Special windows which absorb radiation but allow good visibility, remote manipulators,

---

* By D. H. Stall and A. M. Plummer.

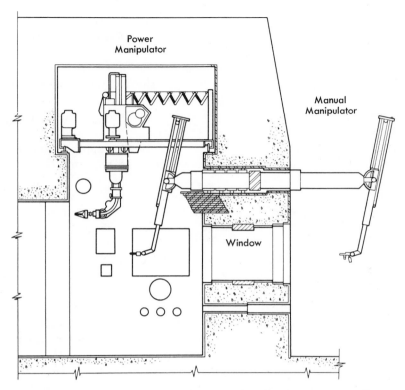

Fig. 8–1. Cross section of an MTR Hot Cell, showing power and manual manipulators for the remote handling of radioactive materials. (Courtesy of Phillips Petroleum Co.)

and automatic equipment are utilized (Fig. 8–1). The hot cell is usually located close to the reactor, so that irradiated objects may be transferred directly into the hot cell by special transfer mechanisms. Water-filled canals, underwater transfer ports, shielded pneumatic tubes, and heavy lead coffins are typical carriers used singly or in combination to facilitate safe transfer of radioactive objects from the reactor to the hot cell.

Hot cells are utilized for a wide variety of physical and chemical studies of radioactive materials from the reactor. For example, before a power reactor is built, it is necessary to determine the radiation stability of the materials to be used in its construction, including materials for fuel elements, moderator, coolant, reflector, control rods, insulation, and general structural and shielding materials. Samples are exposed to radiations in a research or test reactor, and must then be handled in a hot cell for post-irrradiation inspection to determine the changes, resulting from irradiation, in the properties of the material. Frequently this includes remotely measuring weight, density, dimensions, hardness, strength, and electrical and thermal resistivity of the specimens. Also, microstructure change and chemical composition may have to be determined remotely.

Studies of processing radioactive materials are also carried out, including (1) reprocessing nuclear fuels to recover the fissionable materials free from fission products and cladding materials, (2) processing radioactive wastes from fuel reprocessing to a form more suitable for safe disposal or utilization by industry as a source of radiation, (3) processing radio-isotopes into suitable physical or chemical forms for applications in tracer methodology, radiography, radioactive gages, and radiation chemistry or biology.

Radiation levels that the various existing hot cells can contain vary from 100 curies of gamma radiation with an average energy of 1 Mev, to over 1 million curies of the same energy. The design of a hot cell depends largely on the radiation level available at that research reactor and the research purposes for which the reactor was designed.

The hot cells themselves may be small specialized units designed for one repetitive process. When this is the case, the associated equipment is also highly specialized and usually automatic in operation. Large multipurpose cells, allowing greater flexibility, contain standard equipment. For example, if enough highly specific or repetitive evaluation work is expected, a specialized cell may be warranted, but if the nature of the work is unknown or if it is varied, a large (8 by 20 ft) multipurpose cell may be preferred. It should be pointed out that small (8 by 6 ft) single-purpose cells make for better scheduling.

In some nuclear research centers the hot cell is a separate facility requiring its own shielding. However, some hot laboratories are part of the reactor facility, and shielding in these systems may be a continuation of the reactor shielding. The radioactive material may be moved in a pneumatic device, a water-filled canal, a cask on wheels, or a cask moved on a fork truck or overhead rail system.

An example of the separated type of hot-cell facility is shown in Fig. 8–2. The laboratory contains two large cells and the associated auxiliary equipment. The walls of the cells are of high-density (ferrophosphorus) concrete to provide radiation shielding. Inside, the cells are 18 ft long, 8 ft wide, and 12 ft high. One cell has shielding 3 ft thick, sufficient to permit safe handling of about 10 million curies of a radioactive material emitting gamma rays of 1 Mev energy. The second cell, with shielding walls 2 ft thick, will accommodate about 10,000 curies of gamma radiation. Cell doors are solid steel slabs, each weighing about 20 tons and operating hydraulically. Each cell has three viewing windows of high-density glass.

Manipulations in the cells are conducted with a variety of remote-handling equipment. Preparing a chemical solution or positioning a

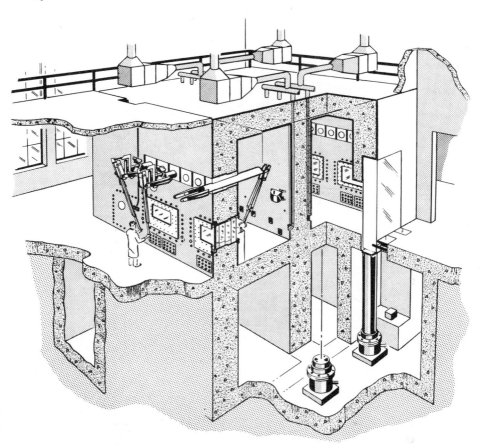

Fig. 8–2. Cutaway view of a hot cell which is separate from the reactor facility. The subterranean cells are used for storage, or to accommodate high experiments.

metallographic specimen is accomplished with master slave manipulators similar to those shown in Fig. 8–3. Individual pieces of equipment, such as standard machine tools and instruments, are modified for remote operations by mechanical or electrical connections through shielded holes in the walls of the cells. In this particular laboratory, one end of the cell, for the lower radiation level, has a remotely operated metallograph and hardness tester permanently installed. Equipment in the cell for high radiation level is portable, mounted on wheels or wheeled tables for maximum motility and flexibility. This equipment includes a milling machine, a tensile tester, an abrasive cutoff wheel, a vacuum dilatometer, a mounting press and polishing equipment for metallography, a gas-sampling system, analytical balances, and special micrometers. The subterranean

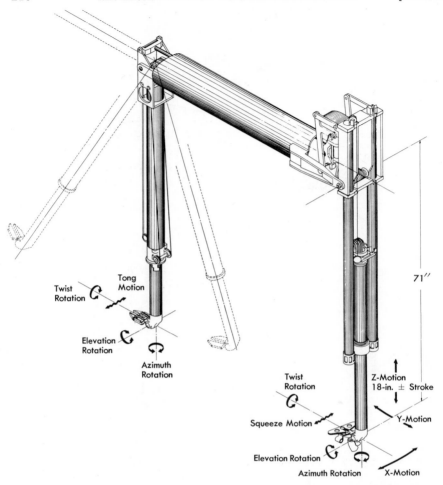

Fig. 8–3. The Argonne National Laboratory Master Slave Manipulator trans-lates the motions of operators' hands into similar motions for the tongs located in the hot cell. These manipulators penetrate the cell wall above the operators' heads. (Courtesy of Argonne National Laboratory.)

cells, a unique feature of the laboratory, are useful for the storage of radio-active material and for handling radioactive solutions.   (See Fig. 8–2.) Small access holes are provided in the floors of the main cells, in addition to the large access ports from the operating area.

Other facilities associated with the hot cells include a decontamination room for cleaning equipment, an underground dry-storage area for solid radioactive materials, a water tank 14 ft deep for transfer and storage of radioactive materials, a photographic laboratory, locker rooms, general laboratory space, machine shop, and offices (Fig. 8–4).

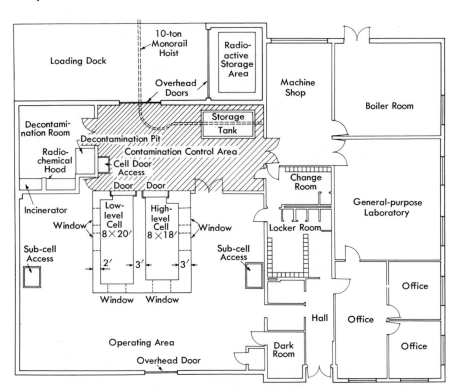

FIG. 8–4. Floor plan of the Battelle Hot Cell Facility showing the location of the cells and associated facilities.

An example of an "attached" facility is the combination research reactor and hot-cell facility at the Naval Research Laboratory in Washington, D. C. An extension of the reactor shielding wall provides the shielding for the hot-cell laboratory. Materials made radioactive in the research reactor may be shifted directly into the hot-cell area through any of three underwater transfer chambers or ports. The cell has three special windows for direct viewing operations in the hot cell. Each 3-ft-thick window is a metal tank having two sides of plate glass 1-in. thick. The volume is filled with a saturated solution of zinc bromide, a dense liquid with good optical properties, and an excellent shield against gamma radiation. A master slave manipulator (similar to those shown in Fig. 8–5) is positioned at each window and, in addition, a heavy-duty electrically powered manipulator can be operated remotely to reach any part of the cell.

The three-cell hot laboratory shown in Fig. 8–6 is an example of a special purpose laboratory. These cells are designed primarily for the preparation, examination, and photographing of highly radioactive metallo-

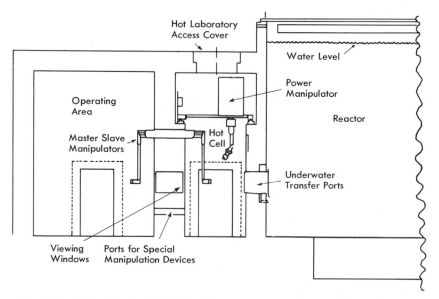

FIG. 8–5. Materials irradiated in the reactor can be transferred to the hot cell through the underwater ports. They can be operated on in the cell with manipulators, and eventually transferred out of the cell through a lead door.

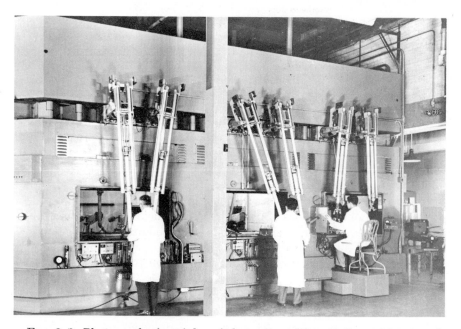

FIG. 8–6. Photograph of a triple-unit hot cell used in metallographic research at Argonne National Laboratory. Each unit has a zinc bromide window, 58 in. by 30 in. (Courtesy of Argonne National Laboratory.)

graphic specimens. Each cell is 7 ft by 6 ft by $12\frac{1}{2}$ ft high. The outer walls are of high-density concrete 2 ft thick, while the roof of the cave is a steel pan filled with magnetite. The windows are filled with a zinc bromide solution, and are several inches thicker than the concrete walls, to provide a comparable amount of shielding.

Access to each cell is provided at the rear directly opposite the window. The shielding doors (steel shells filled with magnetite) can be moved horizontally on an overhead I-beam. Each cell is equipped with a pair of mechanical master-slave manipulators. The partition between the cells is made up of three vertical sections (8 in. thick) of laminated steel. The lower section extends from the floor to a height of 4 ft and is fixed in position. The middle section, about 3 ft high, can be moved out through the back of the cave. The upper section can be raised into the roof shielding. Consequently, two pairs of manipulators can assist each other when the upper partitions are removed; equipment can be transferred from one cell to the other without opening the doors.

8–3. RADIOISOTOPE LABORATORIES

The diverse applications of a research reactor require that the associated facilities be designed for maximum versatility. An indispensable adjunct to a research reactor is the radioisotope laboratory for experiments not feasible in standard laboratories because of the slight radioactivity associated with the materials, which is not high enough, however, to require expensive hot-cell laboratories. Numerous service functions associated with the operation of a reactor, such as foil counting, are also performed in these facilities.

8–3.1 Typical facility. A radioisotope laboratory for a research reactor resembles a general chemistry laboratory (Fig. 8–7). The distinguishing features result from the need for carefully handling the radioactive materials and maintaining working areas and equipment as free from contamination as possible. In addition, limits on the allowable radiation background from stored materials and detailed procedures to be used in the experimental work within the laboratory must be determined. Operating procedures determine the usefulness and versatility of the laboratory to a greater extent than does the specialized equipment and facilities. Personnel working in a radioisotope laboratory must be trained to constantly evaluate possible hazards and to observe regulations closely.

A radioisotope laboratory has more of its working area hooded or vented than does a general laboratory, since there is a possibility of releasing radioactive material to the laboratory atmosphere. Standard chemical hoods or ventilating structures can be used. These include fume and vacuum-frame hoods for experiments with moderately hazardous solutions

Fig. 8–7. View of a radioisotope laboratory, showing hoods for handling radioactive materials. (Courtesy of Pennsylvania State University.)

and solids, and gloved dry boxes for extremely hazardous materials and for those which tend to powder or volatilize (Figs. 8–8 and 8–9). Shallow pans on the floor of the hoods prevent distribution of spilled material, and the inside surfaces of the hoods are protectively coated to enable better contamination control. Service controls are usually outside the hood to prevent their contamination. Rubber gloves are worn at all times when radioactive materials are handled, and some temporary form of plastic or lead shielding is used as protection from external radiation. Rudimentary remote control by laboratory tongs and "over the shield" pipettors is sufficient for millicurie amounts of energetic gamma emitters. More elaborate remote operations and shielding are required for multimillicurie (over 50 millicuries) amounts of gamma emitters. Air-flow rate into the hoods should be at least 100 ft/min (at the hood face), and the air should be exhausted through a high-efficiency filter. "Absolute" filters are not required unless multimillicurie amounts of very hazardous materials are handled in a form that can powder or volatilize.

FIG. 8–8. View of a radioisotope laboratory showing (from left to right): an experiment in an open hood, an experiment in a hood using lead bricks as a shield, and an experiment in a dry box. (Courtesy of the University of Michigan.)

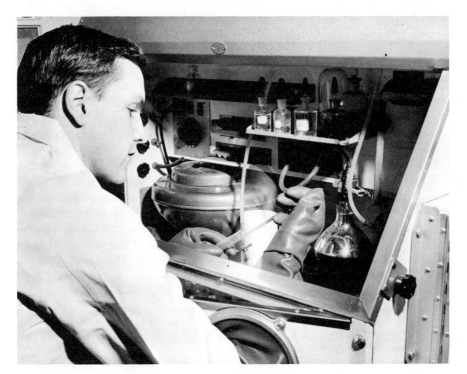

FIG. 8–9. An experiment being carried on in a dry box. (Courtesy of the University of Michigan.)

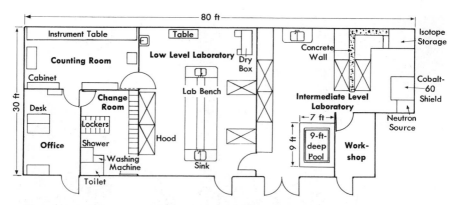

FIG. 8–10. Floor plan of the Battelle Radioisotope Laboratory, showing the relationship of the various facilities.

Radiation monitors to detect surface contamination by weak beta or alpha emitters should be available to all laboratory workers. High-level monitors or survey meters which range from 0.1 to as high as 10,000 mr/hr should be provided.

Proper physical facilities (Fig. 8–10) and properly trained personnel safely permit a variety of research with radioisotopes.

A counting room should be equipped with instruments for quantitative assay of alpha, beta, and gamma radiation. Other laboratories associated with the reactor may share this room. Protective clothing must be worn by all persons entering the laboratory and, consequently, a change room is required. Safety glasses and face masks should also be furnished to laboratory personnel.

8–3.2 Uses of a radioisotope laboratory. *High-level counting room.* Metal foils and wires of materials such as cobalt, when used for neutron-flux determination at high reactor powers, become sufficiently radioactive to require some subdivision or dilution prior to radioassay. The possibility of contaminating the working area in these operations necessitates the use of a controlled area such as a radioisotope laboratory. The postirradiation experiments with gamma dosimeters that have been exposed to mixed neutron and gamma-ray fields frequently require similar controlled areas.

A room for measuring high levels of radiation can use:

(1) A well-type sodium iodide thallium-activated scintillation crystal for measuring gamma rays.

(2) End-window Geiger-Mueller tubes for measuring beta particles.

(3) Geiger-Mueller tubes for measuring beta particles and gamma rays in solutions.

(4) Two gas-flow proportional counters for measuring alpha particles and low-energy beta particles.

(5) A recording gamma-ray scintillation spectrometer to identify radioisotopes.

Coolant analysis. In operating a research reactor, the integrity of the fuel and the coolant system are checked at regular intervals. This is easily accomplished by radiochemical analysis of the coolant to detect fission products released by a fuel element failure, corrosion products from the structural materials, or impurities such as sodium, calcium, etc., from leaks in the secondary coolant system. The analyses are simple but require an area with a low background for good results.

Activation analysis. Some materials become radioactive in a reactor flux and the subsequent decay is easily detected and recognized (see Chapter 10). With proper equipment, the extremely minute quantities of an impurity can be measured. Frequently, chemical separation after irradiation is required before this activation-analysis technique can be used. A radioisotope laboratory with its highly versatile facilities can be used to separate and measure the constituent of interest. Activation analysis is used in many scientific fields; samples can be metallic, ceramic, or even plant or animal tissues.

Postirradiation measurements. In studies of radiation effects, the induced activity of some materials is low enough that instead of the hot cells the radioisotope laboratory can be used. To minimize the possibility of contamination, these operations should be carried out in a controlled area where there is shielding and rudimentary remote control equipment. Hoods can be converted into "junior hot cells" for handling up to 5 curies of 1-Mev gamma-ray equivalent by temporary lead brick shielding, small lead-glass windows, and special long-handled tongs. Irradiation capsules and some experiments can be disassembled in these facilities; density, electrical conductivity, and other items can be measured.

Waste disposal. Disposal of radioactive waste is a problem with almost every reactor experiment. In most cases it is desirable to convert liquid wastes to solids by evaporation or by absorption in plaster or some other material. This requires chemical operations in a controlled area. Solid waste is either buried on site or packaged for shipment to disposal companies.

8–3.3 Activity levels. Approximate amounts of radioactivity which can be handled in a radioisotope laboratory are:

(1) Curie amounts of a pure alpha emitter can be handled in a gloved box, provided there is absolute filtration of the exhaust air.

(2) Curie quantities of a pure beta emitter can be handled with plastic shielding either in standard hoods with efficient filters or in gloved boxes.

(3) Fifty microcuries or so of a gamma emitter with energies over 0.2 Mev require lead or iron shielding; simple, remote-handling techniques are required if the quantity exceeds 1 millicurie, while up to 1 curie may be handled behind 2 in. of lead for limited periods of exposure.

8–4. GENERAL LABORATORIES AND EQUIPMENT

Certain general laboratories and equipment are necessary to each research reactor regardless of the size of the research program. These include a low-level counting room, an instrument repair laboratory, a photographic laboratory, and a machine shop. The minimum equipment for a counting room is that necessary to measure neutron flux in the reactor core (essential for fuel burnup determination and, in some cases, for power calibration) and in the experimental facilities. Equipment should include detectors for both beta and gamma rays, with at least one of these calibrated for absolute counting.

Thin-walled, end-window Geiger-Mueller tubes are adequate for most general purpose beta-ray counting. However, the corrections which must be applied to the observed count rates due to dead time of the counter and to scattering and absorption of the beta rays in the window make G-M tubes undesirable for absolute counting. The thin-window or open-window flow counter is a more reliable instrument for absolute beta counting, but even here corrections sometimes become troublesome.

A scintillation detector is the minimum equipment for gamma-ray counting. A thallium-activated sodium iodide crystal is the most widely used and is available in a variety of sizes. This detector is extremely handy for counting the cobalt and gold foils used for thermal-neutron flux measurements. Calibrated standard foils of these materials make absolute counting simple and convenient. Calibration for other foils commonly used in measuring reactor flux can also be made, either directly from a calibrated foil of the same material or by calibrating several sources of different energies from which the counting efficiency for a gamma ray of a particular energy can be determined. The latter method is especially convenient in the case of materials for which standard foils are not available because of their short half-lives.

Amplifiers, scalers, and power supplies are among the necessary minimum requirements for counting equipment. Many fine instruments are on the market, and there is no need here to recommend specifically. However, it is important to choose these instruments with the future expansion of the counting facilities in mind. With proper planning, and for only slightly higher initial cost, instruments purchased can be the basis for more elaborate counting systems.

Extension of the basic counting system beyond the minimum requirements is dictated to a large extent by requirements of the experimental programs using the reactor. However, for work with the reactor itself, this extension will probably include such additions to the gamma-counting system as a pulse-height analyzer and, for heterogeneous reactors (particularly of the pool and tank types), an automatic counting system for obtaining plots of neutron flux in the core region.

The single-channel pulse-height analyzer used in conjunction with a gamma scintillation detector should fulfill most needs of the reactor. It is a valuable tool in any counting room and, unless other experimental needs justify the expense of a multichannel analyzer, the single channel will serve as well, although perhaps not always as conveniently, as its many-channeled relative.

Multichannel analyzers are essential for many types of experimental work. For example, they are useful in isotope identification (particularly for nuclides of short half-life) and in measurements of reactor gamma-ray spectra using multiple-crystal Compton, coincidence, and pair-production detectors.

Automatic counting equipment becomes a necessity when many specimens are to be counted. In a reactor installation this equipment is required to count smears to determine the extent of contamination on floors, table tops, and equipment in the reactor building, and for detailed flux mapping in the core and experimental facilities. Manual counting is both tedious and time-consuming, and an automatic sample changer can usually pay for itself in a medium-sized reactor facility. Automatic systems which change samples and count and record data can be purchased, and if necessary, systems can be constructed for special applications. Detailed flux maps of the core region can be made by irradiating many wires extending the full length of the core. The wires are then cut into ten short pieces (approximately 1 in.) and counted. In most reactors, a hundred or more such pieces have to be counted, and an automatic system is a necessity. For the Materials Testing Reactor, the irradiated wires are drawn past a counter at a constant rate and the count rate is recorded as a function of position, giving at the same time the quantitative data desired and an actual plot of the flux distribution through the fuel subassemblies.

An easily constructed apparatus for automatic counting is shown in Fig. 8–11. Two channels with circuits containing either photomultiplier or Geiger tubes automatically print the data shown on the scaler, at the end of the period. The third channel operates circuits at the end of preset counts in the two measuring channels, and is used for sequencing the other two channels. The sampler changer moves the foils from the storage hopper to the first counter. The foil is counted and moved under a second

FIG. 8–11. A simple automatic counting device is shown here. The activated foils or pieces of wire are loaded into the plastic storage container at the left. Automatically the samples move to the first counter, and then to the second counter and then to a second storage container.

counter, where it is counted again and then moved to a second storage hopper, all automatically.

The counting room must be located so that radiation background levels from the reactor and other sources in the vicinity are kept at a minimum, but at the same time must not be so isolated that it is inconvenient. Such considerations are particularly important in the case of counting rooms for study of transuranium elements, where the yields of the nuclides of interest may be quite low and the background radiation may be relatively high. If, in addition to low yields, short half-lives are involved, special shielding of the counting room to attain low background may be necessary because the counting room is so close to the reactor.

A well organized and equipped instrument repair laboratory is a necessity. In addition to counting-room equipment, which must be kept in good repair if reliable data are to be obtained, the reactor and experimental control instrumentation must be properly calibrated and in good working order for safe operation. The equipment and procedures necessary to maintain this high degree of reliability do not vary greatly from those of any instrument laboratory. A pulse generator and fast oscilloscope for work with pulse circuits are, in general, the only equipment needed in addition to that ordinarily found in a general instrument laboratory.

A machine shop in a reactor installation is almost a necessity; size ranges from a small shop containing only a bench lathe and a drill press for light work to complete machine shops. Quick repair jobs can often reduce reactor downtime. The operation of research reactors is relatively recent, and very few, if any, installations are free from the annoying effects of equipment failures. Apparatus requirements are quite often unique, and oftentimes can be more conveniently fabricated in facilities close to the job.

In addition to machine tools, the machine shop should also have welding equipment. The widespread use of aluminum as a lightweight material for handling tools and reactor fixtures suggests that equipment for welding this material be included with the conventional gas and arc welders.

Darkroom facilities are included at most reactor installations, although they are seldom extensively needed. One use that should be considered, however, is that of working with neutron-sensitive emulsions for certain experimental work and in checking neutron shielding by photographic techniques.

CHAPTER 9

SAFETY CONSIDERATIONS*

Most reactors produce and accumulate large amounts of radioactive isotopes in the fuel material. In adverse circumstances a reactor may suddenly release amounts of energy which can result in large-scale dispersal of these radioactive materials to the environment, to create an extremely hazardous situation [1]. The probability of such an accident can be made very slight by (1) introducing safety features in the design of the reactor and its control system, and (2) organizing the operation with rigorous safety precautions. The consequences of a release of radioactive material should an accident occur can be minimized by proper location of the reactor and design of its building.

9–1. Physics Aspects of Reactor Safety

Inherent safety can be designed into a reactor because of the physical tie-in between reactor reactivity and period. As mentioned previously, if the reactivity is positive, reactor power increases; if negative, the power decreases; if zero, the power remains constant. The reactor period determines the rate of change of the reactor power, since a stable period is defined as the time required for the reactor power to increase or decrease by a factor of e† (= 2.718). The sign associated with the reactivity indicates whether the power is increasing or decreasing. In every reactor certain inherent reactivity effects occur because of variations in temperature which cause changes in material density, neutron energy, and core size. In a properly designed reactor, these effects are stabilizing factors in any power surge. On the other hand, in an improperly designed reactor, these reactivity effects may lead to instabilities and magnify the seriousness of an accidental power surge.

9–1.1 Reactivity and reactor period. The physical properties of primary importance in the safety of a reactor are the reactivity effects associated with possible changes in the reactor system. The reason for this, perhaps obvious by now, is that the kinetics of a nuclear reactor are governed by the reactivity of the system. If reactivity is positive, the flux level will

---

* By R. F. Redmond, J. N. Anno, Jr., and J. W. Chastain, Jr.

† The base of the Naperian system of logarithms.

increase exponentially with time, and the more positive the reactivity the more rapid the flux increase. Clearly, to avoid rapid flux increases (short reactor periods) the reactivity must be limited to small positive values. Figure 9–1 illustrates the relationship between period and reactivity for reactors having different neutron lifetimes or generation times. The neutron lifetime or generation time in a reactor refers to the average time between successive generations of prompt fission neutrons (those not "delayed"). Prompt-neutron lifetimes range from microseconds to milliseconds, depending on the moderating material used in the reactor, as shown in Table 9–1.

Several features of the curves in Fig. 9–1 illustrate some important facts. First, it will be noted that the period is virtually independent of neutron lifetime for reactivity values less than about 0.007 ($\Delta k_{\text{eff}}/k_{\text{eff}}$). Second, for reactivity values greater than 0.007 ($\Delta k_{\text{eff}}/k_{\text{eff}}$) the period changes rapidly with reactivity at first and becomes strongly dependent upon the neutron lifetime. This behavior is due to the presence of a small fraction of the fission neutrons, termed "delayed" neutrons. The delayed

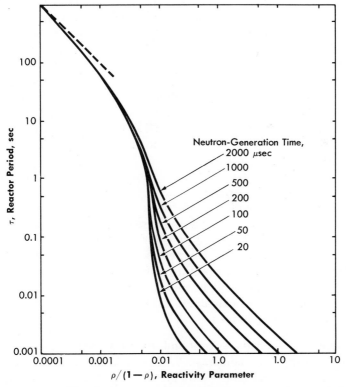

FIG. 9–1. Effect of neutron-generation time on reactor period.

TABLE 9–1

NEUTRON LIFETIMES FOR VARIOUS RESEARCH REACTOR TYPES

Reactor	Type	Neutron lifetime, sec
Bulk Shielding Reactor (Oak Ridge)	Light-water moderated pool	6.8×10^{-5}
Raleigh Reactor II	Homogeneous	1.4×10^{-4}
X-10 (Oak Ridge)	Graphite	1.5×10^{-3}
CP-5 (Argonne)	Heavy-water moderated tank	1.5×10^{-3}

neutrons, unlike the other fission neutrons, which are emitted virtually instantaneously during fission, are emitted after the fission event. Experiments indicate that the total fraction of fission neutrons which are delayed is about 0.0026 for U^{233}, 0.0064 for U^{235}, and 0.0021 for Pu^{239}. The delayed neutrons have half-lives ranging from about 0.2 to 5.6 sec. Even though only a small fraction of the fission neutrons are delayed neutrons, these have an important effect upon the reactor kinetics so long as they are required for criticality. In fact, for small reactivities in thermal reactors, the reactor behavior depends entirely upon the delayed neutrons. However, when the reactivity of a U^{235}-fueled reactor exceeds 0.007 ($\Delta k_{\text{eff}}/k_{\text{eff}}$), the reactor is critical without the delayed neutrons, a condition termed "prompt critical." Hence, as the reactivity exceeds the prompt-critical value, the kinetics will be governed more and more by the prompt neutrons and the reactor period will become much shorter. These features are evident in Fig. 9–1.

As an example of the effect of delayed neutrons, consider a large reactor with a prompt-neutron generation time of 10^{-3} sec. If the delayed neutrons are taken into account, the effective delay time between generations is 10^{-1} sec, and the period resulting from a reactivity increase is lengthened by about the same ratio. As seen in Table 9–1, the heavy-water and the graphite moderated reactors are characterized by a relatively long prompt-neutron lifetime and in this respect are safer than other reactor types.

From a safety standpoint, it is quite important to keep the reactivity well below the prompt critical value. Many safety features and practices are based upon this requirement.

9–1.2 Inherent reactivity effects and stability. When the power level of a reactor changes, the temperatures of the core components also change and this tends to affect the reactivity. Obviously, if a power-level increase causes an increase in reactivity, the system will be unstable in operation. In designing a research reactor, every effort is made to ensure that a power increase causes a decrease in reactivity. This reduces the power transient, and gives a stable system.

The inherent reactivity effects associated with a power-level change are direct consequences of the induced temperature change. In all reactor types temperature changes are reflected by changes of the nuclear parameters, such as effective thermal absorption and scattering cross sections, and of the density of the various core materials. In the liquid-moderated reactors, extreme temperature increases can cause the moderator to boil. The resulting void formation has a significant effect upon core reactivity.

Some temperature-induced reactivity changes may be positive and others negative, but for a stable reactor system it is generally only necessary that the sum of these effects be negative. From a safety standpoint, only the reactivity effects due to temperature changes which respond quickly to a power change are of concern. The magnitudes of the various reactivity effects are given by a coefficient of reactivity. Generally, temperature effects (other than void formation) are expressed quantitatively by a "temperature coefficient of reactivity" for a particular reactor. These effects are usually lumped together in a gross temperature coefficient defined by $\partial\rho/\partial T$, where ρ is the reactivity and T is the temperature. Temperature effects producing boiling are expressed by a void coefficient of reactivity, $\partial\rho/\partial V$, where V is the equivalent volume of voids introduced into the system.

Defined in the above manner, the temperature coefficient of reactivity, $\partial\rho/\partial T$, reflects both changes in the nuclear parameters and density of the core materials. Changes in the nuclear parameters of the core are brought about primarily through changes in the effective cross sections of the materials. The absorption cross sections of the fuel and other core materials vary approximately as $1/v$ (where v is the neutron velocity) in the thermal-neutron energy region. Since the average velocity of a thermal neutron is proportional to the square root of the absolute temperature T of the medium in which the neutron is in thermal equilibrium, the absorption cross section will vary as $1/T^{1/2}$.

Since a temperature variation affects the density of the core materials, causing a change in the number of nuclei per unit volume, both the macroscopic cross sections and the neutron leakage vary. Consequently, an increase in power reduces the macroscopic cross section of the fuel because of the density decrease and also because of the reduction in the cross section per atom at the higher neutron temperature. The neutron leakage is increased because of the decreased density. Both of these effects are usually negative. However, if the core volume is increased and the density held constant, the greater size tends to reduce neutron leakage for purely geometric reasons. Also, the temperature increase causes a smaller number of neutrons to be lost in the parasitic absorptions in other core materials. These effects are positive. If the reactor is cooled by a fluid which has a larger absorption cross section than the moderator, its expansion or expulsion from the core contributes an additional positive reactivity effect. This condition is present in a water-cooled graphite-moderated reactor.

For an air-cooled graphite-moderated reactor, the inherent safety is based on (1) changes in effective thermal microscopic cross sections, (2) changes in density which affect leakage and macroscopic cross sections, and (3) variations in core size. Pool and tank reactors have the same safety features but the changes in the density of the moderator are somewhat larger. Solution reactors have still larger temperature coefficients, since fuel is expelled from the core with the moderator.

Typical values of temperature coefficients for over-all temperature changes in the core are shown in Table 9–2.

In liquid-moderated reactors the production of voids by boiling affects the core reactivity by removing the moderator material. This increases leakage, a negative effect, and decreases absorption, a positive effect. In a properly designed system, the sum of these two effects results in a negative reactivity effect, and hence serves as a shutdown mechanism in case of a rapid power increase. However, if the reactor is overmoderated, then removal of a small fraction of the moderator can leave the reactor in a

TABLE 9–2

TEMPERATURE COEFFICIENTS OF REACTIVITY
FOR RESEARCH REACTORS

Reactor	Reactivity, $\%\ \dfrac{\Delta k_{eff}}{k_{eff}}$ per °C
Armour	−0.030
Battelle Research Reactor	+0.0034 (15°C)*
	−0.0027 (38°C)
Bulk Shielding Reactor	−0.006 (26°C)
	−0.010 (55°C)
Ford Nuclear Reactor	−0.00768 (21°C)
	−0.0099 (32°C)
	−0.0125 (43°C)
Materials Testing Reactor	−0.015 (20°C)

* Positive temperature coefficients have been observed below room temperature at both the Battelle Research Reactor and the Pennsylvania State Reactor.

TABLE 9–3

TYPICAL VOID COEFFICIENTS OF REACTIVITY FOR
RESEARCH REACTORS

Reactor	Location	Reactivity, $\% \dfrac{\Delta k_{\text{eff}}}{k_{\text{eff}}}$ per cm^3 of void
Ford Nuclear Reactor	Edge of core	−0.00041
	Center of core	−0.00106
Battelle Research Reactor	Average in core	−0.00017
Spert I	Average in core	−0.00035

supercritical condition. Under these conditions, the removal of the moderator serves only to remove extraneous neutron-absorbing material from the core. Clearly, from a safety standpoint, it would be hazardous to have a positive reactivity effect associated with boiling, since this will tend to continually shorten the reactor period. Table 9–3 shows some representative void coefficients.

The effect of overmoderation can be demonstrated by referring to Fig. 9–2, which shows the critical mass of a fixed-fuel light-water moderated reactor of constant volume as a function of the hydrogen-to-ura-

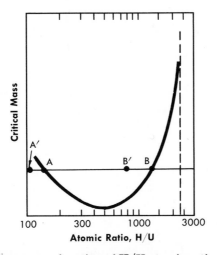

FIG. 9–2. Critical mass as a function of H/U atomic ratio. A reactor designed to operate at point B is overmoderated and the reactivity will increase with an increase in temperature (decrease in water density will decrease the ratio H/U). A reactor operating at point A is undermoderated.

nium atomic ratio. As the temperature increases in the reactor with design conditions represented by B, water is pushed from the core and the hydrogen-to-uranium ratio decreases toward B', since the uranium mass in the core remains constant. The mass of uranium is greater than the required critical mass at B' and the reactor is supercritical. Now consider the reactor at point A. A temperature increase causes a decrease in the hydrogen-to-uranium ratio, which causes the reactor conditions to move toward A'. Since the mass in the reactor is less than the required critical mass, the reactor is subcritical and the reactivity is negative. The Battelle Research Reactor and the Pennsylvania State Reactor have only 10 plates per element and, with their low metal-to-water ratio (approximately 0.4) operate close to the minimum on the curve. In this condition either a negative or a positive temperature coefficient can be measured, depending on the moderator temperature. The MTR has 18 plates in a fuel element and, because of the higher hydrogen-to-uranium ratio (approximately 0.7) the reactor operates closer to point A.

9–2. Built-In Safety Features

Many features can be incorporated into a reactor system to minimize the probability of an accident or, in the event of an accident, to lessen the hazard. In some cases, there are choices of protective measures. For example, the public may be protected against release of airborne radioactivity by an "exclusion area" if sufficient land is available, or by a gastight building or air-processing system for the building if land is not available.

9–2.1 Exclusion area. Enough land around the reactor, under the reactor owner's control, to which access can be restricted offers one means of protecting the public from airborne radioactivity that might follow an accident. The concentration of airborne radioactivity decreases by diffusion with distance from the point at which the material is released. Turbulent weather further diffuses airborne radioactive material and, in addition, radioactivity decays with distance from the source as the material is carried downwind. The actual fraction of the initial release which reaches a given location in the area surrounding the reactor is difficult to calculate. It depends on many factors, such as weather conditions (e.g., wind velocity, inversions), source size, height of source, and amount of fallout along the path of the airborne activity [2,3].

The radius of the exclusion area required for a given reactor is difficult to determine exactly, since it depends on the topography, meteorology, and geology of the site. In addition, the population density and character of land utilization of adjacent areas must be considered. In the case of the

Battelle Research Reactor (a 1000-kw pool reactor), the minimum distance to the exclusion fence is 1250 ft, and in most directions it is considerably more. The nearest dwelling is about 3000 ft from the reactor.

The size of the exclusion area required also depends on the operating power level of the reactor, since the amount of radioactive material in the reactor depends on how much its fuel elements have been used. Additional radioactive material may be formed in the excursion causing the accident, but for the higher-power research reactors the predominant contribution to the activity is due to long-time power operation. To a certain extent, therefore, the exclusion area is influenced by the reactor type.

9–2.2 Gastight building. If a reactor must be located in or near densely populated area, a gastight building or reactor room is often employed as a safety feature. This gastight construction will contain airborne radioactivity until it can be released under control in quantities considered harmless. However, completely gastight enclosures are almost impossible to construct; the term "gastight" generally is applied to structures which leak slowly, usually much less than 5% in 24 hr at a pressure of 0.5 psia. The airborne activity generally consists of a composite of gaseous and particulate matter.

An example of a relatively gastight building is that of the Ford Reactor at University of Michigan, Ann Arbor, Michigan. This is a windowless four-story structure, with 12-in.-thick reinforced concrete walls that are structurally integral with the footings and foundation mats. Doors are fitted with special gaskets and clamping devices. Solenoid-operated dampers in the intake and exhaust ducts of the ventilating system prevent leakage of air when closed. Electrical and pipe conduits and plumbing traps are gastight to a pressure differential of at least 2 in. of water. The building was leak-tested at both positive and negative pressures with respect to the atmosphere. Diffusion tests made by releasing tracer gas in the building showed that for most weather conditions the leakage would amount to less than 10% in 24 hr [4]. The pressure resulting from even a serious accident is rather small in a building of this size, and consequently the diffusion test gives adequate information on leakage.

The Armour Research Reactor, on the campus of the Illinois Institute of Technology, Chicago, Illinois, has two gasket seals on the doors at the entrance to the reactor room. In addition, air from the reactor room is exhausted to a tank, where it can be held for partial decay before release from the building. The leakage rate from this room is about 1% per 24 hr.

The MIT Reactor building leaks less than 1% in 24 hr, with 1 lb difference in pressure between the building and the outside atmosphere.

The Naval Research Reactor building, Washington, D. C., has an estimated leakage rate of 5% or less in a 24-hr period. All exterior walls of the reactor building are sealed with a layer of aluminum foil under the plaster. The exterior doors are heavy, refrigerator types with gaskets.

Lesser measures are taken if "gastightness" is not required. Dampers are sometimes installed on inlet and exhaust fans, many of which close automatically at emergency shutdown. The room housing the reactor may be either windowless or have sealed windows. Often the reactor room is maintained at lower than atmospheric pressure to reduce chances that airborne radioactivity will spread to other parts of the building.

Another protective method consists of filtering the air exhausted from the reactor building. At the Raleigh Research Reactor, North Carolina State College, two 12,500-cfm blowers exhaust reactor room air through a large bank of Airmat Type F filters to reduce the activity in the gas released to the atmosphere from the building after an accident. The Oak Ridge Research Reactor (ORR) also has a gas filtering and cleanup system; a 10,000-cfm blower directs the exhaust air through a "scrubber" bath to capture the iodine nuclides and then to a stack, where the gas is discharged. The system is designed to remove gaseous fission products resulting from an accident, so that release to the atmosphere will not present undue hazard to personnel near the reactor building.

9–2.3 Control safety systems. Such safety features as control rods, instrument interlocks, and fuses are incorporated in the design of the reactor itself.

The purpose of control rods and the manner in which they function in various reactor types have been discussed in previous chapters. The principal safety feature of most control-rod arrangements is their fail-safe functioning. If electric power fails, electromagnets or clutches release the rods, allowing them to fall by gravity into the core to shut down the reactor. In some systems gravity fall is backed up by auxiliary spring or hydraulic mechanisms that increase insertion speed and assure more positive insertion by preventing rods from binding as they drop.

Control-rod materials have large neutron absorption cross sections to provide a large effect on the reactivity. The most common control materials used in research reactors are boron and cadmium. However, other materials, such as hafnium and certain rare earths, are gaining increasing attention. A rod with a large reactivity effect provides safety in two ways: (1) the rate of insertion of reactivity upon release of the rods is greater, and (2) the core is more subcritical in the shutdown condition and hence moving experiments in or out of facilities (or other changes) are less likely to cause accidental startup.

As pointed out previously, it is common practice to use control rods with a total reactivity effectiveness about twice that of the excess reactivity loaded in the reactor. One or more rods (safety rods) are often withdrawn from the core and left in the cocked position for emergency shutdown. Another control rod safety feature is a limitation on the rate of withdrawal. Typical rod-withdrawal rates are on the order of 0.5 fpm. The reactivity effectiveness of control rods used in conjunction with automatic operation is less than the prompt critical fraction, so that no malfunction of the automatic system through electronic failure can bring the core into a state of prompt criticality. Control-rod movement is further restricted by interlocks in the instrument control circuits that require the proper sequence of events in operation, e.g., safety rods must be withdrawn before power is supplied to withdraw the remaining rods.

The use of instrument interlocks is a common feature of all research reactors. These systems were described in connection with instrumentation for particular reactor types in Chapters 3 through 8, and will be mentioned only briefly here. It must be assumed that electronic and mechanical components will occasionally fail and that reactor operators are fallible. Control circuitry, therefore, is interlocked to permit reactor operation only if the system is in order. A discussion of representative instrument interlocks is given in Chapter 3, and a block diagram is shown in Fig. 3–17.

In addition to safety features built into control rod systems and instrumentation, components directly affecting the nuclear state of the core can be provided with fuses. An example is the thermal fuse incorporated in the AGN-201 reactor (see Chapter 7). The lower section of this reactor core is attached to the upper section by a piece of polystyrene with twice the U^{235} density of the other portions of the core. If reactor power increases too much, the high rate of heat generation in the "fuse" section causes it to melt and release the lower section of the core, which falls 2 in. to the bottom of the reactor tank, thus making the reactor subcritical. The thermal fuse is a backup measure that operates if the control rods fail to shut down the reactor. Development work is in progress towards reliable fuses for other research reactor types.

9–2.4 Neutron sources. Auxiliary neutron sources have been found useful and sometimes necessary to ensure safe startup of a reactor. The neutron source increases the neutron flux at startup by subcritical multiplication to a level at which the detecting instruments respond reliably. Most research reactors employ sources of 1 to 20 curies to ensure a positive indication on the instruments at startup. Table 9–4 summarizes the important characteristics of several common auxiliary neutron sources.

When a cold (newly fueled) reactor is started up, the auxiliary neutron source is essential for safety. By triggering the chain reaction and making adequate instrument indication possible promptly, it eliminates the possibility of the operator unknowingly exceeding the critical condition by removing the control rods too fast. Stray neutrons are, of course, present

TABLE 9–4

COMMON AUXILIARY NEUTRON SOURCES USED FOR REACTOR STARTUP*

Source	Neutron-producing reaction	Half-life	Average neutron energy, Mev	Remarks
Polonium-beryllium	(α, n)	138 days	2.5	Easily handled because little gamma radiation emitted; short half-life disadvantageous
Plutonium-beryllium	(α, n)	22,000 yr	4.2	Very stable source of low gamma activity must be protected from burnup by fission in high-flux reactors
Radium-beryllium	(α, n)	1622 yr	2.5	Very efficient source; difficult to handle because of high gamma activity; releases radon gas, so must be contained
Antimony-beryllium	(γ, n)	60 days	0.03	Can be continuously regenerated in high-flux reactors; because of short half-life this source is not well adapted to low-flux reactors which cannot regenerate the source by (γ, n) reaction in antimony

* "The Reactor Handbook," Vol. I, *Physics*, AECD-3645, March, 1955, and J. P. Simpelar, "Neutron Sources for Reactors," KAPL-M-JPS-3, March 12, 1956.

from natural radioactive decay processes, but they appear erratically with weak intensity and cannot be relied upon for startup. After a reactor has operated at high power for some time, there is usually sufficient gamma radiation present to produce enough neutrons for startup by the (γ, n) reaction. This is particularly true of reactors containing beryllium or heavy water which, when bombarded by the core's gamma rays, produce photoneutrons.

9–3. ADMINISTRATIONAL SAFETY

9–3.1 Organization. In organizing an administrative staff for a research reactor, delegation of responsibility must be clear-cut. Potential hazards associated with a reactor require that one person be vested with the authority to make on-the-spot decisions concerning the operation of the reactor. This person, in turn, must have immediate access to his supervisors for advice on urgent matters. As a result, administration of reactor facilities has been almost exclusively of the direct chain-of-command (vertical) type, with responsibility and authority resting in individuals rather than in groups or committees. This general type of organization is illustrated in Diagram (a) of the organizational chart of Fig. 9–3. To the basic organization are added service groups and experimenters, as shown in the second diagram of the chart. Finally, for long-range policy and administration, a system of checks and balances is maintained by separating safety and operation, as shown in the third diagram of the chart. Committees often serve in an advisory capacity for policy and hazards evaluation. The administrative organization for nearly all U. S. research reactors now in operation is patterned after the one shown in the chart.

9–3.2 Hazards evaluation of experiments. To utilize a research reactor efficiently an extensive experimental program must be pursued. Ideally, the reactor should be used to capacity (100% load) at all times. In practice, 80% use is considered near saturation because of scheduling problems, experiment difficulty, shutdown time, etc. A large engineering testing reactor such as the MTR operating at 80% load may be providing radiation for 100 experiments, many operating at high temperature and pressure. For small reactors, the saturation load may be about ten experiments. At any rate, when there are 10 to 100 experiments of different types and requirements in the reactor at the same time, the problem of assuring the safety of the experiment and the reactor is demanding. To complicate the problem, experiments are often in fields unfamiliar to the operating staff—a necessary complication if the reactor is to be exploited as a versatile research tool.

To help keep operations reasonably safe, it is customary for the administration to form hazards-review groups to examine proposed experiments

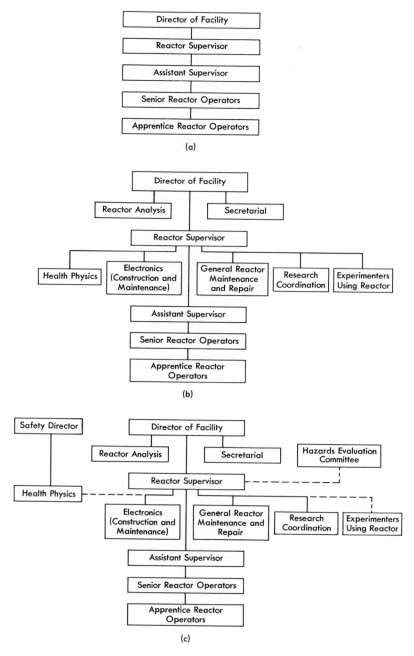

FIG. 9–3(a) Basic organization for reactor administration. (b) Basic organization plus service and research groups. (c) Complete organization.

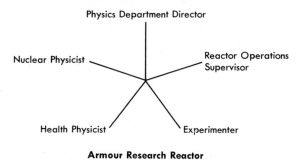

Armour Research Reactor

Battelle Research Reactor

FIG. 9–4. Composition of typical hazards-review groups.

thoroughly from the safety standpoint before they are inserted into the reactor. The group usually includes representatives of reactor operations, health physics, and safety. Frequently technical consultants knowledgeable in the fields of proposed experiments take part in the reviews, which may vary from informal meetings and discussions to formal presentations. To illustrate the structure of the hazards-review groups, the chart of Fig. 9–4 shows the composition of the groups at two reactor facilities. At several large research reactors, a project engineer is assigned to each experiment. This engineer, familiar with the operational and safety aspects of the reactor, guides the experimenter in planning the experiment, designing equipment for it, and preparing the hazards report for the review group.

The hazards report contains all the technical information needed to evaluate safety and the effect on reactor operation. For very simple experiments, such as foil irradiations, this report can be quite brief. However, in a more complex experiment, where operating hazards are present, an analysis of these hazards is required. For elaborate in-pile test loops, the report commonly contains such items as:

(1) Description and purpose of experiment.

(2) Detailed description of apparatus.

(3) A statement of the chain of command of responsibility for the experiment.

(4) Experience of experimenters in irradiation work.

(5) Safety features of the experiment.

(6) Operating procedures.

(7) Test program after removal of specimen from pile.

(8) Consideration of the activation of materials, possible contamination, and handling problems.

(9) Discussion of cleanup procedures in the event of an accident.

(10) Discussion of the maximum possible accident.

(11) Shielding adequacy of equipment.

(12) Heat generation due to gamma and neutron heating.

(13) Heat-transfer and fluid-flow considerations.

(14) Provisions for filters in any flow streams in the apparatus.

Although the primary function of the hazards-review groups is to consider the safety of experiments planned for the reactor, at several research reactor installations this group also reviews the safety of the reactor operations.

9–3.3 Emergency procedures. In the unlikely event that airborne radioactive material is released, it is imperative that measures be taken immediately to minimize spread of the contamination, to protect those exposed to the activity, and to warn, if necessary, other persons who could be affected by the release. Emergency procedures must be established and rehearsed in order to be prepared to avert potentially widespread danger. Although specific emergency procedures are peculiar to each reactor facility, all have common procedures:

(1) Determine the emergency situation and alert all personnel in the vicinity of the reactor. An emergency situation does not necessarily have to be an immediate nuclear accident. A spill of radioactive material somewhere in the reactor building, or a fire in an adjacent structure, might be considered an emergency, since it can affect the operation of the reactor.

(2) Assure reactor shutdown. Since it is likely that the area will be temporarily evacuated, the attention of the personnel will be on the emergency situation rather than on reactor operation. It is therefore important that the operator in charge of the reactor ensure complete shutdown, if possible.

(3) Determine the extent of the emergency. A few quick readings on radiation-survey instruments can turn an unknown emergency situation into a controlled procedure, saving much time in actions of emergency crews.

(4) Evacuate personnel from the immediate danger area. It is important that a judicious choice of "shelter" area be made. If airborne activity is released, it may be safer for personnel to remain indoors than to expose themselves to the active "cloud." If no shelter area exists, emergency procedures should provide for evacuation to upwind locations. The wind direction is often determined by windsocks or smoke bombs.

(5) Isolate the area of the incident. If airborne activity is released, steps should be taken to prevent further spread of the contamination. In the emergency procedures of most reactor facilities, persons are designated to make certain that windows and doors are closed, exhaust fans turned off, etc. In an accident involving radioactive materials, the hazard may be magnified by persons unknowingly tracking the activity out of the immediate area.

(6) Establish an emergency team to take charge of the situation. This team usually consists of health physicists and operations personnel familiar with the reactor facility and experiments. It is usually divided into groups for the special purposes of communications, radiation surveying, and decontamination. The communications group will notify the proper off-site people and relay instructions and messages. Good communication is essential for handling the situation and preventing panic. The surveying group keeps check on radiation levels in the vicinity to determine when the decontamination group can proceed and to determine whether the radiation is spreading to off-site areas.

These general procedures, accomplished in different ways at various reactor facilities, are usually supplemented by specific procedures peculiar to different locations. An example of a typical emergency plan, that for the Pennsylvania State University Research Reactor, is given at the end of this chapter. Most emergency plans provide for notifying Civil Defense and other local authorities to combat possible widespread contamination. These authorities, in turn, have access to radio and television communications.

Equipment to handle emergency situations must be available at proper locations. Typical emergency equipment consists of radiation-detecting instruments, protective clothing, and self-contained breathing units.

9–3.4 Operational rules. Although reactor safety is not solely an administrative problem, the effectiveness of operational rules in averting potentially dangerous situations cannot be overemphasized. In research activities, experimenters quite naturally are anxious to get results and sometimes unconsciously become less alert to hazards. General day-to-day operating procedures (including health-physics procedures) are discussed in a later chapter; the role of operating rules will be considered here only as they relate to reactor safety.

Certain rules are imposed on reactor operation by agreement between the Atomic Energy Commission and the owner of the facility. These are stated in the license issued by the AEC. The following are representative:

(1) The reactor must be operated by personnel licensed by the AEC for operation of the particular reactor or by personnel in training under the direct supervision of a licensed operator.

(2) The reactor must be operated with minimum feasible excess reactivity. (In general, facility licenses stipulate the permissible excess reactivity which can be built into the core.)

(3) All core loadings and core changes must be supervised by experienced personnel.

(4) Proper logs and records of reactor operation must be maintained. (Information required for the record is discussed in Chapter 12.)

(5) Rules for specific operations such as moving the reactor core, removing control rods, etc. must be followed explicitly.

In addition to the rules stipulated in the facility license, the reactor administration formulates additional detailed rules for operation, such as:

(1) The reactor shall not be operated under the duress of a time limit.

(2) More than one reactor operator must be in the reactor building at all times.

(3) Heavy objects shall not be transported directly over the reactor core.

(4) Check lists of all reactor startups and instrument readings must be maintained.

(5) Changes in the nuclear state of the core must be announced over a public-address system.

(6) Safety interlocks cannot be bypassed without approval from the supervisor.

Additional rules of comparable importance are imposed upon experimenters utilizing the facilities. The use of radiation is not new to many of the experimenters, but radiation of such high intensity often presents them with new problems. Also, in most cases, the researcher finds that he must tailor his experiment to the radiation source rather than tailor the source to the experiment. To assure safe and continued operation of the reactor, the experimenter must abide by certain rules, a few of which are listed below:

(1) The experimenter is responsible to the operating staff during his stay at the reactor.

(2) The experimenter must be certified to operate his experiment.

(3) The experiment must have proper radiation shielding at all times.

(4) The experimenter must obtain permission from the reactor supervisor for any significant changes in his experiment.

(5) The experiment must be instrumented to alarm or shut down the reactor if the equipment malfunctions.

(6) The experimenter cannot remove materials from the core or experimental facilities without the approval of the operating supervisor.

Detailed rules for elaborate experiments are usually worked out between the reactor staff and experimenters as the experiments are planned and equipment built for them. These procedures are often examined by the hazards review group.

9–4. Typical Emergency Plan

EMERGENCY PLAN AND EVACUATION PROCEDURE FOR THE PENNSYLVANIA STATE UNIVERSITY RESEARCH REACTOR FACILITY

In case of any abnormal situation arising in the Research Reactor Building, a personnel evacuation procedure will be followed. This emergency plan is prepared to meet an eventuality such as a radiation hazard, a reactor incident, or other hazardous situations which, although highly improbable, could occur at this Facility. This plan is tentative and, from time to time, will be revised to make it more effective.

I. DEFINITION:

This plan is to be put into operation immediately after an accident or incident in or around the Research Reactor Facility. Examples of such an emergency would exist after one of the following conditions:

A. Spill of radioactive material.

B. Insufficient shielding of an experiment utilizing the reactor.

C. Sample container rupture constituting perhaps an air contamination hazard.

D. Fire or chemical explosion.

E. Reactor malfunctioning.

II. ALARM SYSTEM:

The present building alarm system consists of several Edward's heavy-duty industrial buzzers. One is located in the reactor bay, one in the beam-hole laboratory, one in the basement laboratory office area, and one on the roof of the Reactor Building. This alarm system is automatically sounded if the radiation level in the reactor bay or the beam-hole laboratory becomes greater than laboratory tolerance. The alarm system can also be manually actuated from the reactor control console and the main reactor office.

In addition to the alarm sounding in the reactor facility, an alarm signal is also received in the University Telephone Operator's office by means of a telephone line.

III. LINE OF AUTHORITY:

The primary responsibility for establishing a building emergency rests with the reactor supervisor in charge at the time of the emergency. However, if emergency conditions do arise and the reactor supervisor is not immediately available, the reactor operator, health physicist, or individual experimenter must establish a building emergency. After the building alarm system is actuated, the following action must be taken.

1. Reactor Supervisor:
   a. Shall see that the building is evacuated.
   b. Shall check with the reactor operator to ascertain that the reactor is shut down.
   c. Shall, in case of a fire, call Fire Department.
   d. Shall contact the University Health Physicist and Director of the Reactor Facility and report the emergency.
   e. Shall take any remedial action that he deems necessary.

2. Reactor Operator:
   a. Shall shut down the reactor, turn off exhaust fans, if applicable, and evacuate. However, in the absence of the Reactor Supervisor and the Director, the Reactor Operator will assume the above-mentioned responsibilities.

3. Health Physicist:
   a. Upon notification, the Health Physicist shall immediately determine the extent of the radiation and contamination hazard. Determine if re-entry into the area is possible.
   b. If the emergency is due to spillage of radioactive material, airborne activity, or other radioactivity problems under the jurisdiction of the Health Physicist, he will supervise the decontamination of the laboratory, equipment, and personnel.
   c. He will ensure that all personnel involved in any cleanup operation be properly clothed and protected for the operation.
   d. He will, when necessary, direct and assist in the arrangement of emergency shielding.
   e. He shall be empowered to call on any of the reactor staff or other University personnel, including the Campus Patrol, to assist in correcting the abnormal conditions.

IV. EVACUATION:

Upon hearing the emergency alarm buzzer, all reactor staff and laboratory personnel shall leave the Reactor Building immediately. If possible, windows should be closed, and fans and ventilating equipment turned off by the evacuating personnel.

Since at this time there are no buildings of suitable construction near enough to the Reactor Building to be considered as a shelter area, evacuation shall be to the lower parking area gate or to the reactor entrance road if it is deemed necessary by the supervisor in charge.

A telephone is installed in a weatherproof box just outside the lower parking lot gate. Access to the box is by the Reactor Building-and-Gate Key. Additional phone calls for assistance can be made from this emergency phone.

V. SURVEY INSTRUMENTS:

a. An adequate supply of survey instruments is placed on the Health Physicist's shelf in the reactor, on the Health Physicist's shelf in the beam-hole laboratory, and in the emergency phone box at the gate.

b. Additional instruments for emergency use are available from the Health Physicist's office in the University Medical Center.

c. The University Health Physicist and the Director of the Reactor Project each has a survey instrument in his automobile for emergency purposes.

d. A survey instrument shall be maintained in the Alpha Fire Department emergency vehicle by the University Health Physicist.

IV. PROTECTIVE DEVICES:

a. Suitable respiratory filter packs shall be kept sealed in plastic bags in the Reactor Office and additional ones for emergency use shall be available from the Health Physicist's Office in the University Medical Center.

REFERENCES

1. C. K. BECK and others, *Theoretical Possibilities and Consequences of Major Accidents in Large Nuclear Power Plants*, WASH-740, March 1957.

2. O. G. SUTTON, *The Theoretical Distribution of Airborne Pollution from Factory Chimneys*, Quart J. Roy, Meteorol Soc. **73** (1947).

3. O. G. SUTTON, *Micrometeorology*. New York: McGraw-Hill Book Co., 1953.

4. W. K. LUCKOW and J. F. PATTERSON, *The Ford Nuclear Reactor, Description and Operation*, Univ. of Michigan, June 1957.

CHAPTER 10

EXPERIMENTAL RESEARCH WITH REACTORS*

10-1. Introduction

Nuclear research reactors make a variety of experiments possible in the fields of neutron, solid-state, and reactor physics, and in chemistry, biology, and medicine. Most of these experiments utilize the radiations formed in the fission process, and must be carried out at the reactor. However, many can be performed at a distance from the reactor, using the radioisotopes it produces.

When compared with other nuclear machines, the reactor is very versatile, since it can support simultaneously a number of experiments in many research areas. In addition, a reasonably constant source of high-intensity radiation is provided over a large time interval. The reactor has its limitations, of course. The different radiations that a reactor produces curtail its usefulness in radiation chemistry and biology, where it is often desirable to experiment with one type of radiation only, and sometimes with just a small energy range of such radiation. Reactor application in the nuclear physics field is limited to neutron physics and certain aspects of solid-state physics. As a producer of radioisotopes, the reactor can support a great deal of research, but its isotopes are limited to those which can be produced by neutron capture. In most cases requiring a neutron beam, the research reactor is superior to all other radiation sources because of the magnitude of its fluxes and because of its reliability.

A research laboratory should consider its experimental requirements before choosing and investing in a reactor. Many experiments can be adapted to fit an available reactor, whatever its type, but certain experiments, because of flux requirements or physical size, can be conducted more easily in certain types of research reactors. Table 10-1 lists the fluxes required for some research.

The general tendency is to push to higher fluxes, much as nuclear physicists have gone to higher energies with accelerators. Certainly, many experiments require high fluxes to produce appreciable reaction, to give the required sensitivity, or to shorten the length of the experiment. Consequently, experiments with very high flux reactors will lead the way into new and interesting areas of experimentation. However, there are a number of experiments which can be conducted with much lower fluxes, but the experimenter must be content to perform only these experiments,

---

* By J. W. Chastain, Jr.

TABLE 10–1

NEUTRON-FLUX AND GAMMA DOSE REQUIREMENTS

Use	Neutron flux, $n/(cm^2)(sec)$	Gamma dose, r
Cross-section measurements		
Beam	$>10^8$	—
In-pile	$>10^6$	—
Activation	$10^{10}-10^{13}$	—
Shielding	$>10^8$	—
Exponential experiments	10^6	—
Neutron diffraction	$>10^8$	—
Radiation effects		
Metals	10^{14}	—
Semiconductors	$>10^{12}$	$>10^7$
Chemical systems	$>10^{12}$	$>10^7$
Medical therapy	10^{12}	10^3-10^4
Biological and medical research	10^{10}	10^2-10^4
Pasteurization and sterilization	—	10^3-10^6

except for the few cases when ingenuity and careful technique can be substituted for high fluxes.

This chapter discusses some of the more common types of experiments conducted in conjunction with a reactor. If certain reactors have characteristics limiting their usefulness for a particular experiment, this is mentioned. Experiments have been arbitrarily divided into five groups: nuclear and reactor physics, solid-state physics, chemistry, component testing, and biology and medicine.

10–2. NUCLEAR AND REACTOR PHYSICS

10–2.1 Cross-section measurements. The probability of interactions of neutrons with nuclei is expressed in terms of a "cross section" (specific rate of interaction). There are three basic techniques for measuring cross sections: beam or transmission, in-pile, and activation.

In the beam method, a parallel stream of neutrons is brought out of the reactor, passed through a specimen, and the neutron intensity is measured. By measuring intensity with and without the specimen in place, the total or removal cross section (both scattering and absorption) of the specimen can be determined.

In the in-pile method, material for which the cross section is desired is placed in the reactor, and its effect on the reactivity is measured. This permits an evaluation of the absorption cross section alone, since the neutron balance in the core is affected primarily by the disappearance (absorption) of a neutron rather than by a change in direction (scattering) of a neutron.

The activation method consists of irradiating a specimen for a measured amount of time, then determining the radioactivity induced by neutron absorption. The activation cross section may be only a part of the entire absorption cross section, since some neutron absorption may produce a stable isotope and, consequently, no radioactivity.

Beam or transmission experiments. In beam experiments, if the neutron detector subtends a small solid angle at the target, the measured cross section includes the entire absorptions and scattering cross sections. This method measures total cross section because any interaction of a neutron with a nucleus in the sample prevents the neutron from reaching the detector. To separate the scattering and the absorption cross sections requires a second experiment in which the neutrons scattered over a 4π solid angle are measured, or in which the absorption cross section is measured by the actual disappearance of the neutron, as for the in-pile method.

Total cross sections can be measured with great accuracy by the beam or transmission technique because only the ratio of the counting rates with and without the sample is required. When the cross section depends on the neutron energy and when a large range of neutron energies is present (as in the beam from a reactor) the relation between transmission and cross section is complex. Usually, the physicist or reactor designer is interested in the cross section of a material as a function of neutron energy. Consequently, a number of methods have been developed to obtain a beam of monoenergetic neutrons or a pulse of neutrons of desired energy. A variety of methods for measuring cross sections is necessary, since no one method suffices to cover the range from thermal to fission energy of the neutrons found in a reactor.

The research reactor provides beams of resonance neutrons so intense that several new techniques can be used to measure cross sections. Filters, scatterers, and detectors that are particularly sensitive to a certain energy can be replaced by such methods as electronically timing the speed of a neutron to determine its energy (time-of-flight method) and diffracting neutrons with a single crystal (crystal spectrometry) to obtain monoenergetic neutrons.

In general, in spectrometer and time-of-flight experiments well-collimated beams of resonance neutrons with an intensity of roughly 10^8 n/ $(cm^2)(sec)$ incident on the equipment are required. Beams of even higher intensity can be used advantageously for some sample materials. Central core fluxes required to produce this beam strength are determined by the distance of the sample from the core which, in turn, depends on shielding thickness, core size, etc. Pool reactors operating at a power of 100 kw and water boilers operating at 10 kw provide flux levels marginal for these experiments. Graphite reactors like the one at Brookhaven have also been used successfully as sources. However, a light-water tank reactor operating at 1 to 5 Mw (LITR) or a heavy-water reactor in the same power range (CP-5) is probably best for this research.

A beam tube 6 to 8 in. in diameter is required for a collimating system. In addition, sufficient area outside the reactor shield must be available for the experimental equipment. In a method which times the neutron flight, 10 m or so of flight path is required outside the reactor shield.

The high intensity of the resonance fluxes available in reactors makes it possible to resolve neutron velocities (energies) by timing the neutrons over a measured flight path [1]. This method, called the time-of-flight technique, was first developed for use with the neutron pulses produced by a cyclotron. It involves measuring electronically the time required for a pulse of neutrons, several microseconds in duration, to reach a detector. The neutrons from each burst spread out along the line of travel. As the distance from the source to the detector increases, the time difference between the passage of two neutrons of different energies past an observation point also is increased. With a path length of 10 m the time of flight for 10-ev neutrons is roughly 230 μsec, and for 100-ev neutrons 72 μsec. Both times are long enough to be easily measured electronically.

The neutron detector at the end of the flight path is arranged to be insensitive except when a certain voltage is applied to it; consequently, it can be put into operation according to a preset time schedule. Thus the detector counts neutrons whose time of flight, which depends on the energy, corresponds to the time between the initial neutron pulse and the sensitizing of the detector. In practice, a number of neutron velocities are counted simultaneously. This is accomplished by distributing the output of the detector among 100 or so time-of-flight channels according to the time between neutron arrivals.

To obtain a burst of resonance neutrons from a reactor, a high-speed rotating shutter is placed in a beam of neutrons [2]. This consists, in its simplest form, of a long rotor with an axial slot through which the neutrons can pass (Fig. 10–1). If the rotor operates with a stator having a slot, the combination will produce pulses of neutrons with energies above a cutoff value determined by the rotational speed and the design characteristics of the rotor.

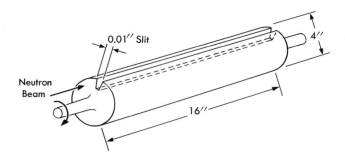

Fig. 10–1. Diagram of a fast chopper rotor. As a rotor slit passes a mating slit in a stator, the combination passes a burst of neutrons. Duration of the burst is determined by the rotational speed and the design of the rotor.

In the time-of-flight method the counting rate per channel is independent of energy for a resonance energy $(1/E)$ spectrum and detector whose sensitivity is inversely proportional to the neutron velocity, called a $1/v$ or $1/E^{1/2}$ detector. The constant counting rate results from the fact that ΔE, the energy resolution of the chopper, varies as $E^{3/2}$ for a constant pulse duration. This factor permits use of the time-of-flight method at energies up to several thousand electron volts.

In the operation of a neutron crystal monochromator or spectrometer, a collimated beam of neutrons from the reactor is directed onto a single crystal [1,3]. Neutrons of a particular wavelength, λ, are reflected according to the Bragg relationship

$$\lambda = 2d \sin \theta,$$

where θ is the internal glancing angle and d is the spacing between lattices of the crystal. Since the neutron wavelength is related to the energy, monoenergetic diffracted beams of various energies can be obtained if the crystal is cut and oriented properly. The energy of a diffracted beam can be changed by merely changing θ.

In practice, the primary neutron beam is partially collimated by a long collimating channel placed in the beam tube. The collimator opening has dimensions roughly 2 by 2 in., and therefore the beam falling on the crystal is very intense (Fig. 10–2). The diffracted beam passes through the sample and on to a well-shielded BF_3 proportional counter. For each position of the spectrometer arm, counter readings with and without the sample are taken. The total cross section can be calculated for each position of the rotating arm, each of which represents a different neutron energy. For resonance-neutron work a beryllium crystal has been found best.

The angular spread of the incident beam plus the additional spread caused by crystal imperfections give an energy resolution of 2% at 1 ev and 16% at 50 ev. In addition to the decrease in resolution, the intensity

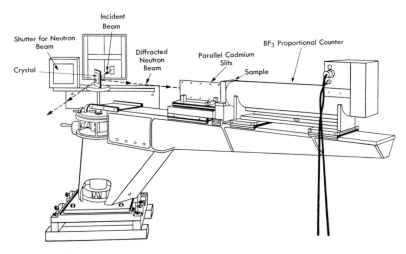

FIG. 10–2. The crystal spectrometer used to measure total cross sections as a function of energy. The counter readings with and without the sample in the diffracted beam can be used to calculate the total cross section. (Courtesy of D. Halliday, *Introductory Nuclear Physics*, John Wiley & Sons, Inc., 1950, and Argonne National Laboratory.)

of the reflected neutron beam also drops off rapidly with energy. This loss in intensity is caused by a combination of the $\Delta E/E$ energy spectrum and the loss in reflectivity of the crystal, which is roughly proportional to $1/E$, in the resonance energy region. Since again the energy resolution ΔE is proportional to $E^{3/2}$, the counting rate with a $1/v$ detector is proportional to $1/E$, in contrast to the constant counting rate of the time-of-flight method under similar conditions. The drop-off in counting rate limits the use of the crystal spectrometer to neutron energies below 10 ev.

Because of the better resolution and intensity of the chopper at higher energies, there is no justification for extending the range of the crystal spectrometers for transmission or beam experiments. These experiments, however, do not exploit the unique feature of the spectrometer, the production of monoenergetic neutron beams. With sufficiently intense beams, activation cross sections as a function of energy could be measured.

The first measurements of cross section for thermal-neutron energies involved transmission techniques using the entire Maxwell-Boltzmann velocity distribution. To eliminate the effect of resonance neutrons, a well-thermalized beam can be used or measurements can be made with and without a cadmium cover on the detector, as explained in Chapter 1. The total cross section is determined, as before, from the ratio of the counting rates with and without the sample in the beam. However, the cross section so obtained is an average over the thermal-neutron energies and is difficult to interpret. Fortunately, the high neutron intensity from a reactor makes it possible to use mechanical monochromators and "beam choppers," eliminating the need for using the entire velocity distribution.

For thermal cross-section experiments an effort is made to secure a high intensity of thermal neutrons with a low background of resonance neutrons. As will be seen later, a slow chopper transmits resonance neutrons continuously, and this causes a significant background count. A well-thermalized beam of neutrons with an intensity of 10^7 n/(cm²)(sec) is adequate for cross-section measurements. However, if experiments with very slow or "cold" neutrons are contemplated, higher intensities are required to obtain counting rates comparable to the resonance-neutron background present in thermal neutron beams.

Graphite-moderated reactors serve admirably in these experiments because of the moderately high flux and the high ratio of thermal to fast neutrons. Other reactor types can be used as sources if provided with a suitable thermal column. Pool reactors operating at 100 kw are marginal, as are water boilers at 10 kw. All tank reactors, whether moderated with ordinary or heavy water, operate at powers sufficiently high to provide ample neutrons for this type of research.

The time-of-flight method for thermal neutrons is the same in principle as the method used for resonance-energy neutrons. However, the mechan-

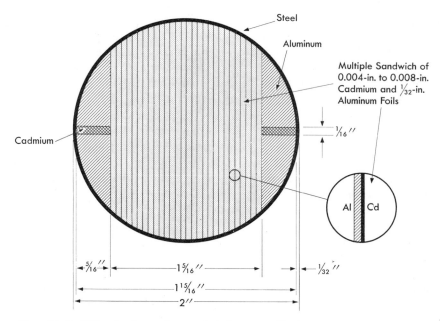

FIG. 10–3. This device, when rotated perpendicular to a thermal-neutron source, gives a pulsed neutron beam. The thin cadmium foils effectively stop the thermal neutrons but the aluminum strips transmit neutrons.

ical equipment is much simpler, since neutron pulses of longer duration allow lower rotational speeds. Also, the chopping or cutoff of thermal neutrons is easily accomplished with thin layers of cadmium rather than with inches of steel [4].

In the slow chopper, a cylinder like the one in Fig. 10–3 is placed in front of the thermal column. Cadmium absorbs thermal neutrons strongly, while aluminum does not. The cylinder, made up of alternate layers of aluminum and cadmium and rotating with its axis perpendicular to the neutron beam, will pass two collimated neutron bursts per revolution. Two small mirrors mounted on the rotating shaft reflect a beam of light to a photocell which activates the detector. The delay between the neutron pulse and the activation of the detector can be varied by changing the angle of the photocell. Six or more scaling circuits are used to record the data. The output from the detector is switched to each one in sequence at definite intervals after the neutron "burst."

In more advanced designs, the plates of aluminum and cadmium are curved slightly, with the result that only neutrons of a given energy band are transmitted; this gives a rough monochromatization. The energy band transmitted depends on the rotational speed and width of the plates.

The ease with which thermal neutrons can be absorbed in thin layers of cadmium permits the use of the mechanical monochromator shown in Fig. 10–4. This device consists of several disks of cadmium mounted parallel to each other on a common shaft which is parallel to the neutron beam. As the disks are rotated, neutrons in a collimated beam pass through

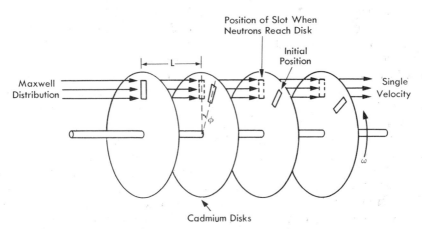

Fig. 10–4. In the mechanical monochromator thermal neutrons with a velocity which bears the proper relationship to the speed of rotation are transmitted. Thermal neutrons with a velocity either greater or less than a narrow velocity band are absorbed.

radial slots in the disks if their velocity v is such that the relation

$$\frac{\omega L}{v} = \phi \tag{10–2}$$

is met.

A number of different designs of mechanical monochromators have been built, but they have never been very successful in use. To obtain good resolution in energy, high rotational speeds are required. The resulting neutron intensity is low, and balance is difficult at high speeds.

In-pile method. The two most important in-pile techniques are the danger-coefficient method [5] and the pile-oscillator method [6]. Both measure the effect of a sample on the reactivity of a reactor. These methods measure absorption cross sections, as opposed to total cross sections or activation cross sections (the activation cross section may correspond to only part of the absorption cross section). In reactor-design work, the disappearance of a neutron is the important thing, whether or not it results in radioactivity.

Danger-coefficient and pile-oscillator experiments can be conducted most effectively in reactors with good neutron economy, i.e., where the fraction of the neutrons which are absorbed in the uranium is high. If, in addition, the reactor is small, then even a small sample can affect this fraction appreciably. Therefore, the reactors best suited to these experiments are small and highly enriched, such as graphite-reflected water boilers, the Argonaut, and the AGN 201. Heavy-water reactors also serve admirably for these measurements. Graphite reactors have been used frequently in the past, but require large samples to obtain sensitivity.

These methods are primarily useful for measuring the thermal-neutron absorption cross section, although the use of cadmium around the sample permits an evaluation of the total resonance absorption.

In the danger-coefficient method, the sample is placed in a region of high flux, and where neutrons are important to criticality, to obtain the maximum sensitivity. The change in reactivity (see Chapter 2) is then measured. The reactivity change can be measured by noting the position of a calibrated control rod for a just-critical condition with and without the sample. A more accurate method in most reactors is to measure the reactor period or the change in reactor period caused by the sample.

A conversion factor to relate the change in reactivity directly to the cross section in square centimeters can be calculated for a particular reactor. However, it is usually more practical to compare the reactivity effect of the sample with that of a standard, such as boron, whose cross section is well known. If the material of interest is a $1/v$ absorber, no correction for epithermal neutrons is necessary, since the specimen and standard are affected the same. In cases where this is not so the resonance absorption can be calculated. For most materials, this method measures only the absorption cross section.

The accuracy of the danger-coefficient method is limited by short-period irregular fluctuations of pile reactivity caused by variations in barometric pressure, temperature, and power.

The pile oscillator uses the same principles as the danger-coefficient method. Here the reactor power does not reach equilibrium because the sample is inserted and removed rapidly and periodically. For these rapid oscillations the change in reactor power is a complex function of neutron absorption. However, the amplitude of the change is proportional to the absorption cross section, and comparison with a standard can again be used to give the cross section directly.

The sample can be oscillated in the reactor core, where the relatively large change in power it causes can be measured. In another design, such as the one at Oak Ridge and Battelle, the sample is oscillated through an annular ion chamber in the thermal column, and the change in thermal-neutron flux ("local power") is measured. If a "boat" of graphite is made to contain two samples, the specimen and the standard can be oscillated simultaneously. This simultaneous measurement eliminates the effect of fluctuations in power, etc. The specimen can be oscillated inside a cadmium tube to measure the resonance absorption.

Activation method. Certain materials become radioactive under neutron irradiation. Elements such as indium, silver, and gold have large enough cross sections to serve in this way as neutron detectors. A knowledge of the activation cross section is important to this use and also to another important application of activation, the production of radioisotopes.

To measure a cross section by this method, a foil of material is exposed to the neutron flux for a time. The foil is then removed, put in a standard position near a counter, and the counts in a given period are recorded. From the counts recorded, the activity at the time counting started and consequently the saturation activity can be calculated. The cross section, σ_{act}, in terms of the neutron flux, nv, and the saturation activity, A_∞, is given by

$$\sigma_{\text{act}} = \frac{A_\infty}{nvN}, \tag{10–3}$$

where N is the total number of atoms in the foil.

Although Eq. (10–3) is for neutrons of a particular velocity, it can be used for a Maxwell-Boltzmann distribution of neutron velocities, provided the cross section is taken as the value for 2200 m/sec (the most probable velocity of a room-temperature Maxwell-Boltzmann distribution).

When the foil is placed bare in the reactor most of the activation is caused by the thermal neutrons, but the effect of the resonance neutrons is likely to be significant. The effect of the resonance neutrons can be determined experimentally by making irradiations with the foil bare and with the foil enclosed in cadmium. The bare foil is activated by neutrons of all energies, while the cadmium-covered foil records essentially those above the cadmium cutoff energy at 0.4 ev. The difference between the two runs can be used to determine the thermal-neutron flux.

Fast-neutron activation cross sections can be obtained by using thermal neutrons incident on a U^{235} plate (fission plate) to produce fission-energy neutrons (Fig. 10–5). The sample being irradiated is wrapped in cadmium and is activated by only the fast flux from the fission plate; another foil of the same material, but bare, records the total flux. After irradiation, both foils are counted and the fast activation cross section, σ_{fast}, can be calculated from

$$\sigma_{\text{fast}} = \frac{\sigma_{\text{th}}}{R} \frac{I_{\text{Cd}}}{I_{\text{bare}} - I_{\text{Cd}}}, \tag{10–4}$$

where I_{Cd} and I_{bare} are the counting rates of the cadmium-covered and bare foils, and σ_{th} is the thermal activation cross section. R is the ratio of fast to thermal flux, and can be calculated from the geometry of the arrangement.

Although the activation method is very simple in principle, in actual practice it is difficult to obtain accurate, reproducible results. Most of the uncertainty arises from errors in measuring the thermal-neutron flux and in obtaining the actual activation from the observed counting rate and the efficiency of the counter. Although the efficiency of the counter does not enter into the fast activation formula, it may be necessary to consider counter efficiency when obtaining the thermal activation cross section.

Thermal activation cross sections can be measured for a number of materials with even the very low flux reactors. For thermal fluxes of 10^6 n/

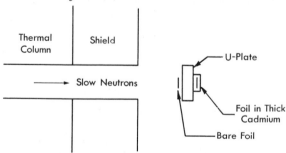

FIG. 10–5. This drawing shows a method for measuring fission energy neutron cross sections. Thermal neutrons from the reactor generate fission neutrons in the uranium fission plate. The cadmium-covered foil is activated by only fission energy neutrons, while the bare foil captures both thermal and fission energy neutrons.

(cm^2)(sec), thin foils of materials with cross sections of less than 10^{-24} cm^2 will give adequate counting rates at saturation. However, the saturated activity is a function of the flux; the combination of flux and radioactive decay in the time between irradiation and counting determines the shortest half-lived materials that can be measured. A long half-life may also be a limiting factor in determining the materials that can be investigated with a given flux. Here, the actual activity, given by

$$I = nv\sigma_{\text{act}}N(1 - e^{-\lambda t}), \qquad (10\text{–}5)$$

may be quite low for a given flux if the half-life $(T_{1/2})$ is long (i.e., small $\lambda = 0.693/T_{1/2}$).

To measure fast-neutron activation cross sections, pure thermal-neutron fluxes of 10^9 n/cm^2(sec) or so are required, since the cross sections are much smaller than the thermal activation cross sections. By use of a fission plate, fluxes of 10^9 n/(cm^2)(sec) from a thermal column can generate fast fluxes several times this value if the geometry of the system is correctly chosen. Measurements of fast activation cross sections are limited to ordinary water and heavy-water reactors of 1000 kw or more, graphite reactors with central fluxes of several times 10^{12} n/(cm^2)(sec), and water boilers of 30 to 50 kw.

10–2.2 Shielding. Shields are frequently designed on the basis of calculations using measured cross sections and relaxation lengths. Indeed, this is the method used in designing shielding for most research reactors. These designs can be conservative, since weight and space are generally not critical and since additional material can be added if the shielding proves inadequate. However, in many applications, weight, space requirements, and economics are very important, and experimental checks on the shielding design are necessary. To verify the design experimentally, a mockup of a portion of the shield is constructed and placed adjacent to a fission source of radiation. The attenuation in intensity and the change in spectrum caused by the shielding mockup are then measured for the fission neutrons and gamma rays.

Pool reactors make a convenient radiation source for these experiments. The original pool reactor, the Bulk Shielding Facility at Oak Ridge, was built with this purpose in mind. The reactor core itself is used as the radiation source and can be moved up to the shielding mockup for the measurements.

Reactors other than pool reactors can be used for such studies if they have thermal columns with fluxes of 10^8 n/(cm^2)(sec) or better, and if the proper research facility is provided. Such facilities have been constructed at Brookhaven and Battelle, both modeled after the original

Shielding Facility at Oak Ridge.   Basically, a shielding-research area consists of a plate of highly enriched U^{235} about 28 in. in diameter placed at the end of the thermal column and a large open tank in which the shielding mockup is placed.   The thermal neutrons from the reactor thermal column cause fissions in the U^{235} source plate.   A large number of the neutrons and gamma rays produced in the plate enter the tank and the shielding specimen.   The intensity of the various radiations transmitted by the shielding mockup is measured by instruments suspended from a small motorized bridge spanning the tank.

Personnel are shielded from the radiation by the liquid filling the tank. The tank can be filled with oil, demineralized water, borated water, etc., depending on the test shield materials.

The fission-plate source strength is controlled by absorbing curtains of various thicknesses which can be lowered between the fission plate and the thermal column.   A large reduction in intensity is desirable for gamma-spectrometer work close to the source.   A thick Boral (B_4C dispersed in aluminum) plate is used to cut out the thermal neutrons almost completely when measurements are not being conducted.

The data obtained from the finite disk source can be readily transformed mathematically to obtain dose rates for other sources in conjunction with the same shield [7].   This transformation can be made for sources of different geometry, size, and power density.

10–2.3 Exponential experiment. An exponential experiment is a mockup of a portion of a reactor, and it has the same composition and intercore configuration as the prototype.   The linear dimensions of the exponential pile are only about a quarter of those of the reactor.   Consequently, it is a subcritical assembly, but by using a source to supply additional neutrons, a steady state can be maintained in it.   Exponential experiments are important because by their use the critical size and behavior of the prototype reactor can be predicted.   The experiments require smaller amounts of material and are much less complex than a true critical-assembly experiment.

The subcritical assembly is built on a base or pedestal of graphite resting on the thermal column.   Theoretical considerations show that the neutron-flux distribution, $nv(z)$, along lines parallel to the vertical axis and away from boundaries can be approximated by

$$nv(z) = Ce^{-\gamma z}, \qquad (10\text{–}6)$$

where C and γ are constants.   If the fluxes along the vertical axis are measured by activating foils, then γ can be determined.   With γ known, the dimensions and mass of uranium required for a critical reactor of the same composition can be calculated quite simply [8]. Once built, the exponential pile provides a quick method for investigating small changes in lattice spacing or material composition and for determining the effect of the changes on the critical size and mass of the prototype reactor.

The fluxes required to conduct exponential experiments are quite low. In fact, before reactor neutrons were available these experiments were performed using radium-beryllium sources. The accuracy of the results is improved if somewhat higher fluxes than those available from sources are employed, but too high a flux requires shielding, which tends to reduce the accessibility to the experiment.

Graphite-moderated reactors have no equal for use in these experiments because of the large space available on top of the reactor with an adequate supply of thermal neutrons. This arrangement permits the experiment to be installed in a vertical position and, if centered with respect to the reactor, provides a symmetrical distribution of neutrons incident on the bottom of the experiment.

10–3. SOLID-STATE PHYSICS

The nuclear reactor is useful in the field of solid-state physics for investigating atomic displacements in solids caused by fast neutrons and gamma rays, and in analyzing crystal structure by neutron diffraction, scattering, and depolarization techniques.

Solid-state research with radiation concerns itself mainly with the study of the effects of atomic displacement caused by radiation. Systems in which atomic displacement is the dominant mechanism of radiation-induced change are generally solids with a crystalline structure. These changes are usually physical in nature (tensile strength, electrical and thermal conductivity) rather than chemical. Hence, solid-state physics is distinguishable from radiation chemistry, which is concerned with chemical changes induced by the radiation effects of ionization and excitation. Solid-state physics includes the study of the interaction of neutrons with bound aggregates of atoms in crystals and molecules, and leaves to the field of nuclear physics investigations of the interaction with nuclei.

In all these experiments the reactor serves primarily as a source of neutrons. Sometimes a collimated beam is used. Thus if a reactor is to be used primarily for solid-state-physics research, it should be designed for fairly high flux and should include beam tubes.

Neutron-diffraction research requires beam intensities incident on the crystal of about 10^8 n/$(cm^2)(sec)$, although some work has been done with somewhat lower intensities. Studies with filtered neutrons (very slow neutrons) require a low background of resonance neutrons. These experiments have been carried out at Brookhaven with thermal fluxes of several times 10^7 n/(cm^2)(sec). The investigation of radiation effects in solids requires a fast-neutron flux and integrated doses (nvt) of 10^9 to 10^{19} n/cm^2. Frequently, it would be beneficial to have very high fluxes for short times. The ordinary water and heavy-water moderated reactors above 100 kw can be used for these experiments, as can the graphite systems such as the Brookhaven Reactor and the Oak Ridge X-10. The neutron-diffraction and filtered-neutron experiments can use higher fluxes to improve sensitivity and selectivity.

10–3.1 Analysis of crystal structure with neutron diffraction. The crystal spectrometer has been mentioned before as a tool for measuring cross sections for neutron-nuclei interactions. However, the most important use of neutron diffraction is in the analysis of crystal structure [9]. Neutron diffraction is similar to and is used in conjunction with x-ray and electron diffraction.

If neutrons or other radiations with wave properties are to be used in investigating the arrangement of atoms in solids, their wavelength (velocity) must be of the same order as the separation distance of the atoms. This accounts for the widespread use of x-radiation from copper of wavelength 1.54×10^{-8} cm. Calculation shows that the wavelengths of thermal neutrons available from a reactor are of just the magnitude desired.

Figure 10–6 shows a typical spectrometer arrangement. Considerable shielding is required to protect personnel and the detector from the direct radiation emerging from the reactor, since only 0.1% or less of the thermal neutrons are diffracted by the crystal and subsequently used in the measurements. The sample at B is generally in the form of powder which is packed into a cylindrical sample holder. The BF$_3$ counter is rotated around the specimen and the data are recorded automatically. A monitor is usually placed in the beam from the monochromator to record any variations in incident intensity due to fluctuations in power, changes in control-rod position, etc.

Unlike x-rays, which are scattered by the electrons of atoms, neutrons are scattered by nuclei and, because of their own magnetic moment, by the atomic magnetic moments. Consequently, neutron diffraction has two principal applications. One is in the investigation of magnetic structures to determine lattice spacing and, in addition, the magnetic moment and orientation associated with each lattice position. The second is in the investigation of structures where the atoms have about the same number of electrons (iron and cobalt) and consequently produce similar x-ray diffraction patterns. A variation of the latter application is the investigation of structures containing two widely different atoms—such as lead and oxygen—where the material of higher atomic number may completely mask the other in x-ray diffraction.

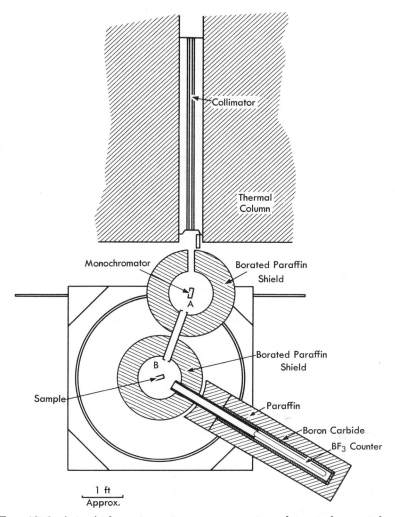

FIG. 10–6. A typical spectrometer arrangement used to study crystal. The diffracting crystal at A is used to produce a monochromatic neutron beam for the study of the crystal structure of the sample at B.

A number of experiments closely related to neutron diffraction but slightly different in character can be carried out with a reactor. These experiments involve neutron scattering, refraction, and polarization techniques, and make use of what may be described as the optical properties of neutrons. For neutron diffraction, collimated beams with an angular spread of several degrees are used. With better collimated beams (about $\frac{1}{2}$-min spread), the slight bending (refraction) that occurs with changes in the index of refraction, and small-angle scattering from polished surfaces can be observed. As pointed out previously, neutron diffraction can be used to investigate the arrangement of atoms in a lattice. Experiments utilizing scattering, polarization, and refraction of neutrons can be used to investigate grain structure, magnetic domains, distortions, and imperfections in crystalline materials. Thus these techniques permit evaluation of the gross structure of these materials.

10–3.2 Studies with very slow neutrons. If a polycrystal with many crystal grains oriented at random is placed in a thermal-neutron beam, most of the neutrons will be diffracted. However, for a given crystal lattice there is a maximum effective lattice-plane spacing, d_m, so that the longest wavelength which is diffracted is

$$\lambda_m = 2d_m. \tag{10–7}$$

Neutrons with wavelengths greater than λ_m will be transmitted practically unattentuated except for nuclear capture. Materials with small capture cross sections and large scattering cross sections for neutrons with wavelengths shorter than λ_m provide a method of securing very slow neutrons. Using such a filter with a crystal spectrometer or mechanical selector can provide a narrow band of very low energy neutrons which is helpful in certain phases of solid-state physics research.

If neutrons with energies close to the thermal equilibrium energy of a crystal are introduced into the crystal, they can either gain energy from the lattice vibrations or they can lose energy to the lattice by exciting lattice vibrations. This inelastic scattering by the lattice provides a means of studying the dynamics of the crystal lattice by determining the energy spectrum of the lattice vibrations. An experimental technique has been developed which scatters the filtered neutrons with a single crystal of the material under investigation and analyzes the energy distribution of the scattered neutron beam [10]. These "cold neutrons" can also be used to investigate imperfections in the crystal lattice [11]. Attenuation of these long-wavelength neutrons occurs because of incoherent scattering from atoms, inelastic scattering by the lattice vibrations, and nuclear absorption. The attenuating effects of nuclear absorption and inelastic scattering by lattice vibrations can be separated, since the former is a function of neutron wavelength while the latter varies with temperature. The incoherent scattering depends neither on temperature nor wavelength, but only on the number of vacancies or displacements in the crystal lattice. Consequently, the difference in attenuation between a perfect and an imperfect lattice can be related to the number of imperfections.

10–3.3 Radiation effects in solids. The radiations from a reactor can markedly change such physical properties as heat conductivity, resistivity, hardness, and elasticity of a crystalline material. When high-energy particles such as neutrons or the electrons produced by gamma rays are stopped in a solid, two types of interactions with the lattice occur. One involves an inelastic energy loss in which electrons are excited by charge interaction. These energy losses appear as heat in conductors, but in insulators some of the energy may be stored by the trapped electrons. The second type involves elastic energy losses by direct momentum transfer to the atoms. This transfer of energy causes displaced atoms and vacancies in the lattice if the incident particle is energetic enough. Frequently, the recoil atoms formed in the initial elastic collision with neutrons are themselves sufficiently energetic to produce further recoil atoms.

The most effective reactor radiation for producing displaced atoms and vacancies is the fast neutron. Its cross section for elastic collision is quite large in relation to other radiations, and since only 10 to 25 ev are required on the average to displace an atom, a fast neutron has sufficient energy to cause many imperfections. The gamma ray produces no atomic displacements directly, since its energy is dissipated through the photoelectric effect and Compton scattering. However, the secondary particles thus formed may produce lattice imperfections.

In recent years the physical changes produced by irradiation have been studied in alloys, single metal crystals, and semiconductors. While the obvious way to obtain high fluxes in the experiments is to place the specimens close to the reactor core, the attendant difficulties are great. If the sample is removed to measure the physical properties, their radioactivity sometimes makes it necessary to work in a hot-cell laboratory. Even if the measurements are made *in situ*, the transmuted material formed by slow-neutron absorption can cause variations in physical properties which in some instances tend to mask the changes caused by atomic displacements. The use of a high fast flux and a thermal-neutron shielding material reduces the transmuted materials and the need for hot cells significantly. In spite of these difficulties, many of these irradiations are performed in or very close to the core to obtain the highest possible fast flux.

In recent work at Battelle [12] an experimental setup has been devised which permits continuous monitoring of electrical resistivity and temperature during the irradiation of semiconductors.

An aluminum structure consisting of five 1-in.-diameter tubes 35 in. long is used to hold the sample tubes in the reactor (Fig. 10–7). Wires connected to the sample are spiraled about 9 ft through $\frac{1}{4}$-in holes in concrete shielding plugs used in the beam tube. With this arrangement the

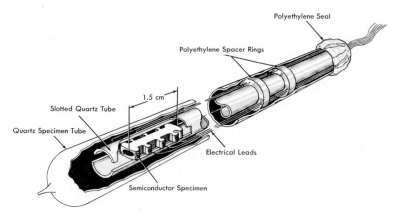

FIG. 10–7. A typical specimen holder for semiconductors. The holder can be placed in a reactor and the resistivity and temperature of the semiconductor monitored continuously during the irradiation.

conductivity can be measured while the sample is being irradiated. A potentiometer circuit is used to make periodic checks of the conductivity of the specimens; their conductivity and temperature are continuously recorded.

Experiments on radiation effects in solids require total fluxes (flux $\times$ time) of from 10^9 to 10^{20} n/cm^2. Five to six months of continuous irradiation at fluxes of 10^{12} n/(cm^2)(sec) is necessary to obtain 10^{19} n/cm^2. These times, although not prohibitive, are frequently longer than an experimenter cares to wait; sometimes he is interested in a large dose rate requiring very high fluxes for short times. This suggests that tank reactors such as MTR are useful for radiation-effects research. Although this is true, many worth-while experiments can be carried out in graphite reactors and in the 1000-kw ordinary water reactors. Water-boiler reactors operating at 30 kw or above also have adequate flux for many of these experiments. Such facilities for this work include beam tubes and other positions of high fast flux around the core. In many experiments, a cryostat to provide controlled low-temperature conditions for the irradiation is essential. The low temperatures prevent the effects induced by the radiation from annealing out.

10–4. CHEMISTRY

The chemist uses the nuclear reactor in many research areas, including the effects of radiation on chemical systems, the chemistry of radioactive elements, and the study of chemical reactions by use of radioisotope tracers. Both neutron and gamma radiations, in a range of intensities, are available from a nuclear reactor. These characteristics of a reactor provide the flexibility which the chemist needs in radioisotope and radiation-effects research.

Radiation chemistry is the study of the how and why of radiation effects in chemical systems. When a chemical substance is irradiated with neutrons, gamma rays, or electrons, chemical bonds are broken and chemical changes occur. A fast neutron breaks a chemical bond by transferring momentum to a bound atom during a neutron-atom collision. The recoil atom is ejected from the molecule at high velocity, and ionizes and excites other molecules before it comes to rest. In the case of gamma rays, recoil atoms are not produced and the energy of the gamma ray is absorbed by ionization and excitation processes entirely [13].

Energy can be transferred to an atom by other means than the processes just described. For example, if a Br^{82} atom in a molecule captures a slow neutron, Br^{83} is produced, and a 7-Mev gamma ray is emitted. The Br^{83} atom is left with 322 ev of recoil energy. Since chemical binding energies are usually less than 5 ev, the recoil energy is sufficient to break the chemical bond between the bromine atom and the rest of the molecule. The recoiling bromine atom breaks other chemical bonds in the neighborhood in slowing down, and dissipates its remaining excess energy by ionization and excitation processes in neighboring molecules.

The ionized and excited molecules produced by these mechanisms initiate chemical reactions. Studies have been made on chlorination, oxidation, and dehydrogenation of hydrocarbons, polymerization of organic substances, and the synthesis of organic compounds and simple gases. There is considerable interest in the fields of oil additives, lubricating oils, and catalysis.

The effect of radiation on plastics and polymers is an important area for study, since it changes their physical properties. The heat stability of polyethylene, for example, is improved by radiation. Radiation will also polymerize many organic compounds such as ethylene, the silicones, the polyesters, vinyl acetate, and vinyl ethers. Polymers produced by this method often have melting points and mechanical properties different from the polymers produced from the same starting materials by conventional polymerization techniques. Many of these studies on radiation polymerization are directed toward developing of better polymers and plastics for commercial applications.

The experiments in radiation chemistry are carried out by irradiating capsules or batch lots, or circulating or continuous feed systems. In general, batch irradiations are quite easy to carry out, since the material can be simply encapsulated. Capsule materials most frequently used are aluminum or polyethylene, which cause little flux depression or lowering of the flux incident on the specimens. Also, they become less radioactive than most other materials, making the handling problems after irradiation much easier.

Radiation chemistry experiments can often be conducted in the fast irradiation or "rabbit" tube. In this facility, high fast-neutron and gamma-ray fluxes are available, and the specimen can be removed quickly and immediately after a predetermined dosage. A batch operation of longer duration or of larger size can be performed in a beam tube or in the space around the reactor core.

Irradiations in a chemical process reactor vessel with provision for circulation of the reactants are much more complex. These experiments are most easily carried out in the beam tubes, although exposure in or close to the core is possible. To carry out these experiments in the beam tubes, special beam-tube shielding plugs must be designed and constructed (Fig. 10–8). In typical reactors such a plug is about 10 ft long over-all, with about 7 ft of this length made up of alternate layers of Boral, barytes concrete, and lead. The lead attenuates the gamma rays, the barytes is effective for both neutrons and gamma rays, while the Boral is a very good absorber of thermal neutrons. The 3 ft or so of tube nearest the core is available for experimental equipment.

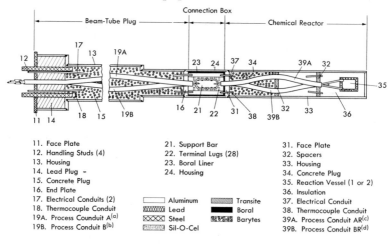

11. Face Plate
12. Handling Studs (4)
13. Housing
14. Lead Plug –
15. Concrete Plug
16. End Plate
17. Electrical Conduits (2)
18. Thermocouple Conduit
19A. Process Counduit A[a]
19B. Process Conduit B[b]

21. Support Bar
22. Terminal Lugs (28)
23. Boral Liner
24. Housing

Aluminum   Transite
Lead   Boral
Steel   Barytes
Sil-O-Cel

31. Face Plate
32. Spacers
33. Housing
34. Concrete Plug
35. Reaction Vessel (1 or 2)
36. Insulation
37. Electrical Conduit
38. Thermocouple Conduit
39A. Process Conduit AR[c]
39B. Process Conduit BR[d]

(a) Contains 2 process lines, tubular heater, and metal-sheathed thermocouples. Voids filled with bubbled alumina.
(b) When 1 reaction vessel used, contains 2 tubes for carrying coolant. When 2 vessels used, contents same as Conduit A. Voids filled with bubbled alumina.
(c) Contains 2 process lines and tubular heater. Voids filled with bubbled alumina.
(d) When 1 reaction vessel used, contains 2 tubes for carrying coolant. When 2 vessels used, contents same as Conduit AR. Voids filled with bubbled alumina.

FIG. 10–8. A special beam tube shielding plug used in radiation chemistry research where circulation of the reactants is required.

To obtain a fairly uniform irradiation of all material, the chemical reactor vessel must be kept short. The diameter is determined by that of the beam tubes, which varies from 6 to 12 in. For chemical systems which do not absorb the radiations too strongly, the chemical reactor vessel can be made as much as 7 to 8 in. long and still maintain fairly uniform dose rates along its length.

The necessary feed and product lines, heaters, electrical leads, and thermocouples are spiraled through the materials of the plug before they are brought outside the reactor, to avoid direct leakage or streaming of the radiation through the plug.

Ordinarily, the materials of interest in the chemical and petrochemical fields do not become intensely radioactive. The resultant activity and also the activity of the process reactor can be reduced by shielding the process reactor with Boral to absorb the thermal neutrons producing most of the radioactivity. This assumes that the thermal neutrons are not of prime importance in the experiment. With the low radioactivity in the feed and product material it is usually possible to operate with chemical flow equipment outside the nuclear reactor. This means that standard chemical procedures and equipment can be used, and that the valves, gages, sight glasses, etc., are readily accessible. The fact that the radioactivity of the process reactor itself is kept lower means easier handling and, eventually, easier disposal. Disposing of the intensely radioactive chemical vessel is a difficult and costly procedure.

The chemical process reactor can often be used over and over for a variety of experiments. At present, experiments are being operated at temperatures up to 1000°F and pressures up to about 800 psi. The flow rates, although low, are adequate for laboratory-scale experimentation.

The nuclear reactor also plays an important role in radiochemistry, the chemistry of radioactive elements. Materials irradiated with neutrons become radioactive. Many new radioisotopes have been produced in this way, and the determination of their characteristics, such as energy, half-life, etc. is an active research area.

The use of reactor-produced radioisotopes as tracers in studying chemical reactions [14] has increased with their increased availability. Tracers are useful in studying isotope effects in chemical reactions, molecular decomposition and rearrangement, kinetics, and diffusion. When tracer studies require short-lived radioisotopes, there can be little delay. It is therefore advantageous to have the nuclear reactor near the place where the radioisotopes are to be used.

As mentioned previously, the thermal fluxes from a reactor can be used to induce radioactivity in materials, and this radioactivity can be used in chemical analysis. The sensitivity of activation analysis varies greatly, depending on the activation cross section, the flux, and the characteristics

TABLE 10–2

SENSITIVITY OF NEUTRON ACTIVATION ANALYSIS FOR A
FLUX OF 10^{12} N/(CM^2)(SEC)

Element	Radioactive product		Sensitivity of detection, μg
	Identity	Half-life	
Europium	Eu^{152}	9.2 hr	1.2×10^{-6}
Gold	Au^{198}	2.7 days	1.1×10^{-5}
Cobalt	Co^{60}	5.3 yr	1.5×10^{-5}
Vanadium	V^{52}	3.9 months	6.2×10^{-5}
Arsenic	As^{76}	26.8 hr	1.1×10^{-4}
Gallium	Ga^{72}	14.1 hr	3.1×10^{-4}

of the induced activity. In favorable circumstances, impurities as low as 10^{-12} g can be detected. Table 10–2 lists the sensitivities of several materials in a flux of 10^{12} n/(cm^2)(sec) [15]. Neutron-activation analysis is already a powerful tool in analytical chemistry.

There are, of course, restrictions on this method. For example, if arsenic, bromine, and selenium are all present in a specimen radioactivity, As^{76} is formed from all of them by (n, γ), (n, p), and (n, α) reactions, respectively. In complex examples like this it is not always possible to correct for interfering radioactivities.

10–5. COMPONENT TESTING

In a reactor, the fissioning or burnup of the nuclear fuel causes the major portion of the damage to the fuel-element material. As the fuel is burned, every fission produces two atoms (as well as varying number of neutrons) for the one atom of fuel previously present, and this loading up with fission products (some of which are gaseous) appears to be the major cause of fuel-element swelling and of changes in physical properties. This is not a true radiation effect. However, radiation damage caused by fast neutrons, fission gamma rays, and decay gamma rays from the radioactive fission products does occur in reactor components. The damage may appear as embrittlement, changes in thermal conductivity, changes in density, etc. In addition, corrosion of structural materials and the fuel-element cladding by the reactor coolant may be accelerated greatly by such physical changes.

Consequently, another extremely important use for the research reactor is to test various reactor components. Most of this experimentation is carried out in test reactors such as the MTR, with the very high fluxes necessary to perform the test in a relatively short time.

In the early stage of reactor design, small samples of the various core components may be irradiated in a static system. A radiograph of a typical capsule used for such irradiations is shown in Fig. 10–9. In testing fueled materials, it is important to duplicate the temperature, uranium loading, and uranium burnup which will occur in the prototype reactor. Frequently, fissioning of the fueled samples can be used to produce the required temperatures. In any event, because of the damage caused by the fission products, thermal neutrons are important in tests on fuel-element materials. This is in contrast to most radiation-effects studies in other fields.

At a later stage in the work on a reactor design it is helpful to check a prototype fuel assembly in an environment closely duplicating the one that will be present in the proposed reactor. To do this, a system in which coolant can be circulated and in which other prototype parameters can be duplicated is constructed. This system is frequently called an in-pile loop. Factors that must be simulated are:

(1) Inlet and outlet temperature of the coolant.
(2) Geometry.
(3) Uranium loading.
(4) Pressure.
(5) Coolant flow rate.
(6) Uranium burnup and, to some extent, the neutron flux and energy spectrum.
(7) Time.

The part of the loop in the reactor consists of a unit fuel cell from the core of the new reactor design. Neutrons from the research reactor cause fissions and heat generation in this fuel element in an environment like that of the final reactor. The loop includes a blower or pump to provide coolant flow, a heat exchanger to dissipate the heat generated in the fuel element, and the necessary piping and valving. A gas-cooled loop for checking out fuel element performance is shown in Fig. 10–10.

Frequently, if the fuel elements are to operate in the prototype reactor core for a long time, it may be impractical to duplicate the time in an experiment and acceleration is desirable. This is accomplished by operating the test fuel element in a higher neutron flux than that which will be present in the actual reactor. This means the test will be off-design in some aspects, but the design values for fuel temperature and the total fuel burnup are usually preserved.

In designing an accelerated experiment, the higher flux required is not always easily available in even a high-flux research reactor. Consequently,

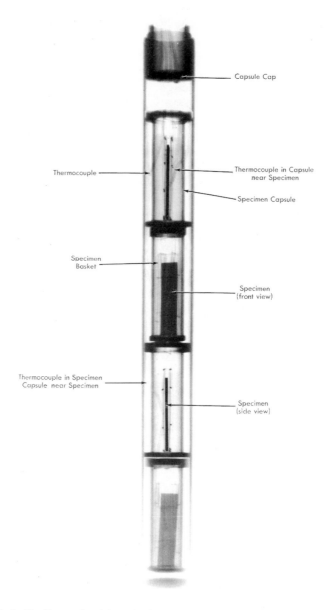

FIG. 10–9. Radiograph of four fuel specimens encapsulated for high-temperature irradiation. The specimens are submerged in sodium, which serves as a high temperature heat-transfer medium.

Fɪɢ. 10–10. A gas loop for checking the operation of a complete fuel subassembly under operating conditions. The fuel element is placed in the 4-in.-diameter pipe on the left of the support structure and moved up to the reactor core. The gas blower is located in the large tank on the rear of the support tower.

the construction materials of the loop around the test cell can be very important. Generally, the system is operated at pressures and temperatures which restrict the use of aluminum. In many loop designs an annular construction is used in which there is an inner annulus of high-temperature corrosion-resistant material. Unfortunately, most of the materials with these properties also have a large cross section for neutron absorption and must be used as thin tubes to reduce neutron loss. The outer annulus, separated from the inner by a dead air space, is heavier walled and of aluminum or some other material with a small absorption cross section. The outer tube holds the pressure and the inner tube withstands the temperature and corrosion. The combination causes a much smaller flux depression than would a heavy-walled stainless-steel tube.

In general, these experiments require very high fluxes to accelerate the component testing. Consequently, the high-flux test reactors (MTR, ORR, and ETR) are best suited to a large portion of this research.

10–6. Biology and Medicine

Reactor-produced radioisotopes have been widely used in clinical applications and in biological and medical research. Since many of the isotopes of interest can be purchased from commercial or government laboratories, it is not essential for an institution to have a reactor to carry on extensive programs in radiobiology and nuclear medicine. A nearby reactor will, however, enhance such programs by making numerous short-lived isotopes available. It can also be used to provide direct irradiation with neutrons and with gamma rays.

The biological and medical use of ionizing radiation, whether from radioisotopes or by direct radiation from reactors or other machine sources, is a subject beyond the scope of this discussion. Applications in medicine [16] and biology [17] have been extensive and, for the most part, have not been reactor dependent. The sterilization of foods and pharmaceuticals [18,19] by reactor radiation has been studied; here, only the gamma rays are used, since the neutrons, if not filtered out, would induce radioactivity in the product.

In cancer therapy, reactors have been particularly helpful in producing useful radioisotopes of high activity. Such reactor-produced isotopes as Co^{60} and Au^{198} have proved valuable to the radiation therapist as supplements to radium and radon in interstitial and intracavitary therapy [20].

Some attempts have been made to use direct reactor irradiation in cancer therapy. One of the most interesting of these, neutron therapy of brain tumors, has been reported by C. S. Shoup of Oak Ridge [21] and L. E. Farr of Brookhaven National Laboratory [22]. The effectiveness of the treatment is based upon two characteristics of thermal neutrons:

(1) they produce little ionization and can pass through tissue with relatively little effect; and (2) they interact with B^{10} to produce alpha particles that cause intense local ionization. Highly enriched B^{10} injected into the blood stream tends to be absorbed selectively, but only briefly, in cancerous tissues. An intense collimated beam of thermal neutrons directed at the tumor produce destructive alpha particles. Unfortunately, the residence time of the boron is short and there is some question that there is adequate differential uptake of the boron in the cancer cells.

Reactor radiation facilities specifically for biological research have been constructed at Brookhaven, Oak Ridge, and Los Alamos. A sketch of the facility at Brookhaven [23] is shown in Fig. 10–11. A 5-ft section of the reactor shield is replaced with graphite to form the facility. A layer of

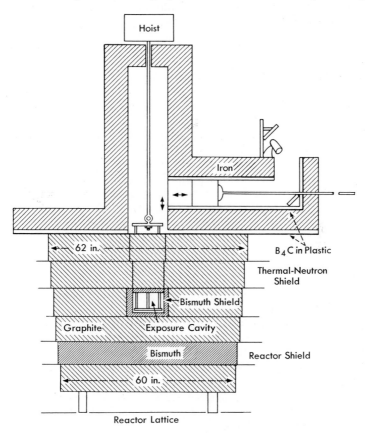

Fig. 10–11. A facility for use in biological studies on plants and animals. The specimen is placed in the tunnel at the right and pushed into the exposure cavity which has been hoisted up to receive the specimen. The cavity is then lowered into place in the graphite and bismuth assembly. (Courtesy of *Nucleonics*.)

bismuth 9 in. thick is used to absorb the gamma rays from the reactor core before they reach the exposure cavity. Additional bismuth is placed around the cavity to shield out capture gamma rays. The material to be irradiated is placed in a plastic box which is, in turn, placed in the exposure cavity. Fast neutrons can be obtained by placing a U^{235} fission plate in the bottom of the exposure box. The fission plate is covered by a layer of bismuth to cut down the fission gamma rays.

The graphite reactor at Brookhaven provides thermal fluxes of 9×10^8 and fast fluxes of 2×10^7 n/(cm^2)(sec) in the biological facility. A lethal dose of thermal neutrons to a mouse is delivered in $1\frac{1}{2}$ hr and of fast neutrons in 10 min. At Los Alamos a water boiler used as a radiation source for biological studies gives a thermal flux in the vicinity of 10^{10} n/(cm^2)(sec). Other reactors which could be used include the light- and heavy-water reactors operating at 1000 kw or above.

REFERENCES

1. D. J. HUGHES, *Pile Neutron Research*. Cambridge, Mass.: Addison-Wesley Press, Inc., 1953.
2. W. SELOVE, Resonance-Region Neutron Spectrometer Measurements on Silver and Tungsten, *Phys. Rev.* **84**, 869 (1951).
3. S. BERNSTEIN et al., Slow Neutron Crystal Spectrometry: The Total Cross Sections of Co, Er, Hf, Ni^{58}, Ni^{60}, Ho, and Fission Sm, *Phys. Rev.* **87**, 487 (1952).
4. T. BRILL and H. V. LICHTENBERGER, Neutron Cross Sections with the Rotating Shutter Mechanism, *Phys. Rev.* **72**, 585 (1947).
5. H. L. ANDERSON et al., Method for Measuring Neutron-Absorption Cross Sections by the Effect on the Reactivity of a Chain-Reacting Pile, *Phys. Rev.* **72**, 16 (1947).
6. J. D. HOOVER et al., Measurement of Neutron Absorption Cross Sections with a Pile Oscillator, *Phys. Rev.* **74**, 864 (1948).
7. S. GLASSTONE et al., *Principles of Nuclear Reactor Engineering*. Princeton, N. J.: D. Van Nostrand Co., Inc., 1955.
8. S. GLASSTONE and M. C. EDLUND, *The Elements of Nuclear Reactor Theory*. Princeton, N. J.: D. Van Nostrand Co., Inc., 1952.
9. G. E. BACON, *Neutron Diffraction*. London: Oxford, Clarendon Press, 1955.
10. R. S. CARTER et al., Energy Distribution of Cold Neutrons Scattered by Lattice Vibrations, *Phys. Rev.* **99**, 611 (1955).
11. J. J. ANTAL et al., Long Wave-Length Neutron Transmission as an Absolute Method for Determining the Concentration of Lattice Defects in Crystals, *Phys. Rev.* **99**, 1081–1085 (1955).
12. R. K. WILLARDSON et al., *Theoretical and Experimental Studies Concerning Radiation Damage in Selected Compound Semi-Conductors*, USAEC Report WADC-TR-57-593, Battelle Memorial Institute, September 1957.
13. J. L. MAGEE, Radiation Chemistry, *Ann. Rev. Nuclear Sci.* **3**, 171 (1953).

14. R. R. EDWARDS, Isotopic Tracers in Chemical Systems. *Ann. Rev. Nuclear Sci.* **1,** 301 (1952).

15. A. A. SMALES, Radioactivation Analysis, in *Proceedings of Isotope Techniques Conference at Oxford, July 1951*, Vol. II. London: Her Majesty's Stationery Office, 1952 (pp. 162–171); or *Ann. Repts. on Progr. Chem. (Chem. Soc. London)* **46,** 285–291 (1950).

16. P. C. AEBERSOLD, *Am. J. Roentgenol. Radium Therapy Nuclear Med.* **25**(6), 1027–1039 (June 1956).

17. A. H. SPARROW and F. FORRO, JR., Cellular Radiobiology, *Ann. Rev. Nuclear Sci.* **3,** 339 (1953).

18. S. A. GOLDBLITH et al., *Food Research* **18,** 659 (1953).

19. H. J. GOMBERG et al., Design of a Pork-Irradiation Facility Using Gamma Rays to Break the Trichinosis Cycle, *Chem. Eng. Progr. Symposium Ser. No. 13,* **50,** 89 (1954).

20. W. G. MYERS, Applications of Artificial Radioisotopes in Interstitial Radiation Therapy, in *Proceedings of the Second National Cancer Conference,* Vol. 2. New York: American Cancer Society and National Cancer Institute of the U. S. Public Health Service, Federal Security Agency, 1954. (pp. 1652-1662)

21. C. S. SHOUP, Some Biomedical Uses of Reactors, in *Proceedings of the University Research Reactor Conference Held at Oak Ridge, Tennessee, Feb. 17–18, 1954,* USAEC Report AECU-2900, Oak Ridge Institute of Nuclear Studies, 1954. (pp. 135–142)

22. L. E. FARR et al., Use of the Nuclear Reactor for Neutron Capture Therapy of Cancer, in *Proceedings of the International Conference on the Peaceful Uses of Atomic Energy,* Vol. 10. New York: United Nations, 1956. (P/177, p. 182)

23. H. J. CURTIS et al., Calibrating a Neutron Facility for Biological Research, *Nucleonics* **14**(2), 26 (February 1956).

CHAPTER 11

PREROUTINE REACTOR OPERATIONS*

11-1. INTRODUCTION

The transition period from the time facility construction is completed and routine reactor operation begins is very important. During this period the operating staff becomes familiar with the characteristics of their particular reactor. This chapter describes common procedures and problems and considers experiments that should be performed on the reactor system before routine operation starts. Both precriticality and postcriticality experimentation are discussed.

Careful attention during this period can give much insight into problems of routine reactor operation, sometimes exposing potential trouble sources which, if corrected, can greatly reduce later difficulties. Preroutine operation also affords an opportunity to establish practical operating procedures. The importance of allowing sufficient time free from pressures and interruptions for preroutine operations cannot be overemphasized. Management frequently underestimates the time needed for these operations, imposing hardships on an operating crew which is usually undermanned. A mature evaluation of the problems encountered during this period and the time required to solve these problems will enable the staff to operate a more reliable facility.

11-2. PRECRITICALITY EXPERIMENTS

Many experiments and checkouts should be performed on the reactor facility before initial criticality is attempted. A complete understanding of the instruments, control system, and equipment is essential, plus as much background information as possible and the complete assurance that the equipment is functioning properly.

An outline of precriticality work done at various operating reactor facilities before initial criticality is included here. Because of the variation of reactor types and equipment, it is not complete or universally applicable, but it may serve to indicate what is involved in such work and to help in devising a detailed checkout for a particular reactor facility.

11-2.1 Instrument checkout. The operator relies on instrumentation for information on the nuclear state of the reactor core. It is therefore

---

* By J. N. Anno, Jr.

extremely important that the instruments and their functions be understood and that the instrument readings be accurate and dependable. Familiarizing the operating staff with the instrumentation is a significant part of the preroutine checkout. A few research reactor facilities now in operation (for example, the Naval Research Laboratory Reactor and the Raleigh Research Reactor) use instrumentation designed and constructed by their own personnel. Consequently, some of their staff are highly familiar with the instruments. However, facilities with such experience are in the minority. In the interests of economy and time, most facilities have purchased their instruments from commercial sources. In such cases the instruments are usually checked by the manufacturer before they are turned over to the reactor staff; operating, calibration, and maintenance instructions are usually supplied with the package unit. If they are not, it is highly desirable that the operating staff prepare this information.

For familiarization, and as a final check, reactor staffs have found it worth-while to (1) trace circuitry of each instrument completely, (2) test all electronic tubes and relays, (3) age the tubes by applying power to the instruments for several days, and (4) calibrate and check the response of each instrument. Several facilities have constructed calibration and test racks containing all the auxiliary instruments and circuitry to calibrate and test their instruments.

Once the instruments have been checked and calibrated, it is common practice to perform "dry runs" with them, observing the effects of temperature and humidity. With all instruments installed in the console, runs are made to make sure the instruments are not overheating. Several reactor facilities have found that a large percentage of instrument (tube) failures have been due to overheating, which is readily corrected by proper ventilation of the console.

The radiation detectors (primarily neutron detectors) that supply signals to the console instruments must be checked out. Most of the detectors are supplied by industrial concerns and are extensively tested before delivery. Compensated ionization chambers (CIC) and parallel-circular-plate chambers (PCP) are usually purged thoroughly with dry nitrogen gas, sealed, and leak-tested before installation. Since the reactor is not yet generating neutrons, the response and sensitivity of the neutron detectors can be checked by using an auxiliary neutron source (see Chapter 9). A neutron source provided by the (α, n) reaction, such as polonium-beryllium or plutonium-beryllium, is used to prevent gamma radiation from contributing to the output signal. During reactor operation both gamma rays and neutrons impinge on the detectors; hence it is important to know the gamma sensitivity of the detectors also. Auxiliary gamma sources, such as Co^{60}, can be used for this purpose.

After both the instruments and the associated radiation detectors have been checked out, it is common practice to perform dry runs with the combined equipment. Time behavior of neutron multiplication in the core is simulated by placing neutron sources near the radiation detectors and observing the functioning of the instruments. Reactor periods can be simulated by moving the source with respect to the ion chambers. Many of the instrument safety interlocks (short period, high flux, etc.) can be tripped by conditions simulated by the source. The general behavior of the instruments and the time response of the scram circuits can be checked in this manner.

11–2.2 Checkout of control components. The third link in the control of the reactor is the control-rod system (control rods, magnets, rod drives, and miscellaneous components). The signal generated by the radiation detector and indicated on the console instruments is ultimately transferred either manually or automatically to the control-rod system. Quick release and insertion of the control rods are important to the safety of the system if a power transient occurs. Response time of the safety instruments and the insertion time of the control rods should be determined during the preroutine testing period. An example of this type of experiment is the response-time experiments performed on the Livermore Water Boiler [1]. In these experiments, a burst of neutrons was detected by a compensated ionization chamber and the resulting signal amplified to actuate a relay. When this relay closed, a second relay opened, interrupting the current in a solenoid holding the safety-rod mechanisms. The safety rod travels a total of 3 ft horizontally and is accelerated by the force of a lead weight. General arrangement for the experiment and the response time for the various components of the control system are shown in Fig. 11–1. Total response time for the system (from initiation of the signal to complete insertion of the control rods) is 1.56 sec.

Times for release and drop of control rods in the Battelle Research Reactor were also measured. The time from initiation of the scram signal at the safety amplifier to the release of the control rods from the holding magnets was about 30 msec, and approximately $\frac{1}{2}$ sec more was required for the rods to drop completely into the core. A curve of distance of rod drop versus time after breakaway is shown in Fig. 11–2. The theoretical curve for free fall of the rod is also shown in this figure. Note that the theoretical curve predicts a total drop time about 15% less than the measured value, indicating that the resistance to rod movement by the reactor pool water and core structure is fairly small.

For precise measurements of reactivity, the control rods must be accurately positioned with respect to the fuel, which means that considerable effort must be expended to calibrate the inductors and the drive mech-

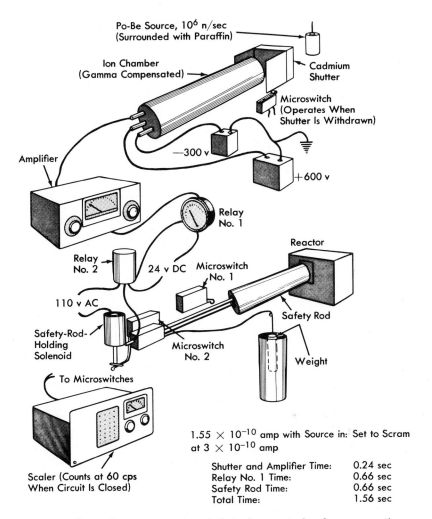

Po-Be Source, 10^6 n/sec
(Surrounded with Paraffin)

Ion Chamber
(Gamma Compensated)

Cadmium
Shutter

Microswitch
(Operates When
Shutter Is Withdrawn)

Amplifier

−300 v

+600 v

Relay
No. 1

Relay
No. 2

24 v DC   Microswitch
No. 1

Reactor

110 v AC

Safety Rod

Safety-Rod-
Holding
Solenoid

Microswitch
No. 2

Weight

To Microswitches

1.55 × 10^{-10} amp with Source in: Set to Scram
at 3 × 10^{-10} amp

Scaler (Counts at 60 cps
When Circuit Is Closed)

Shutter and Amplifier Time: 0.24 sec
Relay No. 1 Time: 0.66 sec
Safety Rod Time: 0.66 sec
Total Time: 1.56 sec

FIG. 11–1. General arrangement and data for control-rod response time experiment for the Livermore Water Boiler.

anisms. The control-rod drive speed is usually checked during this time (a typical rate of rod withdrawal is 0.5 fpm). Other items checked are (1) control-rod shock absorbers, (2) the switches indicating when magnets are seated on control rods, and (3) the automatic control system (servo system) by simulating imput signal changes and observing system behavior.

The above checks for the control-rod system are representative of those performed on research reactors; other checkouts may be needed for specialized features.

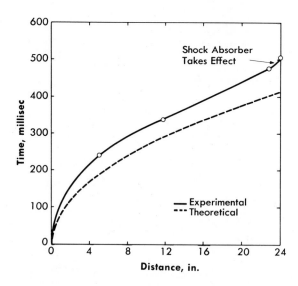

FIG. 11–2. Distance of rod drop vs. time after breakaway for the Battelle Research Reactor. Theoretical curve is computed for free fall in water.

11–2.3 Equipment checkout. As with instrumentation, the contractor supplying the mechanical components of a reactor system (pumps, valves, demineralizer, etc.) usually tests the equipment thoroughly before turning it over to the purchaser. In some cases manuals of testing procedures are supplied. However, members of the operating staff should familiarize themselves completely with the auxiliary equipment by a second testing of all equipment just before the approach to initial criticality. With so much emphasis being placed on the nuclear aspect of reactor operation, the staff may not pay enough attention to the operating of the auxiliary equipment. This can be detrimental to continued reactor operations. Functional testing of auxiliary equipment consists of such items as:

(1) Continuous operation of the cooling system long enough to evaluate performance and check for leaks, overheating of moving components, vibrations, etc. Calibration of pressure gages and flow meters.

(2) Measurements of the liquid or gas flow rates and pressures in the cooling and purification systems (or gas-sweep and gas-recombiner systems in the case of homogeneous reactors).

(3) Calibration of all temperature monitors on auxiliary equipment.

(4) Checkout of all alarms concerned with functioning of the equipment.

(5) Checks on the performance of purification systems (demineralizers, filters, etc).

Checks on proper alignment and tolerances of equipment items are also made. Control rods have already been mentioned. Other items, such as support towers and magnet guide tubes, must also be very accurately aligned.

Although the equipment is usually cleaned by the contractor before assembly, a final cleanup of the system should be made at the conclusion of precriticality testing. Foreign materials, such as tramp iron in cooling and purification systems, can greatly increase corrosion as well as clog the lines. System cleanup demands considerable attention, but because of its distasteful nature it is frequently neglected.

Still another item to be taken care of, not associated with instrument or auxiliary equipment testing, is a health-physics or radiation check. The period before criticality affords the last opportunity to obtain important background activity data before the reactor is operated. Background activity data should be collected at least several months before operation.

In summary, it is extremely important to extensively test before the reactor goes critical. Tests include hydraulic, dimensional, instrumental, and mechanical checks of the reactor and associated equipment. Complete testing can save much time and trouble in later operation of the reactor.

11–3. INITIAL CRITICAL EXPERIMENTS

The first nuclear experiment of preroutine operation is initial criticality. This experiment, the first check on the nuclear behavior of the core, is very important. Consequently, the events, procedures, and precautions typical of an initial critical experiment will be described in detail. Here is the usual sequence of events after completion of facility construction and precriticality experiments:

(1) Fuel elements or solution received and inspected.

(2) Instruments calibrated and checked out for final time.

(3) Mechanical equipment checked out.

(4) Neutron source tested.

(5) Initial fuel charge loaded (usually less than 50% of the calculated critical mass).

(6) Fuel loading increased incrementally, with observations of neutron flux level.

(7) Criticality attained.

(8) Reactor shut down.

After receipt and inventory of the fuel, a careful visual inspection should be made. A detailed mechanical inspection has already been performed by the supplier of the fuel, but a final review of the results of these inspections should be made by those participating in the experiment.

The complete instrumentation system is then given a final thorough check and the results are reviewed by the operating group. It is advisable to activate the neutron-detecting chambers with the neutron source to assure proper indication. The auxiliary equipment for reactor core operation is also given a final checkout; this is particularly important with homogeneous reactors, where the components (gas recombiner, fuel flow system, etc.) are more directly related to the nuclear state of the core than are those of other types. Finally, before adding the initial fuel charge to the core, neutron-source tests are conducted by measuring the neutron count rate with the source at various distances away from the detectors in the core environment (source strength through various distances of water in the case of a water-moderated reactor).

The procedures and precautions for an initial critical experiment vary with reactor type but generally follow a similar pattern. As a precaution, several detectors are employed to indicate the neutron multiplication in the core. Neutron-detecting instruments are sometimes checked by measuring foil activations at various stages in the core-loading process. Before adding the initial fuel charge, the neutron source is positioned as near as possible to its final location and readings are made on all instruments to provide data for determining the multiplication of the core.

The initial fuel is then loaded into the core and the neutron level again measured. Neutron level is measured with the control rods completely withdrawn and completely inserted. The difference between the two conditions indicates the worth of the control and safety rods and aids in determining the amount of the next incremental loading. After each addition of fuel (usually no more than one-tenth the estimated amount required in addition to the original loading to obtain criticality), the neutron level is measured again. Since the subcritical multiplication is given approximately by $M = 1/1-k_{eff}$, as criticality is approached (i.e., as $k_{eff} \rightarrow 1$) the multiplication which is proportional to the counting rates observed on the instruments becomes very large. Hence, the inverse multiplication or inverse counting rate approaches zero as the reactor nears criticality, and a graph of inverse count rate versus fuel content can be extrapolated to zero inverse count rate after each incremental core loading to give an indication of the critical mass. Obviously, the estimate of the critical mass by this extrapolation improves as the core approaches the critical condition.

A typical approach to criticality for a homogeneous reactor is shown in Fig. 11–3. Curves, given for "rods in" and "rods out," show the rods to be worth roughly 80 g of U^{235}. The approach to criticality in a homogeneous solution reactor, shown in the graph, is quite uniform, since the core geometry is fixed and only the fuel concentration is varied. However, in a heterogeneous reactor, where the core is built up by adding fuel elements, core size and neutron leakage change with each addition, and approaches to criticality are not so uniform. Nevertheless, the gross multiplication with

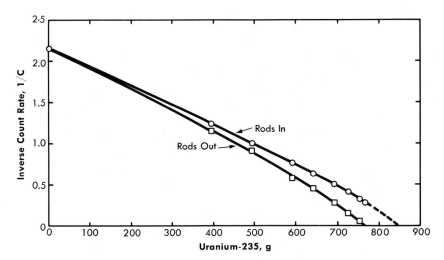

Fig. 11–3. Approach to criticality for the Raleigh Research Reactor II.

total fuel content is similar, and the procedure is valuable for critical experiments with heterogeneous reactors.

The critical experiment is usually conducted by a loading "team." A typical team consists of (1) the reactor supervisor, who operates the reactor controls and is in command of the team, (2) several recorders, who keep running accounts of the data and advise the operator, (3) a fuel loader, and (4) an observer, who checks the loading and advises the operator. It is advisable to train this team in practice core loadings before the initial startup.

11–4. POSTCRITICALITY EXPERIMENTS

After criticality is first attained and before routine operations begin it is important for the operations staff to learn all the details of reactor behavior. A number of important experiments can be performed during this time. Some of these are outlined here, with the results and their uses.

11–4.1 Critical-mass experiments. In general, research reactor cores can be classified as fixed or variable. Graphite-moderated and homogeneous reactors usually have a fixed core size; hence experiments performed on these cores to determine critical mass are limited to changes in the reflectors or in fuel concentration rather than to changes in core size or shape. On the other hand, the cores of heterogeneous water-moderated reactors, comprised of individual fuel elements, are generally variable. Latitude in positioning these fuel elements is usually provided by a grid plate containing more holes or "sockets" for the fuel elements than is necessary

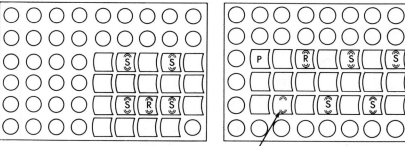

Total Uranium-235 = 2809.2 g
Excess Reactivity = 0.543% $\Delta k_{eff}/k_{eff}$

Initial Criticality, Loading 1

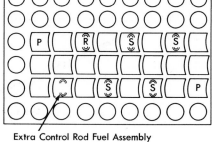

Extra Control Rod Fuel Assembly

Total Uranium-235 = 3412.3 g
Excess Reactivity = 0.276% $\Delta k_{eff}/k_{eff}$

Slab Geometry, Loading 3

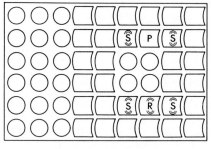

□   Standard Fuel Element
P   Partial Fuel Element
B   Beryllium Reflector
R   Regulating Rod
S   Shim-Safety Rod

Total Uranium-235 = 4793.8 g
Excess Reactivity = 0.090% $\Delta k_{eff}/k_{eff}$

Block "O" Geometry, Loading 5

(a)

Fig. 11–4. Critical-mass experiments. (a) Effect of core geometry on critical mass of the Battelle Research Reactor. (b) Effect of control-rod locations on critical mass of Naval Research Reactor. (c) Effect of reflector on critical mass of Bulk Shielding Reactor.

for a minimum core loading. With this arrangement, the critical mass of the core can be varied greatly by changing the shape of the core. The various configurations possible affect the critical mass by changing the size of the core and the neutron leakage.

In general, for an operating reactor, the primary purpose of critical-mass experiments is to determine the core loadings to be used in future special applications. An important secondary purpose is to provide the

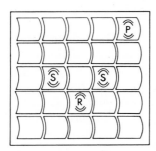

Total Uranium-235 = 3273 g
Excess Reactivity = 0.10% $\Delta k_{eff}/k_{eff}$

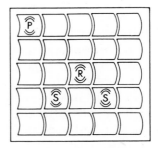

Total Uranium-235 = 3203 g
Excess Reactivity = 0.01% $\Delta k_{eff}/k_{eff}$

(b)

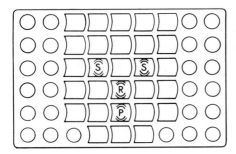

Total Uranium-235 = 3700 g
Critical Mass = 3500 g

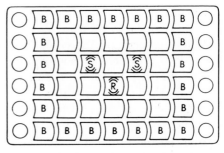

Total Uranium-235 = 2600 g

(c)

☐   Standard Fuel Element
P   Partial Fuel Element
B   Beryllium Reflector
R   Regulating Rod
S   Shim-Safety Rod

FIGURE 11–4 (*continued*)

operators with information about the reactivity worth of fuel elements in various locations in the core in a solid-fuel reactor.

The effect of the core configuration on the critical mass is demonstrated in Diagram (a) of Fig. 11–4. These core loadings are from critical experiments performed on the Battelle Research Reactor [2]. Note that the more compact loading, Loading No. 1, contains only 2800 g of U^{235}, which is close to the minimum water-reflected critical mass of the reactor.

The slab loading, Loading No. 3, requires 3400 g, while the annular loading, Loading No. 5, requires 4800 g of U^{235} for criticality. Thus the critical mass for this type of reactor is not restricted to a narrow range but is significantly affected by core shape and size. The same general effect of geometry on critical mass is observed for all reactors of this type.

In heterogeneous reactors, the critical mass for a particular core geometry is very hard to determine precisely because the fuel is not uniformly distributed in the fuel assemblies, and control-rod channels introduce inhomogeneities. The latter is generally the more important, since the fuel content of standard fuel assemblies varies only a few percent (except for specially constructed partial elements). The effect of location of the control-rod channels on the critical mass is demonstrated in Diagram (b) of Fig. 11–4, which shows two core loadings for the Naval Research Reactor [3]. As seen from this diagram, shifting the control channels toward the edge of the core reduced the critical mass by about 50 g (considering the differences in the U^{235} content and the excess reactivity of the two cores).

Many research reactors have several materials which they use as a reflector to surround the core. Although use of ordinary water as the reflector is prevalent in pool reactors, reflection by graphite, beryllium, or beryllium oxide is not uncommon. Since these materials are better reflectors than ordinary water [4], the critical mass of a particular core can be considerably reduced by using these materials. This fact is illustrated in Diagram (c) of Fig. 11–4, which shows a water-reflected and a beryllium oxide partially reflected core loading of the Bulk Shielding Reactor [5]. Note that the beryllium oxide reflector reduced the critical mass by nearly 1 kg of U^{235}. Removing a 4 by 4-in. reflector block from the graphite reflector surrounding the Raleigh Research Reactor II increases mass needed for criticality by 20.5 g.

11–4.2 Flux measurements. Early in preroutine operation, the magnitude and distribution of the thermal-neutron flux in the reactor core should be measured to determine the power level in the core and, later, to permit accurate determination of the fuel burnup. The reactor power can, in some instances, be determined by a heat balance, (the normal method of power calibration for homogeneous reactors equipped with cooling systems), but it is undesirable to operate the reactor at sufficiently high powers for this determination in the early experimental work. If the reactor is designed so that calorimetric power calibration is possible, calibration by flux measurements provides a worth-while check.

The exact power of the reactor is not known at initial criticality but, by using data from similar operating reactors, rough estimates can usually be made from the relationship of the detection equipment to the core. Also the thermal-neutron flux measured at one point in the core can be used to normalize the calculated flux distribution, providing an early rough power calibration of the reactor.

If the reactor is very similar to one for which extensive flux power measurements have been made, the power of the new reactor can be estimated by measuring the flux at some point for which the relationship of flux to reactor power is known. For example, in starting up the Ford Nuclear Reactor, which has a core very similar to that of the Bulk Shielding Reactor at ORNL, the power was initially estimated by measuring flux at a known distance from the core in the pool water and estimating the power level from data on the radiation attenuation at various distances from the BSR core [6]. Other measurements were performed for rough initial calibration, but the first estimate gave a good indication of the power level.

A knowledge of the radiations in the experimental facilities and in the core of the reactor is necessary before using the reactor for research. Accurate and complete flux measurements in these facilities during pre-routine operation will permit routine operation with fewer interruptions.

Flux plots are usually made pointwise by activating suitable foil or wire material such as cobalt, gold, indium, and manganese. For precise thermal-neutron flux measurements the activities of these materials must ordinarily be corrected for activation by nonthermal neutrons, usually by determining the cadmium ratio throughout the core. In obtaining a flux distribution it is convenient to use wires rather than foils, since they may be scanned after irradiation to obtain relative flux values along their length. The relative fluxes can then be normalized to an absolute flux determination at a single location in the core.

Complete flux mapping of a core by the activation technique is a laborious measurement for most reactors, but it continues to be the most widely used technique. Other schemes have been proposed, but are seldom used in actual practice because of development problems and space limitations in the core. In the case of a homogeneous spherical core, a single radial flux plot is often sufficient, if the reflector is uniform. Flux plots through the cores of the various reactor types have been shown in the chapters on each type.

Although burnup can be considered uniform for liquid homogeneous cores, where the diffusion process sufficiently mixes the fuel, in other reactors it is not uniform, but proportional to the neutron-flux distribution in the core. Uniform burnup for elements in these reactors can be approximated by rotating the fuel in the core, where such action is feasible. From the flux measurements, burnup weighting functions can be obtained for each cell of the heterogeneous core. Figure 11–5 shows the percent power contributed by each element in a 3 by 9 loading of the MTR.

	1	2	3	4	5	6	7	8	9
1	2.91	3.63	4.22	4.63	4.58	4.27	3.96	3.33	2.39
2	3.00	2.68	4.27	3.43	4.74	3.30	3.77	2.65	2.26
3	3.00	3.80	4.40	4.95	4.83	5.03	4.09	3.26	2.61

Fig. 11–5. Percent power contributed by each element in a 3 by 9 core loading of the Materials Testing Reactor.

The extent to which the fluxes must be known in the experimental facilities depends on the proposed use of the reactor. In facilities used for radiation effects studies (see Chapter 10) the thermal- and fast-neutron fluxes and the gamma dose rate (and in some cases the energy spectrum of these radiations) are required. On the other hand, in a facility used to provide a beam for experiments external to the reactor, radiation magnitudes must be known only well enough for design of equipment. Detailed flux mapping of experimental facilities, like similar operations in the core, is a laborious process complicated by changes in the radiation spectrum and intensity with time. These time-induced changes, more noticeable in the higher-power reactors, are caused by changes in neutron distribution due to burnup of U^{235} and buildup of fission products that capture neutrons, changes in gamma dose rate due to fission-product buildup or decay, and changes in flux distribution due to other experiments using the core. Accurate dosimetry over extended periods of time in experimental facilities usually requires continuous monitoring devices. Examples of thermal- and fast-neutron flux measurements in a beam-tube facility are shown in Figs. 3–33 and 3–34.

In higher-power reactors, flux measurements are sometimes desirable in locations of the reactor environment not intended for experimental use, to assess the engineering design. The flux measurements provide information on heat generation in shielding materials, radiation damage to reactor components, etc., and permit checking the design calculations.

11–4.3 Reactivity studies. These are important in evaluating the effect on reactivity by various core parameters, and components and experiments that can be moved in and around the core. Operational and safety characteristics of changes in a reactor can be determined from the results of these measurements. In operating a reactor, such studies are absolutely necessary to hold excess reactivity at the minimum value commensurate with the operating and experimental requirements.

Reactivity measurements can be divided into two principal categories: (1) measurements of the reactivity worths of components of the reactor system and (2) measurements of the reactivity effects of physics parameters of the core. The first category includes experiments to determine the reactivity worth of fuel elements in various locations, control-rod channels, core environment (beam tubes, thermal column, etc.), control rods, and experiments typical of those planned for the reactor. The second category includes the reactivity effects more inherent to the core: effects of voids, temperature coefficient, and poison buildup (for the higher-power reactors). The reactivity effects can, for the most part, be measured at low reactor-power levels.

Reactivity worth of control rods. To measure reactivity effects, the control rods are calibrated in terms of reactivity worth per unit rod movement. Both the inhour and the distributed poison methods are used for rod calibration [7], but the former has received wider usage. The inhour method relates the reactor period to reactivity through the properties of the delayed neutrons and, for short periods, to the neutron lifetime of the core. For precise calibration, a control rod with small total reactivity worth is usually used, so that small reactivity changes will be reflected in large movements of the rod. A representative calibration curve for the regulating rod of the Bulk Shielding Reactor is shown in Fig. 11–6. Near the center of the rod, where the graph is fairly linear, the reactivity worth is approximately $2 \times 10^{-4} \Delta k_{eff}/k_{eff}$ per cm of rod travel. Thus, very small reactivity changes can be detected.

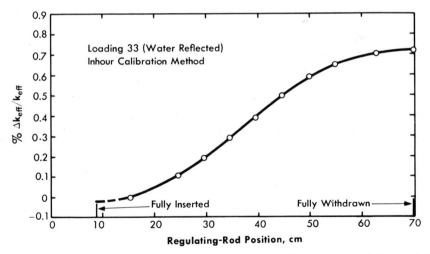

FIG. 11–6. Integral calibration curve for the stainless steel regulating rod in the Bulk Shielding Reactor.

As mentioned in Chapter 9, for safety a rule-of-thumb minimum total reactivity worth of the control rods is about twice the excess reactivity requirements of the core. Typical safety and shim-safety rod worths for reactors operating at 1 Mw or less are on the order of 0.02 $\Delta k_{eff}/k_{eff}$ per rod. Rod worth, of course, varies with location in the core.

Reactivity worth of fuel. The reactivity worth of fuel added to the core must be measured in order to estimate the excess reactivity of the core, which must match reactivity requirements for routine reactor operation. The reactivity worth of a fuel element can be measured by the change in position of a control rod (calibrated in terms of reactivity, see Fig. 11–6) necessary to maintain the reactor in a critical state after the addition (or removal) of the fuel. For a homogeneous reactor, the reactivity worth of additional fuel is free from geometry effects. As an example, the mass coefficient of reactivity of the Raleigh Research Reactor II was found to lie between 3.07×10^{-4} and 3.69×10^{-4} $\Delta k_{eff}/k_{eff}$ per g of U^{235}. For a heterogeneous reactor, the worth of the added fuel is a strong function of location. This is illustrated in Fig. 11–7, which shows the reactivity worth of a fuel element containing 153 g of U^{235} for various locations

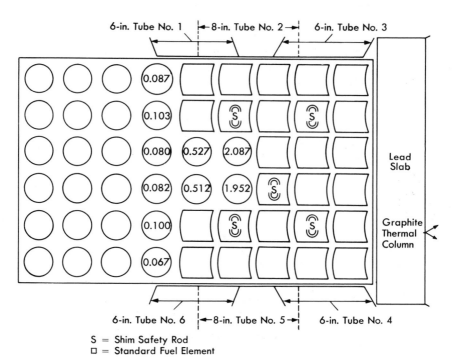

S = Shim Safety Rod
□ = Standard Fuel Element

Fig. 11–7. Reactivity worth of a fuel element in various locations in the Battelle Research Reactor. Numbers in circles indicate percentage reactivity.

around the edge of the core of a 1-Mw ordinary-water reactor. Similar variances of reactivity with fuel location are observed in graphite reactors and heavy-water reactors.

Reactivity effects of core environment. Components of the reactor system near or in the core acquire reactivity worth through their effect on the moderation, reflection, absorption, and scattering of the core neutrons. Experimental facilities (beam tubes, thermal columns, etc.) often terminate very near the core face and hence acquire reactivity worth.

Removing the graphite plug from the beam port of the Livermore Water Boiler leaves a void in the graphite reflector surrounding the core. The opening begins $\frac{1}{2}$ in. from the sphere surface and is 2 in. in diameter. Removing the plug causes a loss of reactivity of 4.6×10^{-4} $\Delta k_{eff}/k_{eff}$. More extreme changes in reflector conditions occur in the Naval Research Reactor in moving the core from the stall or "niche" position (where it is graphite-reflected on three sides) to the open pool (where it is entirely water-reflected). This change in reflection reduces the reactivity by about 0.03 $\Delta k_{eff}/k_{eff}$. The CP-5 Reactor uses the reactivity worth of the heavy-water reflector above the core as a safety device. The heavy-water reflector can be dumped in about 15 sec to remove 0.035 $\Delta k_{eff}/k_{eff}$. Typical reactivity effects of beam tubes are illustrated by the effects of the three $6\frac{1}{2}$-in.-diameter ports at the rear of the Pennsylvania State Reactor core when the core is moved adjacent to the beam tubes at the end of the pool. Near the core the tubes are constructed of aluminum with end plates $\frac{1}{2}$ in. thick. The effect on the reactivity of the water-reflected core of filling the ports with water is shown in Table 11–1. The arrangement of the ports with respect to the core is shown in Chapter 3.

TABLE 11–1

BEAM-HOLE REACTIVITY EQUIVALENCE

Unit	Increase in reactivity, %
Hole No. 1	0.1*
Hole No. 2	0.38*
Hole No. 3	0.1*
Aluminum material of beam extensions	0.25
Total effect of beam holes	0.83

* Changing from air-filled to water-filled.

Reactivity effects of experiments.   In using reactors, negative reactivity effects—(caused by neutron absorption or scattering by experiments placed adjacent to or in the core)—must be compensated by additional fuel.   To aid in estimating the reactivity requirements and to assist in evaluating the safety of certain experiments, such effects are often measured in the experimental mockups in preroutine operation.   For example, the effects of absorbers in the "glory hole" of the Livermore Water Boiler (see Chapter 5) were studied by inserting samples of boron powder into the center of the hole.   For the experiment boron powder was brushed uniformly on cellophane tape in quantities varying from 8 to 36 mg.   A negative effect of approximately 0.035 $\Delta k_{eff}/k_{eff}$ per g of boron was observed.

These results indicate that a large amount of reactivity is required to compensate for strong absorbers placed in the hole and that considerable caution must be used to prevent possible withdrawal of such absorbers during operation.   Materials which scatter and moderate neutrons effectively can cause positive reactivity effects.   Removing this type of material is not considered as dangerous as removing absorbing material, since loss of moderator reduces reactivity.   However, care is necessary to ensure that the experiments are not inserted with the reactor operating or when their positive effect may be comparable to the shutdown effect of the rods.

Reactivity effects of voids in core.   The void coefficient of reactivity has been discussed in Chapter 9 in its relation to reactor safety.   Preroutine operation is the most opportune time for measurements of this type since (assuming that the reactor has been operated most of the time at low power) the reactor is still relatively free from the disturbing effects of fission-product poison buildup or decay and from changes in fuel distribution due to burnup.

An accurate and meaningful measurement of the void coefficient is difficult to obtain because test voids do not duplicate those formed in a reactor transient.   In addition, a research reactor core is somewhat less accessible than a reactor core designed for such measurements, and the measuring techniques are therefore cruder.   However, general indications of the sign and magnitude of the void coefficient can be obtained.   For a liquid homogeneous reactor the reactivity changes introduced by voids from radiolytic gas formation are commonly measured (together with other reactivity changes) by measuring the "power" coefficient of the reactor.   The power coefficient of reactivity indicates the amount of reactivity required to change from one power level to another.

For heterogeneous reactors, indications of the void coefficient can be obtained by inserting small voids in the moderator between the fuel elements.   For example, in studying the effects of voids in the Spert-I reactor, inflated sausage casings were placed between the fuel plates. The effects of a uniform distribution of small voids in the moderator can be mocked-up by inserting plastic or some other material with a hydrogen density different from that of the normal moderating material between the fuel. Polyethylene (CH_2) or aluminum are commonly used for this purpose.

The reactivity effects of internal voids are not always negative as might be expected, since moderator material is removed from the core. In regions of the core with a surplus of moderator, the effect of removing some of the moderator is to remove neutron-absorbing material even though moderators in general have a small absorption cross section. Removal of the neutron-absorbing material causes a positive reactivity effect. This fact must be considered in determining the void coefficient throughout the core since, in regions such as control-rod channels, the net effect may be positive, partially offsetting the negative effects in other core regions. At the NRL Reactor a 2-in.-diameter empty aluminum cylinder inserted into the center of the core gave a positive reactivity effect of $0.0075 \; \Delta k_{eff}/k_{eff}$. The aluminum tube filled with water had a positive effect of only 8×10^{-4} $\Delta k_{eff}/k_{eff}$.

Reactivity effect of temperature. As with the void coefficient, the temperature coefficient of reactivity has been previously discussed in its relation to inherent reactor safety. Two principal types are of interest: the slow temperature coefficient and the fast (or prompt) temperature coefficient. The former is due to the gradual heating of the core as the power level is increased or as the coolant temperature increases due to reactor power input. This temperature coefficient is important primarily from an operational standpoint, since enough excess reactivity must be incorporated into the system to compensate for temperature changes as the power of the core is increased. An indication of the temperature coefficient is obtained by externally heating the core at criticality and noting the change in control-rod position (reactivity) necessary to maintain the reactor critical for a range of temperatures. Examples of coefficients measured in this manner (or by reactor-period measurements due to temperature changes) are the temperature coefficient of the Livermore Water Boiler, 1.47×10^{-4} $\Delta k_{eff}/k_{eff}$ per °F between 50 and 100°F, and the coefficient of the MTR, $8 \times 10^{-5} \; \Delta k_{eff}/k_{eff}$ per °F between 60 and 95°F. As can be seen from the magnitude of these values, the reactivity requirements for normal change in temperature are small compared with requirements for experiments.

The second type of temperature coefficient, the fast or prompt coefficient, is of interest primarily in reactor safety. This is the coefficient associated with temperature changes in the fuel plates, which are faster than thermal diffusion times in the core. The reactivity effects due to this coefficient are significant in rapid power excursions. Measurements of the fast temperature coefficient are difficult and usually done by power oscillation experiments.

Reactivity effects of fission-product poisons. Several of the products of the fission process are strong neutron absorbers (poisons). The concentration of these products in the core depends on reactor operating time and power level. The effect of neutron absorption by these products, primarily Xe^{135} and Sm^{149}, is important in reactors with fluxes greater than 10^{12} $n/(cm^2)(sec)$. Xe^{135} is radioactive and decays with a 9.2-hr half-life to nonpoisoning Cs^{135}. Hence the concentration of Xe^{135} reaches an equilibrium value during operation when the production of xenon is equal to the loss of xenon by radioactive decay and by burnup through absorption of neutrons. Xe^{135} absorbs a neutron to form Xe^{136}, which has a small absorption cross section. However, the other principal poison, samarium, is stable, and hence continues to build up with operating time, the only losses being due to burnup from neutron absorption.

Figure 11–8 shows the reactivity losses as a function of time for 5-Mw operation of the MTR. As seen from this graph, at the end of about 48 hr the loss of reactivity approaches a constant rate, the continuing loss being due to burnup of the fuel and the continued buildup of samarium poison. Note that 8.8 hr after shutdown (actually the power level was reduced to 50 kw so that the effects of shutdown poison buildup on core criticality could still be observed) the reactivity loss reaches a maximum value of 0.086 $\Delta k_{eff}/k_{eff}$. This buildup after shutdown is due to the fact that

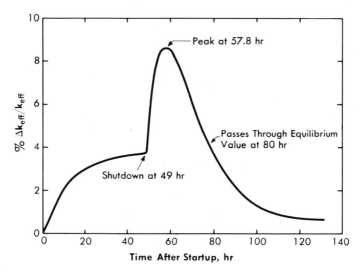

Fig. 11–8. The production and decay of fission-product poisons for 5-Mw operation of the Materials Testing Reactor.

besides being a direct fission product, Xe^{135} is also formed from the radio-active decay of another fission product, I^{135} (see Chapter 3). After shut-down, the I^{135} is still decaying to form Xe^{135}, and since the I^{135} decays more rapidly than Xe^{135}, and since the Xe^{135} is not being burned up by neutron absorption, there is a buildup in the Xe^{135} concentration. In this particular example 30 hr was required after shutdown before the Xe^{135} had returned to its value at shutdown.

The effect on the core behavior of fission-product poisons is a serious operational problem for high-power reactors. Excess reactivity must be loaded into the core to overcome the formation of these poisons. To oper-ate for extended periods of time, reactors with fluxes of 10^{13} n/(cm²) (sec) require about 0.03 $\Delta k_{eff}/k_{eff}$ excess reactivity to compensate for poison effects. Xenon "shutdown" poison buildup is not very important for fluxes less than 10^{13} n/(cm²)(sec).

Note that for homogeneous reactor systems the gaseous fission products are continuously evolved and removed from the fuel. Hence fission-product poisoning is considerably reduced.

11–4.4 Shielding studies. As the power level of the reactor is increased from criticality to design power, shielding adequacy must be checked. These measurements are also useful for other phases of reactor operation. For example, it is often important to determine whether the shielding can be reduced in any of the experimental facilities to aid in carrying out particular experiments.

At the Armour Research Reactor, large sheets of photographic film were exposed at the faces of all beam ports and at other locations where there was possibility of radiation streaming paths. The remainder of the shield was divided into 1-ft-square areas and surveyed with a Geiger-Mueller counter. General neutron and gamma-radiation checks were made with portable instruments around the reactor and throughout the building.

The type of shielding survey mentioned above has been common at most reactor facilities. Similar surveying at the MTR during initial power stepup detected no radiation leaks from the bulk shielding (final biological shield of barytes concrete about 9 ft thick). However, the principal experimental holes emitted gamma radiation which was streaming around the shielding plugs in the holes (only one step was incorporated in the beam-tube design). Special external shielding plugs were added to reduce the radiation-beam intensity below tolerance levels. A few areas of activ-ity were observed near utility lines running into the shield. These were easily shielded. Neutron activities were well below tolerance values over the entire shield.

Although shielding calculations are still primarily of the recipe type, attenuation of radiation through bulk shielding can be predicted with fair accuracy. For this reason, except for failures in the construction of the shield, little difficulty has been encountered in excessive radiation leakage from the bulk shielding. Most weaknesses in the shield, as pointed out in the above MTR shielding survey results, are cracks around special facilities inserted through the shield, through which radiation streams.

Excessive weight or thickness of shielding is of little importance in the construction of research reactors (except from the standpoint of beam-tube length). Most reactor biological shields are overdesigned simply to be conservative. This can be seen by comparing the shield thicknesses of reactors with widely differing power levels, in Chapter 2. Conservatism has advantages when it is decided, after routine operation, to raise the operating power level of the reactor. Shielding measurements during pre-routine operation can yield information useful in predicting the maximum power at which the reactor can be effectively shielded during routine operations.

11–4.5 Reactor control. As soon as the reactor has been taken critical, several experiments can be performed on the control system to determine its operability and to ensure safe and accurate control. Typical experiments are:

(1) Automatic operational stability (if this feature is provided).
(2) Response to step changes in power level.
(3) Power decay after shutdown.

As the reactor power level is increased by several decades, the ion chambers can be compensated for gamma sensitivity.

To check automatic operational stability, the reactor can be put into "automatic" at low powers and the behavior of the system observed. Perturbations can be created by moving control rods not in the automatic system. The general response time can be measured by rapidly moving another rod and observing the time for the automatic system to compensate for this movement.

As a general check of reactor stability to sudden power changes, experiments such as those performed at the Bulk Shielding Reactor (BSR) can be made. In the BSR experiment [7], the reactor was brought to high power (100 kw) and operated at this power with the automatic system for 20 min. The rod positions were noted when the system was near equilibrium. Power was then reduced to 100 watts and the reactor again stabilized at this reduced power. Because of temperature and poison effects on reactivity, the control rod was inserted 1.3 in. to decrease the power from 100 kw to 100 watts. After the system had stabilized at 100 watts, the control rod was suddenly withdrawn to its former position (i.e., withdrawn 1.3 in.) and the behavior of the power change observed. The data recorded by the power-level ion chamber are shown in Fig. 11–9. There

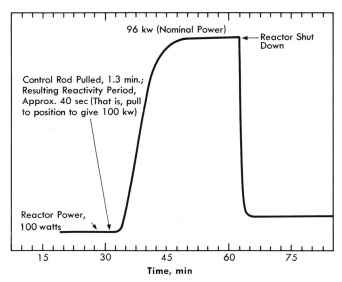

96 kw (Nominal Power)

Reactor Shut Down

Control Rod Pulled, 1.3 min.; Resulting Reactivity Period, Approx. 40 sec (That is, pull to position to give 100 kw)

Reactor Power, 100 watts

15   30   45   60   75

Time, min

FIG. 11–9. Stability test of the Bulk Shielding Reactor.

was no power overshoot or oscillation indicated by this test. The experiment was repeated for other step changes in power.

For accurate power settings, power drift and power reproducibility are determined by observing the behavior of the reactor during a long period of operation. The linearity of instruments indicating power can also be checked, either by using several independent instruments (i.e., by checking fission-chamber count rate against current output from the ion chambers as the power is increased) or by activating foils for various power levels. Assurance of power linearity allows flux plotting, dose measurements, etc., to be made at low power levels and the results to be extrapolated directly.

In understanding control of the reactor, it is useful to know the behavior of the core upon shutdown. Two features are of interest: (1) the behavior with time of the power decay at shutdown, and (2) the shutdown power level. The latter is due to decay gamma rays and subcritical multiplication from neutron sources. If large negative reactivity (several percent) is suddenly inserted into the core for shutdown, as in the case of reactor scram, the power level will drop very rapidly at first, due to reduction of the source of prompt neutrons. Then the decrease will gradually diminish as the delayed neutrons become prominent and eventually predominate in determining the period of power decay. The final shutdown period is on the order of 50 to 100 sec. The time behavior of the power decrease at shutdown is illustrated in Fig. 11–10. This shutdown curve is for a scram of the BRR, where the control rods introduce a negative reactivity effect $0.05 \; \Delta k_{\text{eff}}/k_{\text{eff}}$.

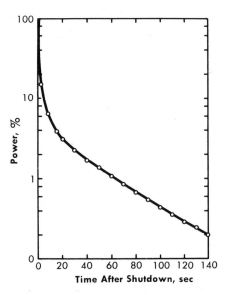

Fig. 11–10. Shutdown power curve for the Battelle Research Reactor; Approximately 5% reactivity inserted.

These data are also important to the safety analysis of experiments where the variation of heat generation with time after shutdown is important. The steady-state shutdown power of the reactor is important from a control standpoint in determining the number of decades the power level must be increased from shutdown to full power and hence the range to which the instrumentation must respond.

The shutdown power level is usually determined by standardized foil activation. For example, the shutdown power level of the Livermore Water Boiler was determined by measuring the activation of standardized foils placed in the center of the core sphere. It was found to be 0.12 Mw with the safety and control rods fully inserted and the startup source (polonium-beryllium, 10^6 n/sec) 13.6 in. from the center of the sphere. Normally, the reactor operates around 1 kw, so the instruments must respond to a power range of 10^7 from startup to full power.

After the reactor power level has been increased so that several decades of power behavior with time upon shutdown may be observed on the instruments, the ionization chambers should be "compensated." Most reactors employ compensated ionization chambers (CIC's) for reactor power level detectors. The compensated ionization chamber is really two chambers in one. One region of the chamber is sensitive to neutrons plus gamma rays, and the other region to gamma rays alone. The currents from

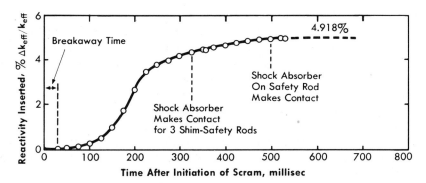

FIG. 11–11. Reactivity insertion following a scram for normal rod positions for Battelle Research Reactor.

these two regions are "bucked" against each other in an attempt to cancel the effects of gamma ionization. The volume of one region is variable, so that the output current can be varied to cancel the gamma effect. The compensation, usually by trial-and-error, can be checked by comparing the shutdown power decay curve of the ion chamber with the neutron decay curve detected by an instrument fairly insensitive to gamma ionization, such as a fission chamber. Because the gamma level in the core is so variable (changes with fission-product buildup), it is common procedure to recheck the initial compensation at full power and then again after considerable operation at full power. The voltages on the electrodes of the ion chambers can also be adjusted to aid in obtaining good compensation.

Using data from the precriticality experiments on control-rod drop distance versus time after initiation of a scram, and the complete reactivity calibration of the control rods, the reactivity supplied by the control rods as a function of time after the initiation of a scram can be obtained. A graph of such data is shown in Fig. 11–11. This curve was obtained for reactivity insertion from "normal" rod positions; that is, one rod (designated the pure safety rod) was completely withdrawn, the regulating rod was withdrawn nearly 50%, and the other three shim-safety rods were equally withdrawn to the position necessary to maintain criticality. Since the regulating rod is not inserted for a scram, and the shim-safety rods are dropped from a partially-in position, the effective total reactivity insertion is about 5%, as compared with the total worth of the rods, more than 7%.

11–4.6 Supporting functional facilities. In addition to experiments performed on the core and core environment, many must be performed during preroutine operation days on the supporting functional systems (cooling and purification systems, gas recombination systems, etc.). These experiments aid in understanding the operation of the facilities and point out likely trouble spots which might develop in routine reactor operation. Since these experiments depend on the particular supporting facilities of each reactor, examples will be given of experiments performed at several reactor facilities.

At the Armour Research Reactor, water transfer rates from the recombiner tank to the core were measured. It was found that with the reactor shut down and all equipment operating, approximately 10 ml/hr of solution were transferred from the recombiner tank (12 liters capacity) to the core. During 10-kw operation about 80 ml/hr of water are transferred from the core to the recombiner tank and back to the core. These measurements show (1) that significant water volume is transferred in the system, and (2) that if the core reactivity increases during shutdown, transfer of water to the core from the recombiner should be suspected. Radiation levels are also measured throughout the system; significant changes from the initial radiation values can indicate regions of fuel deposition.

At the Brookhaven graphite reactor, an experiment was performed to determine reactor behavior if the cooling system failed and the control system did not shut down the reactor. It was found that the negative temperature and barometric reactivity coefficients would reduce the reactor to a subcritical state rapidly enough to prevent excessive fuel-temperature rise.

Radioactivity measurements are made in all accessible components of the auxiliary systems. Typical measurements are of the radioactivity in exhaust systems, activity buildup in demineralizers and filters, and N^{16} activity at various locations in the system if water is the primary coolant.

11–4.7 Miscellaneous experiments. The above listings and illustrations of preroutine operation experiments are by no means complete. Each reactor facility, according to the purposes for which it was intended and the backlog of previous information on similar reactors, will demand certain special experiments. In some cases, many of those outlined above will not be applicable or necessary.

In graphite reactors and water boilers, in addition to temperature and void coefficients of reactivity, the pressure of the air (or other cooling gas) can affect core reactivity, and measurements are often made of the pressure coefficient of reactivity. In high-power reactors, temperature and pressure drops through the core are extremely important, as is gamma heating. Other properties of special importance in certain reactor types have been indicated in Chapters 3 through 7.

11–5. Duration of Preroutine Operation

As has previously been pointed out, the preroutine operation period is an important phase in reactor operation. Time required for this phase is proportional to the complexity of the reactor. For example, 3 months (apparently a near minimum) is typical of the low-power homogeneous and pool reactors, which have a considerable backlog of information from similar operating reactors. For reactors with intermediate power range (100 kw to 5 Mw), about 6 months is commonly spent in preroutine operation. For the large engineering-test reactors, the time may exceed a year. For these high-power reactors, much preroutine operation data must be obtained at full design power and it is difficult to distinguish precisely the transition between preroutine and routine operation. For example, the MTR achieved criticality on March 31, 1952, and within 2 months had attained full design power. However, once at design power, much time was spent in obtaining what this chapter has termed preroutine operation data.

The amount of time to be spent in preroutine operation is also determined by the staff's degree of familiarity with the reactor operations. Preroutine operation is ideal for training personnel. A few extra months of training during preroutine operation may save considerable trouble in the transition to routine operation.

References

1. J. W. Flora et al., *Operating Characteristics of the Water Boiler*, USAEC Report LRL-151, Livermore Research Laboratory, California Research and Development Co., June 1954.

2. J. N. Anno et al., *A Summary of Preliminary Experiments on the Battelle Research Reactor*, Battelle Memorial Institute, Mar. 7, 1957.

3. E. I. Norstrup et al., *Preliminary Measurements on the NRL Research Reactor*, paper presented at the American Nuclear Society, Third Annual Meeting, Session 13, June 11, 1957, Naval Research Laboratory.

4. S. Glasstone and M. C. Edlund, *The Elements of Nuclear Reactor Theory*. Princeton, N. J.: D. Van Nostrand Co., Inc., 1952.

5. U. S. Atomic Energy Commission, *Research Reactors. Selected Reference Material. United States Atomic Energy Program*, USAEC Report TID-5275, 1955. (p. 106)

6. F. C. Maienschein et al., *Attenuation by Water of Radiations from a Swimming Pool Type Reactor*, USAEC Report ORNL-1891, Oak Ridge National Laboratory, Sept. 19, 1955.

7. R. G. Cochran et al., *Reactivity Measurements with the Bulk Shielding Reactor*, USAEC Report ORNL-1682, Oak Ridge National Laboratory, Nov. 19, 1954.

CHAPTER 12

OPERATION AND MAINTENANCE OF
RESEARCH REACTORS*

12–1. INTRODUCTION

The beginning of routine operation of any research reactor is accompanied by many problems not foreseen during the test operational period. The ultimate goal of preroutine operation is, of course, the establishment of a smooth schedule unhampered by shutdowns caused either by equipment or human failure. Attaining this goal is always slow and often a disappointingly tedious process. Although trouble is a *sine qua non* of any beginning routine operation of a facility, present or potential reactor owners may benefit from a discussion of typical problems. Although no attempt will be made to give solutions that are universal in application, the discussion itself may bring about a greater understanding of the scope and involvement of general reactor operation.

Several important differences exist between the preroutine and the routine operation: (1) more stringent demands are placed upon the components of the reactor system during routine operation since operating cycles, which may be as long as several weeks, involve reliability requirements for controls, instruments, and cooling systems not previously encountered; (2) round-the-clock operation requires a full-time staff of trained operating and supervisory personnel; (3) personnel accustomed to operation without experiments installed in the reactor must continually be made aware of the effects of experiments on operation; and (4) the presence of a comparatively large amount of radioactive material enforces emphasis on health-physics procedures, some of which are not necessary during preroutine studies. Ideally, these differences should be kept in mind during preroutine operation so that procedures can be formulated to provide safe and efficient routine operation. In this way any necessary procedural changes brought about by actual operating experience can be included as they arise with a minimum of confusion.

12–2. CONTINUING OPERATIONAL PROBLEMS

The day-to-day problems encountered in keeping a reactor in continuous operation are centered around the necessities of core operation, i.e., instrumentation, supporting facilities functioning as a part of the reactor system, and experiments tied to reactor operation by safety interlocks.

---

* By A. M. Plummer.

12–2.1 Instrument maintenance.   The majority of instrumentation problems may be eliminated by careful scrutiny of reactor instruments during preroutine testing. Causes of failures can be determined in this period and measures taken to prevent recurrence. The keeping of maintenance records is invaluable, since recurrent breakdowns can be detected early and the necessary modifications made. In general, reactor personnel who have a backlog of operating experience are not plagued unduly by instrument failure; they have translated experience into good preventive-maintenance practices.

Occasional failures, particularly of electron tubes, are of course unavoidable. The operational requirements of the reactor determine the measures taken to prevent these failures from disrupting experimental work. In most cases, shutdowns, if infrequent, can be tolerated without serious disruption of the experiment. Spare instruments kept on hand may be sufficient to meet the demands placed upon the reactor. But in some instances unscheduled shutdowns from any source can be quite serious.   To eliminate this hazard the Materials Testing Reactor, for example, because of its high operating power and the accompanying possibility of "poisoning out" following a shutdown (loss of reactivity due to buildup of xenon poison), has a spare set of instruments installed and under power. Any faulty instrument can be replaced by changing cable connections from one chassis to another. Replacement must be effected quickly, because a few minutes' delay in restarting may mean a shutdown of many hours.

Another example of measures taken to prevent a shutdown due to instrument failure is the use of coincidence-connected emergency shutdown trips. With this arrangement, shutdown by either the period or high-level interlocks is not effected unless signals are received through two of three coincidence circuits. This system is used at several reactors, e.g., Brookhaven, MTR, ORR, because of experiments which require a constant power level over a relatively long period of time. The additional expense of such a system is not justified for all research reactors.

One type of instrument failure that occurs in routine operation but not in the early stages of operation results from radiation damage to equipment placed near the reactor core. This is particularly true of organic insulating materials used in electrical connections to ion chambers and safety-rod magnets (in tank and pool reactors). Elimination of this type of trouble is a matter of design and choice of materials. In some cases there is no substitute material available and breakdown must be expected after a period of exposure.   Preventive maintenance is accomplished through periodic insulation-resistance checks.

A carefully planned and executed preventive-maintenance schedule is the best solution to most instrumentation problems. This schedule should include periodic checking and replacement of electron tubes in critical circuits, the use of high-reliability tubes wherever possible, frequent attention to cleaning of relay contacts, and aging all tubes before use. A representative maintenance schedule is given in Table 12–1.

TABLE 12–1

INSTRUMENT MAINTENANCE SCHEDULE

Weekly maintenance checks:
1. Make complete operational check of all console instruments.
2. Check all safety interlocks for proper operation.
3. Recalibrate linear and log N power instruments.

Monthly maintenance checks:
1. Check insulation resistance of all cables to ion chambers and fission chamber.
2. Check insulation resistance of safety rod magnet leads and core winding.
3. Check linear power channel recorder slidewire voltage.

Bimonthly maintenance checks:
1. Check all common (nonpremium) tubes.

Semiannual maintenance checks:
1. Remove all console instruments for complete check, including tubes, and perform recalibration; replace with calibrated instruments.
2. Replace all electron tubes in recorder amplifiers with aged tubes.
3. Clean and adjust all relay contacts.

12–2.2 Maintenance of supporting facilities. Routine operation places the requirement of continuous trouble-free operation on the reactor's cooling system, demineralizers, or gas recombiners. The mechanical nature of these facilities makes them somewhat less prone to failure than the instrumentation but, at the same time, any failure is quite likely to be of a more serious nature, causing extended periods of shutdown. Preventive maintenance is therefore of prime importance, and inspection schedules should be set up early. A typical maintenance schedule is shown in Table 12–2.

TABLE 12–2

MAINTENANCE SCHEDULE FOR THE AUXILIARY EQUIPMENT OF A 1000-KW POOL REACTOR

Daily maintenance checks:
1. Check cooling tower for proper water level and makeup water supply operation.

  2. Check cooling-tower water-filter screens and clean if necessary.
  3. Check pool water level and add makeup demineralized water as necessary.

Weekly maintenance checks:

  1. Backflush primary bypass filter.
  2. Check conductivity of primary bypass demineralizer and regenerate when necessary.
  3. Check conductivity of secondary cooling water and adjust blowdown valve as necessary to maintain desired salt concentration.
  4. Inspect cooling-system pump and valve packings for leakage.

Monthly maintenance checks:

  1. Inspect cooling tower for evidence of deterioration.
  2. Clean cooling-tower diffuser trays.

Quarterly maintenance checks:

  1. Inspect heat-exchanger tube bundle for evidence of corrosion.

Semiannual maintenance checks:

  1. Lubricate pump bearings and couplings.
  2. Lubricate rod drive mechanisms.

Until the characteristics of the various systems are well known through operating experience, their performance should be watched carefully, even to the point of more frequent attention than may be thought necessary. During preroutine operation, when most attention is focused on the reactor core, there is a tendency to think of these facilities as being auxiliary. It is especially important during this period to avoid undesirable maintenance habits that may lead to trouble later.

Although these supporting facilities are basically conventional and familiar, in a reactor system they often present special maintenance problems. The chief difference is the presence of radioactivity, particularly in the cooling systems and gas recombiners, which precludes maintenance work during normal operation, and limits it to periods of shutdown. It is likely that this latter point will have some effect on the length of the operating cycle.

Demineralizers are usually located in a loop which bypasses the main cooling loop, and their shutdown for maintenance does not affect the normal operation of the reactor. Accordingly, it is best to locate the demineralizer at a sufficient distance, or to shield it from the main loop, to allow regeneration and maintenance whenever necessary. Radioactivity from ions retained in the resin beds of a demineralizer presents no serious hazard to personnel if properly shielded, but the disposal of wastes obtained during the regenerating process should be watched carefully. A decay holdup tank should be provided for these wastes and arrangements made to monitor their activity before release from the tank for final disposal.

12–2.3 Experiments. The operating philosophy of a research reactor is based on a desire to provide radiations for experiments and to maintain operating schedules consistent with the requirements of these experiments. The conditions of operation—power level and operating cycle time—are determined initially to be those best suited for the type of experiments anticipated. Once operation is under way, the aim of reactor operations is to provide these radiations under the prescribed conditions.

In addition to failures in the reactor system which inhibit the achievement of this goal, the experiments themselves can contribute problems which make routine operation difficult. This is especially true of experiments, such as in-pile loops, that operate under conditions that may constitute a hazard to the safe operation of the reactor if a failure of some sort occurs. These experiments must be monitored and appropriate emergency shutdown interlocks provided so that any experimental malfunction which can possibly damage either the reactor or the experiment will shut the reactor down.

The interlocks related to an experiment are just as important in maintaining trouble-free operation as the reactor interlocks themselves, and their design and maintenance should receive the same attention as the reactor components. Usually they are required to undergo a period of test operation before installation in the reactor.

Radiation monitoring of all experiments that bring irradiated materials outside the reactor shield is necessary to detect any release of radioactive material in the building. Failures of this type, of course, can be extremely hazardous to personnel in the building.

12–3. Personnel Training

As the number of research reactors increases, the demand for trained reactor operators increases also. There is no supply of such operators available, and the training of personnel is a responsibility of each reactor facility.

Manpower requirements vary widely, according to the size of the reactor and its experimental commitments. The organization chart for the Ford Nuclear Reactor of the University of Michigan [1] is shown in Fig. 12–1. This organization is representative of most reactor staffs. In practice, for a reactor of this size two trained operators are required. They serve part time as reactor operators; the remainder of their time is given to the duties of either reactor mechanic or electronics technician.

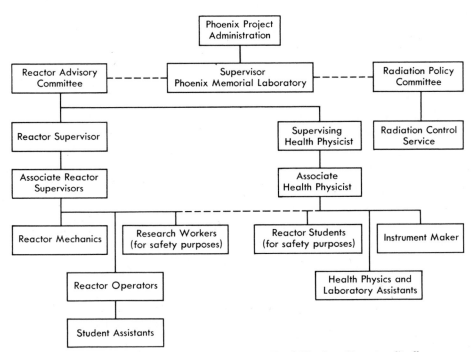

FIG. 12–1. Organizational chart of the Ford Nuclear Reactor Staff.

From the standpoint of safety, a minimum of two operating personnel per shift is required. On the other hand, large installations such as the Materials Testing Reactor require an operating staff of about twenty men per shift.

It is well to have the manpower requirements well organized prior to the initial operation of the reactor, because the many startups, shutdowns, and tests made during preroutine operation offer an excellent opportunity to train personnel in the manipulation of the reactor controls. Once routine operation commences there is little time to obtain this type of training.

Educational requirements for operating personnel will vary somewhat with the type of reactor, but it is generally agreed that for reactors operating on a round-the-clock schedule technicians with no formal engineering background serve most efficiently. Use of technicians as operators frees professional personnel for other work during routine operation. In the case of training or special-purpose reactors, however, this may not hold true.

The training program should be organized to sufficiently prepare personnel for licensing as reactor operators. The licensing test given by the United States Atomic Energy Commission is designed to determine the operator's ability to start up and shut down the reactor in a safe and prescribed manner, and also to test his knowledge of the reactor controls and instruments, normal and emergency operating procedures, core-loading procedures, basic reactor physics, and radiation safety practices. Reactor operator's licenses issued by the USAEC permit the licensee to manipulate the controls of a particular reactor only; no general licenses are issued. At the present time license requirements for various facilities differ with operating policy. For example, at installations where instrument maintenance is done by personnel other than operating personnel, licensing does not require a detailed knowledge of instrument circuits.

A representative training program for reactor operators includes the following:

(1) An orientation period in which the trainee learns the over-all operation of the facility, its principles of operation and operating rules, and the very elementary principles of reactor physics. Instruction is given through formal or informal lectures and prescribed reading material.

(2) A period of supervised operation of the reactor. Under direct supervision at the reactor console, the trainee becomes familiar with the location and function of reactor controls, learns the relationship between instrument readings and control manipulations, and applies the basic principles of reactor physics to control functions.

(3) Supervised startup and shutdown of the reactor. This phase follows after the operator is thoroughly familiar with the controls and instruments. He is checked carefully at this time to see that his knowledge of operating rules is complete.

(4) Participation in core-loading drills and instruction in the duties of all members of the loading team (see Chapter 11).

(5) Lectures on radiation safety practices. This instruction begins with the orientation period and continues through the entire training period.

12–4. Operating Procedures

Procedures for normal operation are similar for all reactors. The reactor operator on duty is responsible for proper manipulation of the reactor controls and for keeping the reactor log. Periodic readings are taken from the various instruments and recorded by the operator; a page from a typical reactor log is shown in Fig. 12–2. He also keeps a record of all emergency alarms and shutdowns, and it is his responsibility to notify the proper authority of abnormal conditions. The operator is vested with the authority to shut down the reactor if, in his judgment, conditions warrant such action to assure the safety of personnel and equipment.

In all cases, authority to increase the power level (including startup) must come from the reactor supervisor. Whether an operator may start up without direct supervision depends on the operating policy of the installation and the training standards and educational background required of operators. Startup is preceded by a thorough checkout of all instruments and safety interlocks and a visual check of the reactor and experiments to see that all are in ready condition for startup. Before the control rods are withdrawn, warning lights are turned on and an audible signal signifying startup is given. An abstract of a startup procedure is shown in Table 12–3.

TABLE 12–3

TYPICAL OPERATOR'S INSTRUCTIONS FOR REACTOR STARTUP*

1. Assure that startup has been authorized by the supervisor.

2. Assure that the control-system checkout has been completed.

3. Make visual check from control room of beam ports to provide additional assurance that ports in use are shielded.

4. Record run number, date, and time of startup in reactor log.

5. Assure that "Reactor On" signs are illuminated.

6. Announce over P.A. system that reactor is being started up.

7. Check log book to determine the safety rod shim positions for the current core loading and position.

8. Observe the three operational lights on the console; the Safety-Rod Withdrawal light will read "Ready" only when the following conditions are satisfied: (1) period safety circuits ready, (2) level safety circuits ready, (3) log channel monitors ready, and (4) safety-rod drive "Up" interlock is not on.

9. When the Safety-Rod Withdrawal light reads "Ready," carefully raise the safety rods until they are in shim range, watching fission-chamber count-rate recorder and period recorder to detect any approach to criticality; the safety rods shall then be further withdrawn one at a time; the last safety rod shall be withdrawn in a stepwise manner, allowing sufficient time after each movement to be sure that the neutron flux is leveling off as indicated by the count-rate recorder.

10. Observe the next operational light labeled Control-Rod Withdrawal; when all safety rods are in shim range this light reads "Ready"; carefully withdraw and adjust control rod manually to maintain reactor on a 20 to 30-sec period until the desired power level is reached; if the control rod reaches the limit switch, adjust one safety rod to return the control rod to its operating range.

11. As the reactor power increases, adjust range switch on the linear channel amplifier until range switch setting is for the desired operating power level.

BATTELLE RESEARCH REACTOR DATA

Page ____

DATE ____

ROD POSITIONS AT CRITICALITY | **TIME DATA**

OPERATOR ____ SHIM-SAFETY #1 ____ SHIM-SAFETY #4 ____ START CHECK-OUT ____ PERIOD GOING UP ____

REACTOR LOADING ____ SHIM-SAFETY #2 ____ REG. ROD ____ FINISH CHECK-OUT ____ REACTOR AT POWER ____

REACTOR POSITION ____ SHIM-SAFETY #3 ____ FINISH CORE LOADING ____

TIME	JORDAN RADIATION READINGS, MR/HR						POWER	LOG N	LINEAR POWER		PCP % POWER		MAG. B+	ROD POSITIONS					TEMPERATURE DATA						OTHER	INITIALS
	#1	#2	#3	#4	#5	#6			RECORD-ER	SCALE	#1	#2		#1	#2	#3	#4	REG.	#1	#2	#3	#4	#5	#6		

FIG. 12–2. A page from a typical reactor log.

12. When the desired power level has been reached, switch control rod drive to "Automatic."

13. Adjust one safety rod until the control rod is operating approximately in its center of travel.

14. Announce power level over P.A. system.

15. Withdraw fission chamber to the "Up" position.

16. Enter on recorder charts the run number, date, and time.

17. Record in log the run number, date, time, and power level.

Normal shutdown of the reactor is done in one of two ways. At some installations, shutdown is effected by inserting the control rods by means of their drive motors. Other reactors shut down by actuating one of the safety interlocks with a simulated signal; this method has the advantage of checking interlocks under operating conditions. Both shutdown and startup are carefully controlled at some installations (the Brookhaven reactor, for example) to prevent excessive temperature cycling of the fuel elements. Some fuel-element failures have been attributed to thermal stresses encountered during startups and shutdowns.

12–5. ADMINISTRATION

The role of administration in research reactor safety has been discussed in Chapter 9. Its role in routine operation is equally important, and indeed, the success of a research reactor in its job of supplying to experimenters their radiation requirements depends to a large extent on the ability of the administration to coordinate efforts of the operating and experimental staffs into a smooth-functioning research team.

12–5.1 Responsibility. With the administration rests the responsibility of seeing that reactor and experimental operations are conducted in such a manner as to make the most efficient use of manpower and equipment without undue hazard to plant equipment, personnel, and the general public. Facets of this duty include the formulation of sound operational policies and a comprehensive program of personnel training. The acceptance of a reactor installation by the general public can be greatly facilitated by a well-organized administration whose actions command respect and confidence.

The supervisor of the reactor facility, in order to execute the above responsibility, is generally given authority to have complete control over the operating status and condition of the reactor. In addition, he has authority over the experimenters using the reactor and control of visitors touring the facility.

---

* From operating procedures for the Naval Research Reactor.

12–5.2 Evaluation and scheduling of experiments.   Even before a reactor commences operation, the administration is faced with the problems of evaluating experiments.   Unlike some of the problems of routine operation, those of evaluating experiments will continue throughout the life of the reactor.

All experiments proposed for irradiation must pass through various groups which evaluate the hazards involved.   The administration must not only determine what potential hazards exist and what precautionary measures must be taken to prevent damage to either the experiment or reactor, but also determine to what extent it is necessary to interlock the experiment to the reactor emergency shutdown.   The limits to which a

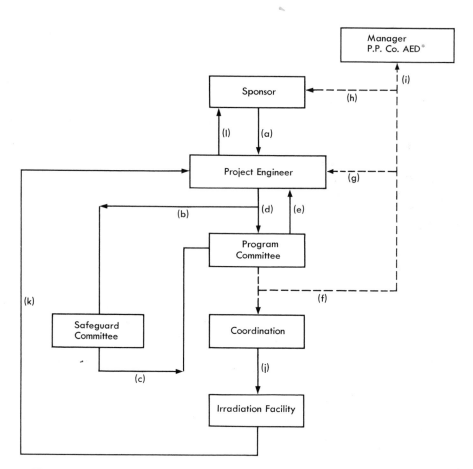

Fig. 12–3. Insertion approval of experimental irradiations in the MTR. Letters refer to Table 12–4. *Phillips Petroleum Co., Atomic Energy Division.

given parameter may vary must be decided and appropriate safety measures defined. As an example of the procedures followed in evaluating experiments, Fig. 12–3 and Table 12–4 indicate the organizational groups through which an experimental irradiation project must pass before actual insertion of the material in the MTR.

TABLE 12–4

INSERTION APPROVAL FOR EXPERIMENTAL IRRADIATIONS
IN THE MTR*

(a)   On receipt of program approval, sponsors submit samples and/or equipment to the Project Engineering Group assigned to follow the program.

(b)   Project Engineering personnel, on receipt of equipment, will check the design and perform all tests and inspections necessary to satisfy MTR engineering and safety requirements; they will then submit their proposal to the Safeguard Committee for final approval of all safety aspects; this review is concerned with the equipment and/or samples as received—in other words, a specific irradiation to be performed under stated conditions.

(c)   The Program Committee considers insertion requests, at which time the technical and operating aspects of the proposed irradiation are reviewed.

(d)   Insertion requests for irradiations not requiring Safeguard Committee action may be submitted directly to the Program Committee.

(e)   Requests may be returned to Project Engineering by the Program Committee if in its opinion further study or safeguard action is indicated.

(f,g,h,i) The result of the Program Committee action is transmitted to the Manager, Phillips Petroleum Company Atomic Energy Division, Project Engineering, Coordination, and the sponsor.

(j)   The Project Engineering coordination group, after satisfying itself that final tests have been completed and all special instructions have been issued to interested AEC branches, will schedule the actual insertion in the irradiation facility.

(k,l) On completion of the irradiation, samples are returned to the sponsor by the responsible project engineer along with all pertinent details concerning the irradiation.

---

* See Fig. 12–3.

TABLE 12–5

PERMISSIBLE WEEKLY DOSE*

| Conditions of exposure | | Dose in critical organs, 10^{-3} rem | | | |
Parts of body	Radiation	Skin, at basal layer of epidermis	Blood-forming organs	Gonads	Lens of eye
Whole body	Any radiation with half-value-layer greater than 1 mm of soft tissue	600†	300†	300†	300†
Whole body	Any radiation with half-value-layer less than 1 mm of soft tissue	1500	300	300	300
Hands and forearms, or feet and ankles, or head and neck	Any radiation	1500‡	—	—	—

* *Federal Register,* "22," No. 19, Title 10, Chap. 1, Part 20.
† For exposures of the whole body to x- or gamma rays up to 3 Mev, this condition may be assumed to be met if the "air dose" does not exceed 0.3 r, provided the dose to the gonads does not exceed 0.3 rem. "Air dose" means that the dose is measured by an appropriate instrument in air in the region of highest dosage rate to be occupied by an individual, without the presence of the human body or other absorbing and scattering material.
‡ Exposure of these limited portions of the body under these conditions does not alter the total weekly dose of 0.3 rem permitted to the blood-forming organs in the main portion of the body, to the gonads, or to the lens of the eye.

Scheduling is also one of the important duties of the administration. Only through carefully planned schedules can the most efficient use of a reactor be obtained. At first glance scheduling may seem to be quite simple, but it must be remembered that large engineering loop experiments may take as long as a year to be prepared for insertion in the reactor. In these circumstances it is apparent that problems exist in scheduling the experiment for reactor use.

12–6. HEALTH PHYSICS

Radiation safety (health physics) procedures play an important role in the safe operation of a research reactor. The purpose of these procedures is to ensure against exposure of personnel to harmful amounts of radiation. Precautions must be taken to protect not only reactor personnel, but the general public. Control must be exercised over all forms of radioactive material, particularly those which may be accidentally disseminated to the atmosphere or to local water supplies.

Recommended maximum permissible exposures to various types of radiation are given in Table 12–5. It should be noted that these values are not the *allowed* permissible exposure. In view of the lack of data on the effects of radiation exposure, the best rule is to perform a given job at exposures well below the maximum.

Good health-physics practices begin with a thorough knowledge by all personnel of the hazards involved, the precautions that should be taken to prevent overexposure, and the operation of personnel monitors provided to guard against overexposure. Personnel should be reminded at frequent intervals of the hazards of radiation by such devices as lectures, movies, and posters, and more forcefully, if necessary, by the presence of health-physics personnel during operations which involve high radiation levels.

Film badges and pocket dosimeters which measure integrated exposures should be provided all persons working in radiation fields or where the possibility of exposure exists. Periodic smears of floors, table tops, and hand rails should be made to detect contamination of areas outside the reactor room. Particular attention must be paid to areas used for eating, to prevent accidental ingestion of radioactive materials. The air should be sampled continuously at strategic points to ensure that unsafe amounts of radioactive materials are not present.

A program to sample all liquid and gaseous wastes released from the reactor site is necessary to ensure that active materials are not disseminated so that outsiders will unknowingly come in contact with them. This program should get under way before the reactor starts operating, so that adequate background information may be collected.

The place of the health physicist in administration of the reactor varies somewhat among installations. In some cases he has authority equal to that of the reactor supervisor and may order the reactor to be shut down or stop any work if he considers that a hazardous situation exists. At most facilities, however, the health physicist is a consultant whose recommendations are acted upon by the operating supervisor. In practice, the methods seem equally effective.

12–6.1 Handling of radioactive experiments and wastes. One of the larger problems connected with research reactors is handling radioactive experiments and wastes. The extent of the problem is determined primarily by the operating power level and type of reactor. Some of the techniques and equipment used by experienced personnel to deal with this problem will be discussed. Regulations governing shipment of radioactive materials will also be pointed out.

12–6.2 Shielding and handling equipment. The major problem in handling irradiated materials lies in transferring them from the reactor to shipping and storage containers. The techniques and equipment for transfer depend on the facility in which the material is irradiated.

Irradiated materials from the core regions of tank and pool reactors are relatively easy to handle from a radiation safety viewpoint because they can be taken from the reactor and transferred to suitable containers without being removed from the water. Experiments are taken from the core with handling tools manipulated from the top of the reactor tank or pool. They are then disconnected from instrumentation and cooling lines and passed through the discharge chute, then transferred to shipping containers in the canal, which is open at the top.

Materials are transferred from beam tubes in a different but equally safe manner. Figure 12–4 illustrates the beam tube transfer mechanism at the Materials Testing Reactor. Experiments attached to the beam tube shielding plugs are pulled from the beam tube into the shield of the transfer mechanism, which is then wheeled to the hot cells where there are pass-through tubes to accommodate the mechanism. A similar transfer procedure is used at the Battelle Research Reactor. Here the shielding and experiment are pulled into the transfer cask and the experiment disconnected from the shielding at a terminal located at a shutter in the shield. Covers are inserted in both ends of the transfer cask, which is lifted from the rest of the mechanism by an overhead crane and transported to the hot cells. Removing the shielding thus before transfer to the hot cells simplifies remote handling. Similar techniques apply to smaller reactors. Shielding, of course, should be consistent with the highest activity levels encountered.

Fig. 12–4. Mechanism for transfer of irradiated materials from the beam tubes of the MTR. (Courtesy of Phillips Petroleum Co.)

Radioactive waste disposal is handled in several ways. Mildly contaminated paper may be burned in incinerators, provided that activity levels of the released material comply with existing regulations [2]. Incinerator ash must, of course, be handled as are other radioactive wastes. Waste materials are buried either in the earth or at sea, or disposed of in limited quantities through sanitary sewer systems. Regulations on permissible concentrations that can be disposed of by any method are specific and must be consulted [2].

12–6.3 Transportation. Transportation of radioactive materials is closely regulated by the Interstate Commerce Commission and the Atomic Energy Commission [3]. Regulations define the methods of marking containers and maximum permissible radiation levels. Containers for shipments involving activities of less than 2.7 curies must meet certain requirements of size, ruggedness, and shielding. They must be large enough so that they cannot be carried in a pocket (no dimension smaller than 4 in.) and rugged enough to withstand shocks in transportation without allowing leakage of radioactive material. Liquid radioactive materials in breakable containers must be shipped with sufficient absorbing material surrounding the container to absorb all the liquid material contained. The package in any case must be sufficiently large or have sufficient shielding so that external gamma radiation does not exceed 200 mr/hr at the surface of the package. To protect photographic film that may be nearby during shipment, the gamma radiation from the package must not exceed 10 "radiation units" (for most gamma emitters, 1 radiation unit equals 1 mr/hr at 1 m).

Shipments of materials having activity greater than 2.7 curies must be made in containers approved by the Bureau of Explosives. The Bureau of Explosives must also be given prior notification of any shipments exceeding 2.7 curies.

12–6.4 Records. To prevent accidental dissemination of radioactive materials, careful records should be kept of the disposition of all materials irradiated in the reactor—not only experimental materials, but also containers which are of no interest experimentally. Records of all shipments and disposal of licensed and radioactive materials must be kept.

12–7. VISITOR CONTROL

It is important to the progress of work in the atomic energy field that interested persons be allowed to visit reactor facilities. Such visits should be made safe for people working in the field and for the general public.

Escorts should accompany visitors throughout their tour of an installation. This is desirable for several reasons. Few visitors will be familiar with the details of the facility and its operations and some description is necessary to make visits as informative as possible. Also, many people are unaware of potential hazards around a reactor; they must be accompanied to prevent possible injury to themselves. Conversely, they should be guarded against inadvertent interference with any experimental work in progress.

Visitors can, even at restricted installations, require a significant portion of the time of the operating staff, and plans should be made to include this service in the facilities work load. The Battelle Research Reactor, for example, which allows visits by interested persons on a controlled basis, averages about 300 visitors per month. Other installations have even more visitors. A large part of these are groups from various educational, professional, and civic institutions. Thus it is wise not only to include the visitor load when considering the facility workload but to also plan the handling of visitors when designing the facility. For example, the RRR at Raleigh has a visitors' room with a large glass front and NRL has a balcony above the experimentation area. It is important to keep visitors away from locations where they would interfere with operations.

12–8. Summary

This discussion of reactor operation has, of necessity, been limited to general consideration of those procedures and problems common to the majority of research reactors. With the growth in recent years of the number, type, and potential activity of these reactors, a discussion of specific problems on any comprehensive scale is not possible.

The objective here has been to show that the administration of any research reactor must be apprised not only of the methods of continuous operation of the reactor facility itself, i.e., maintenance, experiments, etc., but of its attendant functions as well. These functions, which make possible successful continuous operation, include the training of personnel, establishment of the general operating procedures maintained by them, and the safeguards provided for them and for the public.

References

1. H. J. Gomberg and A. H. Emmons, Manpower Requirements for a University Research Reactor, *J. Eng. Educ.* **48**(5), 360–363 (February 1958).

2. *Federal Register* **22**(19), Title 10, Chap. 1, Part 20.

3. R. D. Evans, Physical, Biological, and Administrative Problems Associated with the Transportation of Radioactive Substances, Nuclear Science Series, Report No. 11, *Natl. Acad. Sci. Natl. Research Council, Publ. No. 205* (1951).

CHAPTER 13

COST OF REACTOR FACILITIES*

13-1. Introduction

This chapter is intended to help those interested in constructing, operating, and using research and test reactors by giving them information about the costs involved. Since 1942, when the first chain reaction was achieved in CP-1 under the stands at Stagg Field, Chicago, there has been steady evolution in the design of research and test reactors. Progress has not been without growing pains as reactors became more complex and concepts were refined. As each new installation was built, new ideas for improving performance and utilization have been conceived.

Considerable sums of money have been spent by the United States Government for reactor research and development. Until 1954, the Government assumed the cost of almost all work in the field. The Atomic Energy Act of 1954 took atomic energy out of the realm of government monopoly and provided for research and industrial participation by private organizations. Since then an atomic energy industry has come into being. Although it is still relatively small, a foundation has been laid for healthy growth and expansion.

The industry has two basic divisions: one that purchases and uses atomic energy products, and one that designs, constructs, and operates or sells research and power reactors. The second group includes suppliers of materials, components, and services for Federal and private reactors. Both new and existing private companies have entered many phases of the industry, and there have been heavy outlays for nuclear research and development, and for designing, engineering, building, and operating reactors.

From 1942 to 1954 the cost of Government-owned reactors was high because much research and development had to be done. However, reactors built since 1954, when private industry entered the field, generally have cost less than in the preceding period because industry was able to take advantage of research, development and operating experience sponsored by the Government. Furthermore, competition and the desire of some companies to establish themselves in the business sometimes brought prices down still further. Now, it seems, that period is past and the industry is determined to sustain itself financially.

---

*By D. H. Stall.

This chapter considers the five principal types of research reactors developed to date (and discussed at length in this book): homogeneous, pool, tank, with light or heavy water, and graphite reactors.

Three classes of reactor owners are discussed in this chapter: (1) Government, (2) university, and (3) private industry.

Actual costs and rule-of-thumb estimates are given as they apply to the different types of reactors and to the different classes of reactor owners.

13–2. Cost of Design, Construction, and Operation

The design and consequently the cost of research reactors can vary considerably with such factors as the fuel and degree of its enrichment, type of cooling, the moderating material selected, and the location of the reactor. The proximity of the reactor to general services such as power, gas, water, roads, railroad sidings, etc., can decidedly affect the cost of an installation. If the services are not already available, they very likely have to be provided at the expense of the reactor facility.

It would seem that financial histories of reactor installations already completed should be a reliable basis for estimating the cost of similar new projects. In some instances this may be so, but more often it will not hold true because figures are presented in a wide variety of ways, according to various bookkeeping conventions.

A *post factum* indication of what a given reactor has cost may be too low if it fails to take into account such "free" items as the value of the site (the reactor may have been built on ground already belonging to the institution), administrative overhead, cooperation of scientists and technicians loaned to the project, and miscellaneous supplies granted free or at reduced prices from Governmental or private sources connected in some way with the reactor project (this last category often includes the fuel). Such a subjective approach to accounting will indicate the very minimum additional cost to the sponsoring institutions, without taking into account the value of existing resources thrown into the project.

On the other hand, an attempt to present a comprehensive accounting may reflect special difficulties encountered by the project and not likely to happen again. Development costs, for example, may be heavy in a pioneering project and much less in a subsequent model. The costs of rare ingredients, such as heavy water and processed fuel, may show a tendency to decrease. Consequently, comprehensive cost accounting may lead to excessive estimates.

The majority of the research reactors in operation, under construction, or being considered in the United States are pool or homogeneous reactors. The tank-type reactor is a variant of the pool type. The heavy-water reactor combines generous experimental capacity and a high thermal flux

TABLE 13-1

A COMPARISON OF RESEARCH REACTORS BY TYPE

Reactor type	General characteristics	Approximate average thermal-neutron flux, $n/(cm^2)(sec)$	Approximate cost of reactor,* dollars	Typical critical mass
Homogeneous	Good flux at moderate power, very low critical mass, readily adaptable to a variety of research, gross fission-product isotopes (unseparated) are directly available in laboratory quantities	2×10^{11} at 10 kw to 1×10^{12} at 40 kw	125,000 to 225,000	† About 1 kg of U^{235}
Light-water pool	Moderate critical-mass requirements, large degree of flexibility in assembly and positioning of core, very adaptable for wide variety of research	1×10^{11} at 10 kw to 1×10^{13} at 1,000 kw	200,000 to 350,000	† 2.4 to 4 kg of U^{235}
Light-water tank	Highest neutron flux, large experimental capacity, especially valuable for materials testing	2×10^{14} at 30,000 kw	6,000,000	† 4 to 6 kg of U^{235}
Heavy-water tank	Very high flux, relatively low critical mass, large experimental capacity, especially valuable for radioisotope production, enriched fuel not required	2×10^{13} at 1,000 kw	2,000,000 (includes D_2O inventory)	† 1 to 3.8 kg of U^{235}
Graphite	Largest experimental volume, allowing in-pile irradiation of large objects and great research flexibility, enriched fuel not required	2×10^{12} at 28,000 kw	10,000,000	50 to 100 tons of natural uranium
Training	Low flux, low critical mass, limited research flexibility, valuable as training facility	1×10^6 to 2×10^{10}	90,000 to 200,000	$\frac{1}{2}$ to 4 kg

*Cost of reactor proper, not including fuel, or supporting facilities.
†In fuel of 20 per cent or higher enrichment.

with a low critical mass and, although the initial investment is high, this type is receiving increased attention for new projects, since the cost per experimental facility is competitive.   The graphite reactors were designed and constructed before the widespread availability of enriched fuel and are being supplanted by the other four types. In Table 13–1 research reactors of several types are briefly compared, including cost estimates.

The cost estimates given in this table are for a bare reactor. It is interesting to compare the cost of the reactor alone with the cost of complete reactor installations including fuel, housing, and supporting facilities. Complete low-power, low-flux reactor facilities have been built and installed on a budget of not more than $100,000 (Tables 13–11, 13–14, 13–15). A homogeneous reactor installation with a flux of a little more than 10^{12} n/(cm^2)(sec) has been built for something more than $400,000 (Table 13–9).   Pool reactor facilities having a flux of about 10^{13} n/(cm^2)(sec) have cost $0.8 to $1 million (Tables 13–3 and 13–4).   Tank and heavy water reactor installations providing flux of the order of 10^{13} to 10^{14} n/(cm^2)(sec) were completed in the range of $2.5 to $3 million.

The cost of 1 to 3 kg of U^{235} invested in a modern research reactor does not constitute a major item.

Running costs, even more than investment costs, depend on the bookkeeping conventions and on the lavishness (or thrift) of the reactor budget. From the scanty numerical data in the literature, some rough indications can be deduced.

Operation and maintenance of a medium-flux university reactor [around 10^{12} n/(cm^2)(sec)] may cost up to $100,000 per year (mobile equipment and personnel for experiments not included).   Operation and maintenance of a somewhat more powerful facility, operated on a round-the-clock basis, or nearly so, by specialized personnel, may cost around $200,000 per year.

At highest fluxes the cost of fuel and of heat removal become very important. The annual operating costs for the MTR [thermal-neutron flux, 10^{14} n/(cm^2)(sec)] approach 5 million dollars. This heavy cost limits the availability of the highest flux reactors for most research institutions and makes more attractive, for most purposes, the selection of somewhat less powerful types.

Tables 13–2 through 13–15 give cost breakdowns from published literature for specific reactors of the several types. The variety of accounting methods in use is apparent from these tables. The obvious items of cost that appear to be missing may be accounted for in one of three ways: they were free, they were not included as part of the cost of the facility (these two are particularly prevalent in government- or university-owned reactors), or they are included under some other accounting heading.

The costs in these tables represent what was paid for a particular

TABLE 13–2

PENNSYLVANIA STATE RESEARCH REACTOR

Pennsylvania State University, University Park, Pennsylvania

Reactor type	Pool
Power	100 kw
Thermal-neutron flux	1×10^{12} n/(cm²)(sec)
Class of owner	University
Cost of facility	
Design	$ 14,350
Core and instrumentation	76,000
Pool and shield	32,450
Experimental facilities	24,000
Building	134,480
Site improvement (utilities, roads, fence)	26,670
	$307,950
Planned changes	
Future forced cooling (estimate)	$ 23,600
Future hot-cell cost (estimate)	155,000
	$178,600
Operating cost per year (fuel inventory and burnup, depreciation, and taxes are free)	
Manpower	$59,000
Fixed facility cost	15,650
	$74,650

TABLE 13–3

BATTELLE RESEARCH REACTOR

Battelle Memorial Institute, Columbus, Ohio

Reactor type	Pool
Power	1000 kw
Thermal-neutron flux	1.4×10^{13} n/(cm²)(sec)
Class of owner	Industrial
Cost of facility	
Design, engineering, hazards evalua- tion, and license preparation	$ 90,000
Core and instrumentation	96,000
Cooling system	29,000
Experimental facilities	60,000
Initial core loading	30,000
Building and pool	485,000
Site improvement (utilities, roads, but not cost of site)	44,000
	$834,000
Operating cost per year	
Manpower	$ 60,000
Fixed facility costs	140,000
	$200,000

TABLE 13–4

FORD NUCLEAR REACTOR

University of Michigan, Ann Arbor, Michigan

Reactor type		Pool
Power		1000 kw
Thermal-neutron flux		1×10^{13} n/(cm^2)(sec)
Class of owner		University
Cost of facility		
Project staff costs and supplies*		$ 46,679
Design costs		46,523
Building	36,911	
Reactor and auxiliaries	9,612	
Construction costs		774,183
Building (base price)	506,970	
Air drier	10,500	
	517,470	
Reactor (base price, including thermal column)	141,400	
Fast pneumatic system	22,600	
Shipping coffin	10,605	
Transfer coffin	12,895	
System intrumentation	43,894	
Cooling tower	9,830	
Water purification	8,489	
Pool lining (estimated cost of tile)	7,000	
	256,713	
Miscellaneous costs		134,000
Site improvement	30,000	
Construction supervision by University of Michigan supervising architect	4,000	
Hot cave in adjoining building	100,000	
		$1,001,385
Operating cost per year†		$50,400
Manpower	26,400	
Fixed facility	18,000	
Cooling and purification	6,000	

* Includes $7155 for preparation of major safeguards report and $7492 for other hazards studies and license negotiations.

† No charge for fuel or depreciation.

TABLE 13–5

OAK RIDGE RESEARCH REACTOR

Oak Ridge National Laboratory, Oak Ridge, Tennessee

Reactor type	Tank (modified pool)
Power	20,000 kw
Thermal-neutron flux	3×10^{14} n/(cm^2)(sec)
Class of owner	Government
Cost of facility	
Design	$ 545,000
Building, pool and shielding	2,315,000
Reactor and controls	819,000
Water system (includes tank)	887,000
Air system	100,000
	$4,666,000

TABLE 13–6

NAVAL RESEARCH REACTOR

Naval Research Laboratory, Washington, D. C.

Reactor type		Pool
Power		100 kw
Thermal-neutron flux		1×10^{12} n/(cm^2)(sec)
Class of owner		Government
Cost of facility		
Basic building costs		$ 672,000
Architectural and structual	230,000	
Mechanical facilities	349,000	
Fees (design)*	93,000	
Basic reactor costs		298,600
Pool	66,000	
Hold-up tank and cooling system	62,000	
Core and core components	57,400	
Fuel elements	24,000	
Experimental facilities	40,000	
Control electronics	44,200	
Miscellaneous	5,000	
Reactor accessories costs		219,300
Hot cell	111,000	
Chemical-laboratory equipment	9,600	
Water treatment	16,200	
Miscellaneous	82,500	
		$1,189,900

* Costs incurred by the reactor and engineering staff in design of building, reactor, control, and associated facilities and equipment are generally excluded. For example, the control electronics and design and development ran to roughly $100,000.

TABLE 13–7

ENGINEERING TEST REACTOR

National Reactor Testing Station, Idaho

Reactor type	Tank
Power	175 Mw
Thermal-neutron flux	6×10^{14} n/(cm^2)(sec)
Class of owner	Government
Cost of facility	
Reactor	$ 2,900,000
Building	2,200,000
Experimental facilities and services	2,100,000
Cooling system and associated buildings	4,200,000
Electrical	2,100,000
Winter protection	300,000
Engineering, development, and inspection	2,600,000
All other	800,000
	$17,200,000
Operating cost per year of cooling system alone (includes amortization at 9%)	$ 5,659,000

TABLE 13–8

MATERIALS TESTING REACTOR

National Reactor Testing Station, Idaho

Reactor type	Tank
Power	40,000 kw
Thermal-neutron flux	4×10^{14} n/(cm^2)(sec)
Class of owner	Government
Cost of facility	
Site improvement	$ 2,100,000
Reactor	5,900,000
Building	3,500,000
Water system	3,100,000
Air system	300,000
Power plant	1,000,000
Finish detail design*	2,100,000
	$18,000,000
Operating costs per year	
Manpower, maintenance, cooling and purification, fuel fabrication (this is included in use rate)	$ 3,154,000
Depreciation, fuel burnup, fuel reprocessing, overhead (this is not included in use rate)	1,471,860
	$ 4,625,860

* Conceptual design and development $13,000,000.

TABLE 13–9

ARMOUR RESEARCH REACTOR

Armour Research Foundation, Chicago, Illinois

Reactor type	Homogeneous
Power	50 kw
Thermal-neutron flux	$1.7 \times 10^{12}\,\text{n}/(\text{cm}^2)(\text{sec})$
Class of owner	Industrial

Cost of facility (excluding building)

Reactor and biological shield	$ 220,000
Reactor room and containment system (including airlocks and overhead crane)	70,000
Special equipment	15,000
Health physics equipment	12,000
Equipment (spectrometers, etc.)	50,000
Hot cell (kilocurie)	40,000
	$ 407,000

Physics and electrical engineering research building,
including all the nuclear facility but excluding all
other research equipment $1,300,000

TABLE 13–10

RALEIGH RESEARCH REACTOR

North Carolina State College, Raleigh, North Carolina

Reactor type	Homogeneous
Power	500 watts
Thermal-neutron flux	2×10^{10} n/(cm^2)(sec)
Class of owner	University
Cost of facility	
Core and core components, reactor instrumentation, core container, and shield	$125,000
Building	380,000
Miscellaneous equipment	120,000
	$625,000
Operating costs per year*	
Manpower	$ 20,000
Supplies (not including capital equipment)	25,000
Miscellaneous	10,000
	$ 55,000

* Depreciation and fixed costs are not charged to the reactor operations budget.

TABLE 13–11

WATER BOILER NEUTRON SOURCE REACTOR

Atomics International,* Santa Susana Mountains, California

Reactor type	Homogeneous
Power	5 watts
Thermal-neutron flux	2×10^8 n/(cm^2)(sec)
Class of owner	Government
Cost of facility	
Reactor	$75,000
Building and crane	10,000
	$85,000

* Built and operated for the USAEC.

TABLE 13–12

ARGONNE RESEARCH REACTOR (CP-5)

Argonne National Laboratory, Lemont, Illinois

Reactor type	Heavy water
Power	2000 kw
Thermal-neutron flux	3.5×10^{13} n/(cm^2)(sec)
Class of owner	Government
Cost of facility	
Reactor	$ 633,000
Fuel-element fabrication	15,000
Heavy water	400,000
Installation of biological shield, graphite, and reactor tank	403,000
Building (approximate)	1,000,000
	$2,451,000
Operating costs per year (approximate)	$ 200,000

TABLE 13–13

OAK RIDGE GRAPHITE REACTOR (X-10)

Oak Ridge National Laboratory, Oak Ridge, Tennessee

Reactor type	Graphite
Power	3500 kw
Thermal-neutron flux	1.1×10^{12} n/(cm^2)(sec)
Class of owner	Government
Cost of facility	
Reactor	$2,700,000
Building	1,100,000
Air system	900,000
Design	500,000
	$5,200,000

TABLE 13–14

ARGONNE NAUGHT POWER REACTOR (ARGONAUT)

Argonne National Laboratory, Lemont, Illinois

Reactor type	Special
Power	10 kw
Thermal-neutron flux	5×10^{11} n/(cm²)(sec)
Class of owner	Government
Cost of facility	
Building, slab, and foundation	$29,711
Reactor and instrumentation	26,088
Cooling system	3,904
Fuel assemblies	2,830
Shielding and graphite	32,816
Miscellaneous	2,011
	$97,360

TABLE 13–15

AGN SOLID HOMOGENEOUS REACTOR

Reactor type	Special
Power	0.1 watt
Thermal-neutron flux	4.5×10^6 n/(cm²)(sec)
Class of owner	Any
Cost of reactor system with fabricated uranium fuel* and all AGN services, completely set up and operating at any location in the continental United States†	$95,000

---

* U^{235} must be leased from the AEC. Educational institutions and nonprofit research organizations usually do not pay a leasing fee. The leasing fee to industry is approximately $700 per year.

† In addition to the reactor, this cost includes the following services: Hazard Evaluation Report for AEC, Site Survey Report for AEC, necessary assistance in obtaining AEC licensing, and training in reactor theory and operation usually for 1 week.

type of reactor by a particular class of owner at a particular time and should not be taken to be the cost of duplicating the reactor now or in the future.

13–3. Items of Cost to Be Considered by the Prospective Reactor Owner

This section will present the many different items of cost to be considered by a prospective reactor owner. Expenses likely to be encountered in the planning, construction, and operation of a research reactor facility will be described.

13–3.1 Design and engineering costs. There are design, engineering, and research and development costs for every reactor, whether these functions are performed by the owner, the contractor, or both. Often, published design and engineering costs include only the contract fee paid to a contractor and not time spent by the owner.

13–3.2 Hazards-evaluation costs. These costs should include the amounts paid by the owner or contractor for the preparation of the hazards summary report required before a construction permit for the reactor can be issued by the Atomic Energy Commission. This report includes a description of the reactor, its building, the makeup of the surrounding area, and an estimate of the hazards during normal operation and after an accident.

13–3.3 License-preparation costs. These costs are incurred by the owner or contractor for preparation of the application to the Commission for the license necessary before a reactor can be operated. The application contains general information about the owner and the reactor facility, including proposed administration and operating procedures, and special material requirements. These costs apply only when the reactor is owned by industry or a university.

13–3.4 Site costs. The cost of the land on which a reactor facility is located has rarely been included as part of the cost by the owners of research reactors, since the Government and universities have generally had land available. Industry, on the other hand, ordinarily must locate and buy the land specifically for a reactor site, and this cost should be considered by the prospective industrial owner.

13–3.5 Construction costs. These costs include the core and core components, instrumentation, cooling and purification system, experimental facilities (beam tubes, thermal column, etc.), core container (pool or tank), shielding, building, and site improvements (utilities, roads, etc.). They vary a great deal, according to the type of reactor, the class of owner, and the location. A small, low-power, university-owned reactor may not need a special cooling and purification system, may be located in an existing building, and may need few site improvements, whereas a medium-power, Government-owned reactor located in a remote area might incur all this expense, especially high costs for site improvement.

13–3.6 Operating costs. Manpower, amortization, fuel, repair and maintenance, and fixed facility costs are included here.

Manpower includes an administrative staff, operating staff, and health-physics and safety staff. These costs will vary with the type of reactor and with the class of the owner. A pool-type university-owned reactor may operate only three days a week, using students for manpower. A tank-type Government-owned reactor, on the other hand, may operate around the clock 30 days at a time and require a large staff.

Amortization includes the depreciation and obsolescence of the entire reactor facility, plus insurance and taxes. Industry must usually pay all these amortization costs; universities some; and the Government ordinarily none. Depreciation is usually spread over a short period of time (5 to 15 years) because of the rapid obsolescence factor common in a fast-growing industry.

Fuel costs include the 4% paid to the Government on the inventory value, fabrication costs where they apply (none for homogeneous-type reactors), reprocessing costs, and the value of the fuel burned up. Industry must pay all these costs; universities usually do not have to pay the inventory and burnup costs; and Government-owned reactors generally do not have inventory, reprocessing, or burnup costs charged directly to the reactor facility.

Fixed facility costs include power, heat, water, gas, communications, guards or watchmen, and miscellaneous services and supplies. These items vary with the requirements of the various types of reactors but generally must be paid by all classes of reactor owners.

13–3.7 Supporting facilities. The magnitude of costs involved with supporting facilities, such as hot cells and radioisotope laboratories, depends more on the type of research to be carried on by the reactor facility than on the type of reactor or the class of the owner.

13–3.8 General laboratories. The cost of a counting laboratory, instrument-repair laboratory, machine shop, and miscellaneous laboratories, as well as their equipment must be considered. The cost of research laboratories and equipment is not considered here as part of the cost of a complete research reactor facility, although supporting laboratories are an important factor in increasing the usefulness of the reactor.

13–4. GENERAL LABORATORIES AND SUPPORTING FACILITIES

General laboratories (see Chapter 8) include a counting laboratory, instrument-repair laboratory, and perhaps a machine shop. These facilities are considered necessary to the operation of a reactor facility but their costs make up a very small percentage of the total for the complete reactor facility. However, when research and/or training equipment is added to these laboratories or the entire facility, costs can rise very rapidly.

Supporting facilities for a research reactor include hot cells and radioisotope laboratories (see Chapter 8). Radioisotope laboratories are generally present in some form at all research reactor facilities, but represent such a small portion of the facility cost that they are rarely accounted for separately. A small radioisotope laboratory located in an existing building might cost as little as $2000 or $3000. Multi-unit laboratories built for specific research purposes might cost 100 times as much.

Hot cells suitable for handling work with high radiation levels are not found at all research reactors because of their high cost, or because of the type of research work that is to be carried on. Hot cells are usually kept busy with work created by their associated reactor, as well as with work sent from other reactors. Table 13–16 lists some typical hot-cell facilities, their capacity, and cost.

TABLE 13–16

TYPICAL HOT-CELL FACILITIES, THEIR CAPACITY, AND COST

Reactor facility	Number of cells	Maximum cell capacity,* kilocuries	Cost, dollars
Armour Research Reactor	1	50	$ 40,000
Battelle Research Reactor	2	1000	754,000
Ford Nuclear Reactor	2	10	100,000
Materials Testing Reactor	1	20	268,000
Naval Research Reactor	1	3	219,300
Pennsylvania State Research Reactor†	2	0.1	155,000

* Capacity is based on the number of curies of a gamma emitter, with an average energy of 1 Mev, which can be contained in the cell without exceeding the tolerance level external to the cell.

† Estimate of future cost.

13–5. USE-RATE CHARGES

Each reactor facility charging for irradiation service has developed its own method for computing use rates. The different methods are usually based, to varying degrees, on space, time, or radiation level, or combinations thereof. The magnitude of the use-rate costs depends upon the yearly operating cost of the research reactor facility, and whether the facility is being subsidized or is expected to pay its own way. The various methods for charging use rates are attempts by the owners to arrive at an equitable means of recovering operating costs.

Table 13–17 gives the availability of various research reactors to outside organizations for research and service irradiations. Since most of the research reactors built to date are owned by the Government and were built to handle Government research projects, they are usually available only on a limited basis for non-Government research. Tables 13–18 through 13–21 list the use rates for five Government-owned research reactors that are partially available to research organizations, subject to AEC regulations.

TABLE 13–17

AVAILABILITY OF RESEARCH REACTORS

POOL

Bulk Shielding Facility (Government)	Available on a limited basis to research organizations, subject to AEC regulations
Ground Test Reactor (Government)	Operated as the Air Force directs; it is fully scheduled with Air Force research and development programs
Pennsylvania State (University)	Intended for use by faculty and staff; time and space can be made available to outside organizations with priority to those within the state
Battelle Research Reactor (Industry)	Available to organizations sponsoring research programs at Battelle
Naval Research Reactor (Government)	Intended for use by NRL, but facilities can be made available to other Government agencies and private organizations holding Department of Defense contracts
Ford Nuclear Reactor (University)	Facilities will undoubtedly be made available to outside parties, although more than two-thirds of the time and space will be used by the university
Livermore Pool Reactor (Government)	Use to be limited to UCRL research program
Curtiss-Wright Research Reactor (Industry)	Available to any organization requiring a broad research program or merely irradiation services
Industrial Research Lab., Inc. (Industry)	Participating companies will hold priority, but some irradiations may be performed for other organizations

LIGHT-WATER TANK

Low-Intensity-Testing Reactor (Government)	Present full schedule is expected to be relieved when ORR is completed; will then be available to other research organizations subject to AEC regulations
Materials-Testing Reactor (Government) and Engineering Test Reactor (Government)	Available to educational, research, and industrial organizations, subject to AEC regulations; priority given AEC-sponsored work; proposed work must be submitted to MTR/ETR Policy Board for priority

(*continued*)

TABLE 13–17 (*continued*)

Omega West Reactor (Government)	For internal LASL research program and not ordinarily available for other use
Oak Ridge Research Reactor (Government)	Intended for ORNL research program; some small experimental facilities may be available through the radioisotope-production program

HEAVY-WATER TANK

MIT Research Reactor (University)	Intended for MIT fundamental research, for medical radiation investigations, and industrial and government research
Argonne Research Reactor (CP-5) (Government)	Available to authorized educational research and industrial organizations, subject to AEC regulations

GRAPHITE

Oak Ridge X-10 Area Reactor (Government)	Used for major portion of AEC radioisotope production; service irradiations available, subject to AEC regulations
Brookhaven Research Reactor (Government)	Available to research organizations, subject to AEC regulations and laboratory requirements

HOMOGENEOUS

SUPO (Government)	For internal LASL research; not ordinarily available for other use
Water-Boiler Neutron Source (Government)	Almost fully scheduled with Atomics International research program; some space can be made available from time to time
Livermore Water Boiler (Government)	Use limited to UCRL research program
Armour Research Reactor (Industry)	Participating organizations hold priority for use of research facilities; inquiries from other organizations will be considered, and some may be accommodated
Raleigh Research Reactor (University)	Primary purposes are research and instruction by faculty and staff, but irradiation services can be negotiated

TABLE 13–18

CP-5 USE-RATE CHARGES

1. For standard-size (1.5 in. $\times$ 3 in. capsule) service irradiations:
   (a) $15 per week or less, or $45 per month, in the flux region of less than 1×10^{13} n/(cm^2)(sec)
   (b) $25 per week or less, or $75 per month, in the flux region of more than 1×10^{13} n/(cm^2)(sec)

2. For bulky items:
   (a) $15 per week or less, or $45 per month, for each 6 in. of axial hole space occupied in the 4.75-in.-diameter graphite thimbles and the 3.5 by 3.5-in. isotope holes
   (b) $3 per day for each space (4 in. wide by 4 in. high by 6 in. long) occupied in the thermal column, plus $100 surcharge for dismantling the column

3. For in-pile experiments:
   (a) $30 per day for thimbles in the flux region of less than 1×10^{13} n/(cm^2)(sec)
   (b) $50 per day for thimbles in the flux region of more than 1×10^{13} n/(cm^2)(sec)
   (c) $20 per day for isotope holes
   (d) $40 per day for the thermal column, plus $100 surcharge for dismantling the column

4. For handling of irradiated samples:
   (a) $15 per standard-size CP-5 service irradiation, standard reactor unit irradiation
   (b) $30 per bulky-item irradiation for all activity up to 200 mr/hr measured at 2 m and increased by $15 for each 200 mr/hr (or portion thereof) of additional activity

5. For material furnished by the laboratory:
   (a) Cost of sample material if it exceeds $2
   (b) Cost of accessory equipment and material used for special experiments
   (c) $1.50/day demurrage for each returnable shipping container held 21 days

6. For labor furnished by the laboratory:
   Direct-labor costs plus overhead, laboratory work for preparation of targets or other equipment, special preparations and analyses, and unusual loading and unloading services

TABLE 13–19

BROOKHAVEN RESEARCH REACTOR USE-RATE CHARGES

	Rate*	Surcharge†
A. Target conveyor	$10 for first day, $2 for each additional day	None
B. Pneumatic tubes	Same as A	None
C. Water-cooled hole	Same as A	$10
D. Liquid nitrogen hole	Same as A plus cost of liquid N_2 (maximum of $16 per day)	$25
E. Gas-handling system	Same as A	$15
F. Thermal column	Same as A	None
G. Tunnels	Same as A	$10
H. South core hole	$32 for first 2 weeks, $24 for each additional 2 weeks	$50 or $65
I. Experimental holes	Same as H	$10 or $25
J. Fuel channel	Same as H	$35 or $50
K. Air-cooled holes	Same as H	$10 or $25
Holes N-5 and N-8 only	Same as A	$15
L. CO_2-cooled facility	Same as A plus cost of CO_2	$25
M. High-temperature facility	Same as H	$10 or $25

* These rates apply to each package irradiated. The package size, except for the following facilities, is the maximum size given in the table.

Water-cooled hole:	8 in^3 volume
South core hole:	$3\frac{3}{4}$ by $11\frac{1}{2}$ by $11\frac{1}{2}$ in.
Experimental holes:	$3\frac{3}{4}$ by $3\frac{3}{4}$ by 6 in.
Fuel channels:	$2\frac{1}{2}$ in. in diameter by 8 in.
Air-cooled holes:	2 in. in diameter by 8 in.
N-5, N-8	$1\frac{3}{4}$ in. in diameter by 7 in.

† A single surcharge will be made for each irradiation performed at one time regardless of length of irradiation time or package size.

Note: In addition to the above costs, a $20 handling charge is made for each sample, or series of samples, irradiated or shipped as a unit.

TABLE 13–20

LITR AND X-10 USE-RATE CHARGES

Special service irradiations which can be
accommodated in a standard can

Flux, n/(cm^2)(sec)	Cost, dollars	
	Per week	Per month
$< 10^{12}$	$15	$45
10^{12} to 10^{13}	23	68
10^{13} to 10^{14}	30	90

Note: Prices are fob point of delivery to a common carrier and do not include handling charges or applicable target costs.

Charges for handling larger objects and making special arrangements will be quoted by the laboratory upon request.

Cost for contaminated waste disposal is $10 per disposal for packages less than 500 lb and smaller than 4 by 4 by 4 ft. Prices for larger packages will be quoted upon request.

Two types of containers are normally used for the shipment of radioactive materials. One is a returnable heavy lead-shielded container for which a deposit of $125 is required. The other is a disposable light-weight fiberboard box. Customers must furnish shipping containers for samples larger than $\frac{3}{4}$ in. in diameter by $3\frac{1}{2}$ in. long.

TABLE 13–21

MTR USE-RATE CHARGES

The following charge basis is in accordance with
the "full-cost recovery" philosophy of the U. S.
Atomic Energy Commission, based on actual
cost experience during 1956

1. Neutron irradiations performed inside the reactor tank will be charged at the rate of \$55 per irradiation unit of 10^{20} nvt (thermal) for each linear inch of space occupied in any vertical $1\frac{1}{8}$-in.-diameter irradiation facility by capsules containing the specimens to be irradiated plus the cost of any leads that may be required

2. Irradiations involving materials of such high macroscopic absorption cross section as to create excessive shadowing effects in adjacent facilities will, in addition to the charge for the space actually occupied, be charged at the standard rate for any of these facilities that have to be left vacant because of such shadowing

3. Hydraulic-rabbit irradiations will be charged on the same nvt basis as indicated above, subject to the limitation that the minimum length of capsule that can be handled is 3 in.; the charge rate for a 0.813-in. or a 1.125 by 3-in. long capsule in VH-1, VH-3, and VH-4 is \$0.56 per MWD of reactor operation, while the capsule is in its irradiation position; each of these facilities gives an integrated thermal-neutron flux of 3.456×10^{17} nvt per MWD

4. The charge rate for Hydraulic Facility VH-2, which supplies an integrated flux 50% higher than the other hydraulic facilities, is \$0.85 per MWD; the minimum charge for each experiment or capsule handled in any hydraulic-rabbit facility will be \$10.00.

5. Cost information for irradiations performed in beam holes, graphite-reflector positions, or other locations within the reactor will be supplied on request

6. The neutron-irradiation charges specified above include routine insertion and removal of the test specimens from the reactor; they do not include charges made to cover costs of special services which may be requested or required; such services might include, as examples: detailed engineering consultation, special shop work, extraordinary collection of data, nonroutine sample inspections and handling, and the like

7. Shipping is at the customer's expense, and the customer is expected to provide proper shielded shipping containers; the MTR can, in special cases, provide shipping casks at cost, provided prior arrangements have been made for such service

8. All radioisotopes will be charged for on a service-irradiation basis at the space rates specified above; no limitation except that of geometry and macroscopic absorption cross section as indicated in Paragraph 2 above is placed on the quantity of material that can be irradiated in a given facility volume

9. A handling charge of $25.00 will be made for each sample shipment to cover costs of packaging, health-physics inspection, and local transportation to shipping points; shipments may contain more than one sample, so long as they can all be handled at once

Several university and privately owned reactors are available for some service-type irradiations, although these operators prefer complete research programs. University reactors usually operate on an 8-hr-day 5-day-week basis and charge rates sufficient to cover their operating costs. These costs are divided between the various experimental facilities on a somewhat arbitrary basis, with a minimum charge per experiment for each facility.

To date no industry-owned research reactor has published use-rate charges. This class of reactor owner usually prefers to carry out complete research programs with the reactor and tends to discourage service-type irradiations. A rough rule-of-thumb use-rate charge often used in connection with a research program is 10 to 25% of the total research allocation. When a research reactor is owned by a number of participating companies, the companies usually are not charged for the use of the reactor or, if they are, the rate is greatly reduced.

CHAPTER 14

REGULATIONS AND INSURANCE*

I. REGULATIONS

Before generally discussing the regulations applicable to research reactors in the United States, it seems worth while to review the historical background and the events leading up to the passage of the Atomic Energy Act of 1954, a revision and expansion of the McMahon Act (The Atomic Energy Act of 1946).

At the end of World War II, with the dramatic demonstration of the potential of atomic energy, many government and industry leaders turned their attention to the problems created by this revolutionary new development. The McMahon Act, in essence, made atomic energy a government monopoly, administered by a five-man civilian board, the United States Atomic Energy Commission (USAEC, or simply AEC). The Act prohibited private ownership of fissionable material and imposed control upon trade in source materials.

In the years between 1946 and 1954, the succession of events, both political and scientific, emphasized the changed nature of the problems confronting the ultimate peaceful utilization of atomic energy. By 1950, the fond hope of 1946 for international control of atomic energy seemed less likely to be realized. In addition, peaceful utilization of atomic energy seemed imminent rather than distant. As a result of the changed emphasis, in 1952 the Atomic Energy Commission began an intensive study of the problems of atomic power development. In the spring of 1953, the Commission submitted a policy statement on atomic power. The Commission's report emphasized that maximum progress in the area of atomic power development required a greater contribution in manpower and resources from private enterprise and that legislative revisions in the McMahon Act would be necessary to make this possible.

A succession of legislative proposals ultimately produced the Atomic Energy Act of 1954. Perhaps the most significant feature of the 1954 legislation is that the AEC assumed the status of a regulatory body, in addition to its status as a contracting organization. The Atomic Energy Act of 1954 provided the legal framework for the development of an atomic energy industry under private auspices. Regulatory procedures of the Commission and the procedures applicable to private industrial development of atomic energy are in the code of Federal Regulations.

---

* By H. R. Nelson and C. R. Tipton, Jr.

14-1. CODE OF FEDERAL REGULATIONS (CFR)

Under the Atomic Energy Act of 1954, the AEC is responsible for regulating both the processing and utilization of source, by-product, and special nuclear materials.* The regulations governing the USAEC's action in these fields are described in the Code of Federal Regulations, Title 10, Atomic Energy. The CFR has been published in the *Federal Register*, copies of which are available from the AEC. Thorough familiarity with the Regulations is a requisite for any contemplated licensing action. The following parts of the CFR Title 10 are pertinent to the planning or operation of a research reactor:

Part 2 sets out the Commission's Rules of Practice.

Part 9 prescribes the rules governing the AEC's public records.

Part 20 establishes the "Standard for Protection Against Radiation."

Part 30 covers the licensing of by-product material (reactor-produced radioisotopes.)

Part 40 contains the regulations governing source material.

Part 50 is the regulation establishing the licensing system for facilities (the construction and operation of reactors, for example).

Part 55 deals with the licensing of operators of facilities (the persons who actually manipulate the controls of a reactor).

Part 70 sets up the licensing and allocating procedures for special nuclear material (the reactor fuel).

Part 140 establishes the financial protection requirements and the indemnity agreement procedure.

In an introductory sense, Parts 2 and 9 are most important to any group or individual planning to construct and operate a reactor. Parts 2 and 9 set forth the general rules of practice for filing papers, hearings, rule making, and availability of official records relating to license applications.

Part 9 of the Regulations covers the rules governing the AEC's handling of a submission for licensing. While in fact Part 9 provides for the handling of "Business Confidential" information as well as "Classified" (security) information, in practice, the Commission is required to make public as much as possible of all information relating to its proceedings. Any license

---

* These terms have very specific meanings. *Source material* means any material, except special nuclear material, that contains, by weight, 0.05% or more of (a) uranium, (b) thorium, or (c) any combination thereof. *Special nuclear material* means (a) plutonium, U^{233}, uranium enriched in the isotope 233 or in the isotope 235, and any other material which the AEC determines to be special nuclear material, but does not include source material; or (b) any material artificially enriched by any of the foregoing, but does not include source material. *By-product material* means any radioactive material (except special nuclear material) yielded in or made radioactive by exposure to the radiation incident to the process of producing or utilizing special nuclear material.

submission will ultimately appear in the public record either in its original form or in a form modified by the applicant to eliminate either security or "Business Confidential" information. Much time and effort can be saved if all submissions are prepared with the view that they will be made public. Privileged information pertinent to a submission, but not required for the public record, should be included as addenda to any application.

Applicants will find it useful to examine the public records to gain insight into the format and content of applications previously acted upon. By studying these "case histories," they can profit from the experience of others.

14–2. REACTOR LICENSING

Because reactors built to date vary widely in use and type, the procedure for licensing has not become highly formalized. Some of the more important steps, however, are detailed in the following sections to indicate the nature of the procedures and requirements.

The owner of a research reactor will need some, and perhaps all, of the following licenses or actions:

(1) For the reactor facility
   (a) Construction permit (unless a ready-made package reactor is purchased)
   (b) Facility license
(2) For the reactor fuel
   (a) Fuel allocation
   (b) Special nuclear material license
   (c) Source material license (if the reactor uses natural or depleted uranium or thorium)
(3) For operations, in addition to the above
   (a) By-product material license
   (b) Operator's licenses

Since the regulations permit licenses to be combined, it is general practice to include licenses for the fuel and by-product material (fission products) in the facility license. Thus, at a minimum, the reactor owner must have a facility license, one or more licensed operators, and a license for by-product material made radioactive in the reactor.

14–2.1 Construction permit and facility license. Part 50 of Title 10, Code of Federal Regulations, sets forth the procedures for licensing of production and utilization facilities. Production and utilization facilities include all types of nuclear reactors. A utilization facility means any nuclear reactor other than one designed or used primarily to form Pu or U^{233}. A Class 103 license is issued for a production facility of a type

found by the Commission to be sufficiently developed to be of practical
value for production and industrial purposes. A Class 104 license is issued
in connection with reactors or other facilities utilized in medical therapy
or research and development. This also includes research and development to demonstrate the practical value of a facility for ultimate industrial
or commercial purposes.

A Class 104 license is required for research reactors. Generally, a construction permit for the reactor facility is first obtained, and ultimately
this permit is converted to a facility or operating license. Thus obtaining
a construction permit is a step toward obtaining the facility license and is
so considered in the following discussion.

A license application contains general information about the applicant—
his name, address, and business, his corporate organization, his financial
and technical qualifications, and other related information. The hazards
report* is a most important part of the application, usually a separate
document. The essential initial function of the hazards report is to provide the AEC information on which a decision can be made to grant or
deny a construction permit. This report must give:

(1) The design and anticipated features of the reactor facility so
that the hazards can be estimated.

(2) The applicant's analysis of the hazards and the adequacy of
safeguards planned to ensure protection of the public.

In some cases, design details and anticipated behavior characteristics
are not firmly established at the time of the initial application. Because
hazards evaluation depends to a large extent on exact and detailed design
experience and on operating procedures which may be developed as construction of the reactor proceeds, the regulations allow the Commission
to issue a license based on a series of step-by-step hazards evaluations.
Consequently, hazards reports are often submitted in two parts, a preliminary and a final report. To provide the data necessary for a hazards
evaluation by the AEC and the awarding of a construction permit, the
preliminary hazards report should contain the following:

(1) Description of the proposed site.

(2) Description of the reactor.

(3) Description of auxiliary systems and facilities.

(4) Discussion of the potential hazards.

The final hazards report establishes the applicant's final evaluation of
hazards that might arise from operation of the facility, and provides

---

* Hazards reports submitted in support of research reactor licenses are often
published by the Commission. These reports are generally available for a modest
charge through the Office of Technical Services (OTS), Department of Commerce, Washington 25, D. C. Those planning to submit hazards reports should
review the format and content of reports previously acted upon.

enough information to allow the Commission to make an independent appraisal of the ultimate safety of the reactor. In format, the final hazards report will contain:

(1) Description of the facility as constructed.

(2) Detailed description of the reactor.

(3) Description of administration, organization, and procedures.

(4) Final estimate of hazards and safety.

Between the preliminary and final reports, additional reports may be necessary to provide the information for evaluating the hazards involved.

The Commission's decision to award a facility license is based on the cumulative information supplied, on results of an inspection to determine that the facility has been built according to the plans, and on the Commission's own appraisal that the reactor facility as constructed and as proposed for operation will not cause undue hazard to the general public's health and safety. The applicant must also furnish proof of financial protection for the public against loss from a nuclear incident. This requirement is discussed further in the section of this chapter dealing with insurance and government indemnity.

The construction permit gives legal right to build or assemble the reactor. It also provides the prospective owner some assurance that if he proceeds as planned he will eventually receive a facility license.

The facility license permits possession and operation of the reactor under specified conditions. The statements, conditions, and procedures set forth in the license applications are generally made conditions of the license. Licenses for special nuclear material and source material, as required for fuel, are included in the facility license, which also permits by-product material (fission products) and special nuclear material (plutonium, for example) to be made in the fuel.

14–2.2 Fuel allocation and license. Usually a prospective reactor owner requests allocation of fuel when he applies for a construction permit. The allocation is simply a statement that the Commission has obligated itself to assign the required amount of special nuclear material for the specified purpose. It is not a license to possess or utilize the material. In support of an allocation request the applicant must supply detailed information regarding:

(1) Financial ability to pay the Commission's charges (lease and utilization) and to carry out the proposed use for a reasonable period of time.

(2) Estimated dates to receive the initial shipment and a schedule by years for later shipments.

(3) A schedule by years showing production, consumption, and operating losses of material.

(4) Estimated schedule by years for the transfer of material to other licensees or back to the Commission.

In the case of some of the small package reactors the owner may not need an allocation, since the fuel is generally a one-time loading obtained with the reactor from the vendor. Nor is it mandatory to get an allocation for a loading of fuel elements purchased from a manufacturer and supplied from his allocation and inventory of special nuclear material. It would seem to be good business practice, however, to have the assurance of an allocation as early as possible, particularly for a reactor that will consume appreciable quantities of fuel.

As has been indicated, a fuel license is usually included in the facility license. In any case, the amount of special nuclear material permitted is specified. Ownership remains with the United States Government, and a charge of 4% per annum of the value of the material is made for its use.

14–2.3 By-product license. Although a reactor facility license usually conveys the right to make the fission products incidental to operating the reactor, most reactor owners require a by-product material license to cover the handling and use of the materials made radioactive in the reactor. Frequently, the owner has had such a license for some time prior to acquisition of the reactor, but the license may require extension or generalization to cover the new operation.

14–3. Operator's Licenses

The Atomic Energy Act of 1954 provides that no individual shall be allowed to manipulate the controls of a licensed reactor without an operator's license. This is to assure that reactors are operated by competent personnel. Licensing procedure includes a medical examination, as well as a written and an operating test. The medical examination determines whether the applicant has a physical disability that might impair his performance. The written examination and operating test evaluate the operator's competence in the areas of general operating procedures, control and safety mechanisms, control instrumentation, emergency shutdown, and the purpose and function of radiation-monitoring equipment.

For routine work, high-school graduates make good reactor operators. They require intensive training at the controls but need no competency in reactor physics or design. Their supervisors, who must also be licensed operators, do require a good understanding of reactor physics.

II. INSURANCE

Ownership of a research reactor poses unique and complex insurance problems, due largely to the newness of nuclear energy as a source of hazards. There is little experience on which to base evaluation of the risks as needed, on the one hand, by the insurance companies for rate making and, on the other, by the reactor owner for determining the amount of insurance he should carry. There has also been the problem of fitting nuclear insurance into the complex of other insurance coverage to avoid duplication or gaps in coverage.

Most attention, as dictated by the most serious problems, has been given to third-party or public liability. Suitable insurance has been worked out for property coverage, involving only the addition of some new perils to the usual fire and extended-coverage protection of property. It is expected that use and occupancy insurance will soon be supplied by the insurance companies if the demand justifies it. Workman's compensation regulations will undoubtedly undergo modifications in the states to make them more compatible with nuclear hazards, notably with the possibility of delayed appearance of injury.

14–4. The Hazard

A reactor is a source of radiation produced directly in the fission process or indirectly from the radioactive materials made therein. The effect of this radiation is the hazard that is feared. Radiation can injure or kill persons, animals, and plant life. In extreme cases, it can damage inanimate materials. Radioactive materials can contaminate both real and personal property, making abandonment or expensive decontamination necessary.

Accidental release and spread of radioactivity from a reactor is the nuclear incident hazard that may cause damage. The release of activity may be sudden, as might be caused by a chemical explosion or by a reactor runaway, or it may be gradual, the result of a slow leak. In any case, the reactor owner may find that the incident has resulted in claims for damages or that he has suffered loss from damage to his own property. Moreover, not only the owner, but others associated with the operation or construction of the reactor—the designer, builder, or suppliers of parts and equipment—might be sued for damage from an incident allegedly caused by a defective part or negligent performance.

To estimate the probability and severity of a nuclear incident is complex and beyond the scope of this discussion. However, a number of studies have led to several pertinent conclusions:

(1) There is no way that a reactor can cause a devastating nuclear explosion producing widespread blast damage. One cannot make a reactor behave like an atomic bomb. The most severe reactor accidents that have occurred have been so mild as to bear no resemblance to an explosion.

(2) There is, however, a *possibility* of a fast release of energy that may rupture containment vessels and release fission products to the surroundings. Although such an accident is believed to be extremely unlikely, it is the type that is most feared and has been given most attention, from both the standpoint of building safety into reactors and insurance coverage.

(3) Reactor operating experience suggests a high degree of safety. In the few runaway accidents that have occurred (e.g., Chalk River, EBR-1), no one has been injured and there has been no serious release of fission products "off-area." This experience and other safety considerations lead to the belief that the chance of a *given person* being killed or injured by a reactor accident is very low, many thousands of times less than the chance of death or injury by an automobile accident.

(4) Although the record is good, the runaway accidents that have occurred have been in research or experimental reactors and not in the large, routinely operated power or production reactors. Moreover, these accidents could have caused injury to persons on the premises under somewhat different conditions. The conclusion is that the chance that an accident with a given research reactor might cause personal injury is finite and not fantastically low.

14–5. PUBLIC LIABILITY

Financial protection of both the public and reactor owners against nuclear hazards became a matter of concern when private ownership of power reactors became a possibility. Prospective owners of large nuclear power plants felt the need for very large amounts of liability insurance as protection against the possibility of a catastrophic runaway accident. The amount of coverage desired on a single risk and, in fact, on a single occurrence—some $100 million—was far beyond the capabilities of commercial insurance firms.

By early 1955, the problem was being studied intensively. The Atomic Energy Commission, with the dual responsibilities of protecting the public against loss or damage and of promoting the atomic power industry, initiated studies to provide better background information on the nature of the hazards and to formulate plans and recommendations for needed legislation. Groups of insurance companies began to study policy forms, rates, and the organization of syndicates and reinsurance pools for providing the very large amounts of coverage that seemed necessary. It soon became apparent that the private insurance industry, despite syndicates, pools, reinsurance, and the like, could supply only a fraction, perhaps $\frac{1}{10}$, of the liability insurance needed on a single large power plant.

14–5.1 Government indemnity. This conclusion, and the results of other studies, led finally to the enactment of an amendment to the Atomic Energy Act of 1954 to provide means for protecting the public against financial loss from a "nuclear incident." The law, in effect, extends the financial protection of reactor owners (licensees) against public liability claims by an additional $500 million over the amount available from private sources. A minimum amount of financial protection, determined by the AEC, must be provided by the licensee through private insurance, self-insurance, or other proof of financial capability for meeting liability claims. This requirement is a condition of obtaining a license. Once it has been met, the Commission will then enter into an agreement with the licensee wherein, for a small annual fee, the indemnity provisions of the law become effective. Under these provisions, the United States Government will indemnify the licensee, all suppliers, and others against any liability for damage caused by radiation over and above the amount of financial protection the licensee is required to provide.

Because the indemnity amendment was designed principally for large power reactors, some difficulties are encountered in extending it to research reactors. A main difficulty is determination of the minimum financial protection to be required of each licensee. For each power reactor with a capacity of 100,000 electrical kw or more, the law requires financial protection equal to the total available amount of private liability insurance. With about $60 million in insurance presently available and required of the large power reactors, what, then, should be the amount required of smaller reactors, all the way down to fractional-watt research reactors— a range of 10^9 fold? This question has not been settled (March, 1958).*

---

* A temporary regulation was published in the *Federal Register* of September 11, 1957, a few days after the indemnity amendment became effective. It required $150,000 financial protection for each 1000 kw (thermal) authorized in the reactor license, with a minimum of $250,000 for small reactors. Taking 4:1 as the ratio of thermal to electrical power capacity, the 100,000-kw (electrical) reactor specified in the law is defined as a 400,000-kw reactor which, at $150,000 per 1000 kw, must be protected by the $60 million also specified in the law. The required protection drops off linearly with power to $250,000 at 1667 kw. All reactors below this power level, a region embracing most of the licensed research reactors, were required to carry the minimum $250,000 of financial protection. This temporary regulation put the indemnity law into effect, pending further study of the problems involved.

Some general principles bearing on this problem are worthy of brief review because they will probably form the basis of decisions and because they are factors to be considered by the reactor owner in formulating his own insurance program.

The overriding hazard in a reactor lies in the possibility that an accident would release enough accumulated fission products to cause personal injury or to contaminate or otherwise damage property. The probability that such an accident will occur is exceedingly difficult to evaluate, depending, as it does, not only on many physical factors such as the type of reactor, control devices, temperature coefficients, and the like, but also on such personal factors as the responsibility, alertness, and competence of the operating staff. The severity of such an accident depends, to some extent, on the same factors but, even more importantly, it depends on the quantity of accumulated fission products. This, in turn, depends on the average power and the time the fission products have been allowed to accumulate at this power, i.e. power level and fuel cycle.

Another consideration is the possible degree of exposure of the public, which is dependent not only on such factors as containment and exclusion area, but also on the population density in the area surrounding the reactor.

The three factors discussed above—power, fuel cycle, and neighboring population density—have a direct bearing on determining financial protection needed for intermediate-size reactors. Whatever formula may be developed to incorporate these and perhaps other factors, it probably will not apply to most research reactors, which will come instead under some blanket minimum requirement of financial protection. Such a minimum should be adequate to cover the small claims that may arise but not so large as to burden operation of a low-budget reactor. From the reactor owner's viewpoint, the amount of insurance protection required should be reasonably compatible with his other liability coverage.

14–5.2 Small versus large claims. Research-reactor accidents will probably be minor rather than catastrophic, but they might still result in exposure of the public and consequent damage claims. Such an accident might be a runaway that causes a release of fission products or a chemical explosion that blows some radioactive material out of the reactor. An experimenter may turn a wrong valve or press a wrong button, causing a radioactive liquid to flow into an unshielded container. Even though no radioactivity escapes from the building and none reaches more than a small area within the building, someone, perhaps a visitor not covered by workman's compensation, may be injured. Students, nonemployee scientists, and others not covered by workman's compensation, could thus be exposed to injury from research reactors. Such exposures are more likely to occur with research reactors than with power reactors;

consequently, the owners of research reactors may be subject to more small claims.

14–5.3 Immunity from liability. The indemnity amendment of the Atomic Energy Act of 1954 undertakes to protect the public by providing financial responsibility for paying legal claims. It accomplishes this purpose by requiring the reactor owner (licensee) to provide financial protection to satisfy claims against all who may be legally responsible for damages. This requirement is a condition for obtaining a license. A few reactor owners, e.g., some state universities, are immune from public liability. In certain cases, waiving this immunity is prohibited by law, and purchase of liability insurance is illegal. This situation poses a dilemma that may require state legislation authorizing some institutions to waive immunity.

14–5.4 Liability insurance. The Nuclear Energy Liability Insurance Association (NELIA) was formed in May, 1956, as the exclusive agency through which stock insurance companies may offer insurance protection "against radiation liability hazards arising out of or pertaining to (a) nuclear reactor installations designed for experimental, testing or power purposes and (b) operations or facilities related or incident thereto . . . " Among the mutual companies, a syndicate, Mutual Atomic Energy Liability Underwriters (MAELU), performs the same function. The two organizations cooperate in establishing rates, policy forms, etc. Together, they have a coverage capacity of about $60 million per installation. Insurance agents or brokers can supply information on policies and rates for reactor liability coverage by these syndicates.

Conventional liability policies (as of March, 1958) have been amended to exclude the nuclear energy hazard except for handling or use of radioisotopes. The new nuclear energy contracts, as drawn up by NELIA and MAELU, cover liability arising from the nuclear energy hazard alone. Therefore, for the reactor owner, both conventional liability insurance and nuclear energy liability insurance are necessary.

The nuclear energy liability policy covers damage to the property of an insured away from the insured facility. This unique provision means, for example, that if an accident in an insured reactor causes damage to an off-site building or property of the same owner, he can recover from the insurance company just as if he were a third party.

Another unusual feature is that any person who may become legally liable is insured under the policy. For example, designers, builders, or suppliers of insured reactors are insured. Thus, the reactor owner is forced to provide insurance to cover the possible negligence of a large number of persons, some of whom (such as suppliers of minor parts) he may never have heard of.

Of practical interest to the reactor owner is a policy provision that any payment made by the insurers reduces the limit of liability under the policy regardless of the time the policy has been in force. Thus, payments in claims, investigation expenses, negotiation costs, etc., reduce and eventually exhaust the policy limit. To restore the original limit after any such payment requires an additional premium and endorsement of the policy or a new policy. If the reactor owner is carrying the minimum insurance required by his license, this provision is a nuisance, since it necessitates negotiating new insurance after every payment under the policy.

14–5.5 Procedural considerations. The discussion above has attempted to point out a few important problems and features of nuclear energy liability protection. The reactor owner or prospective owner must delve into these complexities much more extensively. He must realize that insurance cannot furnish protection in all situations and that there are certain procedural steps which should be taken to help him avoid falling into liability troubles through an insurance gap. For example, he should make certain that his staff does not ship radioactive waste to someone not covered by nuclear liability insurance. Above all, he should avail himself of competent legal and insurance advice.

14–6. PROPERTY INSURANCE

The Nuclear Energy Property Insurance Association (NEPIA), formed in May, 1956, is an agency through which stock companies offer property coverage for nuclear reactors and related facilities. Mutual companies supply similar coverage with full reinsurance through Mutual Atomic Energy Reinsurance Pool (MAERP). Policies and rates have been standardized. The policy contains a deductible clause, with the amount of deductibility scaled to the face amount of insurance. It is an all-risk contract that covers damage to the installation from ordinary hazards as well as from nuclear hazards. Thus, only one policy is necessary to provide adequate property insurance.

RESEARCH AND TRAINING REACTORS ABROAD BUILT BY U. S.*

Owner	Location	Principal contractor**	Type	Startup	Power, Mw (heat)	Thermal flux, n/(cm²)(sec)	Fuel†
Operated							
Brazil, Government of, University of Sao Paulo	Sao Paulo	B & W	Pool	1957	5.0	10^{13}	U–Al
Denmark, Government of, Atomic Energy Commission	Risoe	NAA	Homogeneous	1957	0.005	1.5×10^{10}	UO_2SO_4
Germany, Federal Republic of, Munich Technical University	Near Munich	AMF	Pool	1957	1.0	1.8×10^{13}	U–Al
Germany, Federal Republic of, Hoechst Dyeworks, Incorporated	Frankfurt	NAA	Homogeneous	1958	0.05	10^{12}	UO_2SO_4
Italy‡ University of Palermo	Palermo	AG	AGN-201-110	1958	100 mw	5×10^6	UO_2–polyethylene
Japan, Government of, Atomic Energy Research Institute	Tokai-mura	NAA	Homogeneous	1957	0.05	10^{12}	UO_2SO_4
Netherlands, Government of, Delft Technical University	Delft	AMF	Pool	1957	0.01	10^{13}	U–Al

Switzerland, Government of, Reactor, Incorporated‡	Wuerenlingen	ORNL	Pool	1955	0.1	7×10^{12}	UO$_2$-Al
Switzerland, University of Geneva	Geneva	AG	AGN-201-111	1958	100 mw	5×10^6	UO$_2$-polyethylene
Being Built							
Belgium, Government of, Center for Nuclear Energy	Mol	NDA-CEN	Tank	1958	25–50	10^{15}	U-Al
Canada McMaster University	Hamilton, Ont.	AMF	Pool	1958	1.0	—	U-Al
China, Republic of, National Tsing-Hua University	Hsinchu	GE	Pool	1959	1.0	—	U-Al
Denmark, Government of, Atomic Energy Commission	Risoe	FW	Tank	1958	5.0	4×10^{13}	U-Al
Germany, Federal Republic of, Society for the Utilization of Nuclear Energy in Ship-building and Navigation, Inc.	Near Hamburg	B & W	Pool	1958	5.0	8×10^{12}	U-Al
Greece, Government of, Atomic Energy Commission	Near Athens	AMF	Pool	1958	1.0	10^{13}	U-Al
Israel, Government of, Atomic Energy Commission	Near Rehovoth	AMF	Pool	1959	1.0	—	U-Al
Italy, Government of, National Committee for Nuclear Research	Ispra	ACF	Heavy water	1958	5.0	6×10^{13}	U-Al

(continued)

Owner	Location	Principal contractor**	Type	Startup	Power, Mw (heat)	Thermal flux, n/(cm²)(sec)	Fuel†
Italy, SORIN Nuclear Center	Chivasso	AMF	Pool	1958	1.0–5.0	—	U-Al
Japan, Government of, Atomic Energy Research Institute	Tokai-mura	AMF	Heavy water	1959	10.0	1.2×10^{14}	U-Al
Netherlands, Government of, Reactor Center	Petten	ACF	Tank	1959	20.0	1.5×10^{14}	U-Al
Portugal, Government of, Nuclear Energy Board	Near Lisbon	AMF	Pool	1959	1.0	10^{13}	U-Al
Spain, Government of, Nuclear Energy Board	Near Madrid	GE	Pool	1958	3.0	2.5×10^{13}	U-Al
Sweden, Government of, Atomic Energy Commission	Studsvik	ACF	Tank	1958	30.0	1.5×10^{14}	U-Al
Venezuela, Government of, Institute of Neurology and Brain Research	Near Caracas	GE	Pool	1958	3.0	2.5×10^{13}	U-Al
West Berlin, City of, Institute of Nuclear Research	West Berlin	NAA	Homogeneous	1958	0.05	10^{12}	UO_2SO_4
Contracted							
Austria, Government of, Study Company for Atomic Energy	Vienna	AMF	Pool	1959	5.0	3×10^{13}	U-Al
Italy, Milan Technical University	Milan	NAA	Homogeneous	1958	0.05	—	UO_2SO_4

FOREIGN-BUILT RESEARCH AND TRAINING REACTORS FOR WHICH U. S. FUEL FURNISHED*

Operated							
Argentina, Government of, National Commission for Atomic Energy	Buenos Aires	CNEA	Argonaut	1958	—	—	U_3O_8
Canada, Government of, Atomic Energy of Canada, Ltd.	Chalk River	Canadair Ltd.	Pool	1958	0.01	2×10^{11}	U-Al
France, Government of, Comm. for Atomic Energy	Saclay	CEA	Heavy water	—	15	10^{14}	U
France, Government of, Comm. for Atomic Energy	Grenoble	CEA	Pool	1958	1.0	1.0×10^{13}	U-Al
Being Built							
France, Government of, Comm. for Atomic Energy	Fontenay-aux-Roses	CEA	Pool	1958	1.0	1.0×10^{13}	U-Al
France, Government of, Comm. for Atomic Energy	Fontenay-aux-Roses	CEA	Pool	1958	100 watts	—	U-Al
Norway, Government of, JENER	Halden	IFA	Heavy water	1958	10	—	UO_2

* All reactors use uranium of 20% enrichment except: Canada, 90%; Netherlands at Petten, 90%; and Sweden at Studsvik, 90%.

** Abbreviations: ACF, ACF Industries, Inc.; AG, Aerojet-General Corporation; AMF, AMF Atomics, a Division of American Machine and Foundry Co.; B & W, Babcock & Wilcox Co., The; CEA, Commissariat a l'Energie Atomique; CNEA, Commission National for Atomic Energy; FW, Foster Wheeler Corporation; GE, General Electric Co.; IFA, Institute for Atomic Energy; JENER, Joint Establishment (of Norway and Sweden) for Nuclear Energy Research; NAA, Atomics International, a Division of North American Aviation, Inc.; NDA-CEN, Nuclear Development Corp. of America and Belgian Center for Nuclear Energy supervising Belgian companies engaged in construction; ORNL, Oak Ridge National Laboratory, operated for the U. S. Atomic Energy Commission by Union Carbide Nuclear Co.

† UO_2SO_4 is aqueous solution of uranyl sulfate. U-Al is alloy of uranium and aluminum. UO_2-Al is mixture of uranium dioxide and aluminum powders. UO_2-polyethylene is a mixture of uranium dioxide and polyethylene. U is cast uranium metal rods.

‡ Reactor has operated but as of June 1, 1958 had not been shipped overseas.

INDEX